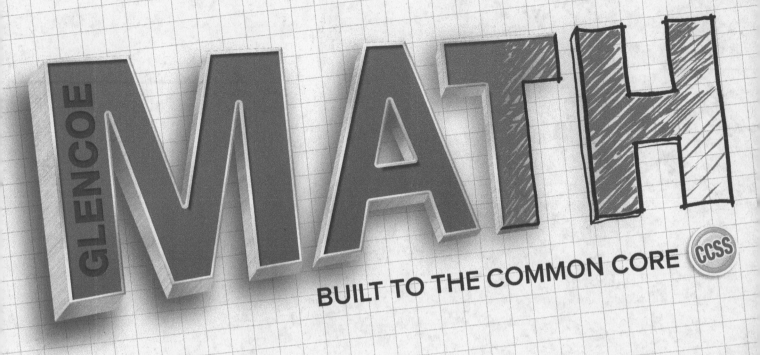

GLENCOE MATH

BUILT TO THE COMMON CORE CCSS

COMMON CORE PRACTICE MASTERS

AUTHORS
Carter • Cuevas • Day • Malloy
Kersaint • Reynosa • Silbey • Vielhaber

McGraw Hill Education

Bothell, WA • Chicago, IL • Columbus, OH • New York, NY

D1295077

connectED.mcgraw-hill.com

Send all inquiries to:
McGraw-Hill Education
8787 Orion Place
Columbus, OH 43240

ISBN: 978-0-02-136277-6
MHID: 0-02-136277-7

Printed in the United States of America.

2 3 4 5 6 7 QVS 20 19 18 17 16

Contents

Lesson 1 Multi-Step Problem Solving

Multi-Step Example

Two teams that have the best win to loss ratio play each other in a one-game playoff. The table shows four teams competing for the playoff spots. Based on the table, which two teams are in the lead to go to the playoffs? 8.NS.1, **MP** 1

Ⓐ Blue Sox and Hawks

Ⓑ Bombers and Bears

Ⓒ Blue Sox and Bombers

Ⓓ Hawks and Bears

Team	Win	Loss
Blue Sox	97	64
Hawks	96	66
Bombers	95	60
Bears	94	61

Use a problem-solving model to solve this problem.

 Understand

Read the problem. (Circle) the information you know.
Underline what the problem is asking you to find.

 Plan

What will you need to do to solve the problem? Write your plan in steps.

Step 1 Write the information for each team as a win to loss ratio.

Step 2 Express each ratio as a _____ and compare _____.

 Solve

Use your plan to solve the problem. Show your steps.

Blue Sox: $\frac{97}{64} \approx$ _____   Hawks: $\frac{96}{66} \approx$ _____

Bombers: $\frac{95}{60} \approx$ _____   Bears: $\frac{94}{61} \approx$ _____

The two greatest values are _____ and _____.

So, the _____ and _____ are in the lead to go to the

play-offs. The correct answer is _____. Fill in that answer choice.

> **Read to Succeed!**
> When comparing decimals, be sure to round each decimal to the same decimal place.

 Check

How do you know your solution is accurate?

_____

_____

_____

Lesson 1 (continued)

Use a problem-solving model to solve each problem.

1 The table below shows the free throws made (FTM) and the free throws attempted (FTA) for three players on the high school basketball team. As a decimal rounded to the nearest thousandth, what is the combined free-throw percentage of all three players? **8.NS.1, MP 1**

Free Throws		
Player	FTM	FTA
Jones	38	42
Mason	9	10
Rice	9	10

- Ⓐ 0.900
- Ⓑ 0.903
- Ⓒ 0.904
- Ⓓ 0.905

2 Express 0.$\overline{461538}$ as a fraction in simplest form. Show your steps below. **8.NS.1, MP 1**

3 A survey was conducted to determine the favorite sport for members of the eighth grade class. The results are shown in the table. How many students selected either football or baseball? Express your answer as a decimal. **8.NS.1, MP 2**

Sport	Part of Class
Football	$\frac{7}{20}$
Baseball	$\frac{1}{5}$
Basketball	$\frac{3}{10}$
Soccer	$\frac{3}{20}$

4 🖐 **H.O.T. Problem** What is the difference of the areas, expressed as a decimal, of the shaded rectangle and the unshaded rectangle? Explain how you determined your answer. **8.NS.1, MP 1**

$\frac{1}{2}$ in. $\frac{1}{3}$ in. $\frac{1}{5}$ in. $\frac{1}{4}$ in.

Lesson 2 Multi-Step Problem Solving

Multi-Step Example

The table shows the approximate number of Earth hours there are in one day for two planets. Which of the following is the longest amount of time? 8.EE.1, **MP** 1

Planet	Length of Day (Earth Hours)
Venus	3^5
Neptune	2^4

Ⓐ 8 Venus days

Ⓑ 20 Neptune days

Ⓒ 5 Venus days and 12 Neptune days

Ⓓ 4 Venus days and 15 Neptune days

Use a problem-solving model to solve this problem.

1 Understand

Read the problem. Ⓒircle the information you know.
Underline what the problem is asking you to find.

2 Plan

What will you need to do to solve the problem? Write your plan in steps.

Step 1   Write an expression with exponents for each of the four times.

Step 2 _____ each expression and _____ the values.

3 Solve

Use your plan to solve the problem. Show your steps.

8 Venus days = _____ Earth days

20 Neptune days = _____ Earth days

5 Venus days and 12 Neptune days = _____ Earth days

4 Venus days and 15 Neptune days = _____ Earth days

The greatest value is _____ Earth days. So, the longest amount

of time is _____. The answer is ____. Fill in that answer choice.

> **Read to Succeed!** 👀
>
> When evaluating an expression such as $8 \cdot 3^5$, remember to follow the order of operations. Evaluate 3^5 before multiplying by 8.

4 Check

How do you know your solution is accurate?

_____

_____

_____

Lesson 2 *(continued)*

Use a problem-solving model to solve each problem.

1 The table shows the approximate number of Earth hours there are in one day for two planets. Which of the following is the same amount of time as 4 Venus days and 6 Neptune days? **8.EE.1, MP 2**

Planet	Length of Day (Earth Hours)
Venus	3^5
Neptune	2^4

Ⓐ 1,036 Earth hours

Ⓑ 1,068 Earth hours

Ⓒ 1,522 Earth hours

Ⓓ 1,554 Earth hours

2 What is the volume of the cube, in cubic units, if $x = 3$? **8.EE.1, MP 2**

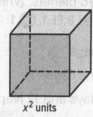

x^2 units

3 If $4^2 \cdot 4^x = 8 \cdot 512$, what is the value of x? Show how you solved the problem. **8.EE.1, MP 7**

_____
_____
_____
_____
_____

4 ✋ **H.O.T. Problem** Consider the following equations.

$$1 = 1 = 1^3$$
$$3 + 5 = 8 = 2^3$$
$$7 + 9 + 11 = 27 = 3^3$$
$$13 + 15 + 17 + 19 = 64 = 4^3$$
$$21 + 23 + 25 + 27 + 29 = 125 = 5^3$$

If the pattern continues, what will be the 10th equation? Explain. **8.EE.1, MP 8**

_____
_____
_____
_____
_____
_____
_____
_____

Lesson 3   **Multi-Step** Problem Solving

Multi-Step Example

The processing speed of a certain computer is 10^{12} instructions per second. A second computer has a processing speed that is 10^5 times as fast. Which statement is true? 8.EE.1, **MP** 2

Ⓐ The processing speed of the second computer is 10^5 instructions per second.

Ⓑ The processing speed of the second computer is 1,000 times as fast.

Ⓒ The second computer processes 1,000 more instructions per second.

Ⓓ The processing speed of the second computer is 10^{17} instructions per second.

Use a problem-solving model to solve this problem.

 Understand

Read the problem. Circle the information you know.
Underline what the problem is asking you to find.

 Plan

What will you need to do to solve the problem? Write your plan in steps.

[Step 1]   Find the processing speed of the second computer.

[Step 2]   _____ the processing speed of the first computer by the increase of processing speed of the _____.

 Solve

Use your plan to solve the problem. Show your steps.

Find the processing speed by _____.

_____ × _____ = _____

The second computer has a processing speed of _____ instructions

per second. Choice _____ is the correct answer. Fill in that answer choice.

> **Read to Succeed!** 👀
> Remember when using the product of powers the base stays the same and you add the exponents.

4 Check

How do you know your solution is accurate?

_____

_____

_____

Lesson 3 *(continued)*

Use a problem-solving model to solve each problem.

1 The table shows the length of samples of bamboo. Which of the following is true about the two samples? 8.EE.1, (MP) 1

Sample	Length (cm)
A	100,000
B	100

Ⓐ Sample A is 100 times as long as Sample B.

Ⓑ Sample A is 10^3 times longer than Sample B.

Ⓒ Sample A and B can be combined for a length that is 10 times as long as Sample B.

Ⓓ The difference between the two lengths is 103 cm.

2 How many times greater is the cube of one million than the square of ten thousand? 8.EE.1, (MP) 1

_____

_____

3 Is $\dfrac{5^{98}}{5^{95}}$ greater than, less than or equal to 25? Justify your answer using exponents. 8.EE.1, (MP) 7

_____

_____

4 🖐 **H.O.T. Problem** What number is triple 3^{15}? Write using exponents and explain your answer. 8.EE.1, (MP) 7

_____

_____

Lesson 4 **Multi-Step** Problem Solving

Multi-Step Example

The models show a square floor and the square tile that will be used to cover the floor. How many tiles will it take to cover the floor? **8.EE.1,** MP 1

(A) $8x^2y$

(C) $64x^4y^2$

(B) $8x^3y^2$

(D) $64x^6y^4$

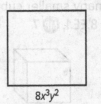

$8x^3y^2$

xy

Use a problem-solving model to solve this problem.

1 Understand

Read the problem. Circle the information you know.
Underline what the problem is asking you to find.

2 Plan

What will you need to do to solve the problem? Write your plan in steps.

Step 1   Find the area of the floor.

Step 2   Find the area of the tile.

Step 3   Divide the area of the _____ by the area of the _____.

3 Solve

Use your plan to solve the problem. Show your steps.

Find the area by squaring the length of each side.

floor = $(8x^3y^2)^2$ = _____   tile = $(xy)^2$ = _____

Then divide to find how many tiles it will take to cover the floor.

$\dfrac{\text{floor}}{\text{tile}}$ = _____ = _____

The correct answer is that it will take _____ tiles to cover the floor. The answer is _____. Fill in that answer choice.

> **Read to Succeed!**
>
> To find the area of a square just square the length of the side.

4 Check

How do you know your solution is accurate?

_____

_____

_____

_____

Lesson 4 *(continued)*

Use a problem-solving model to solve each problem.

1 How many smaller cubes will fit in the larger cube? 8.EE.1, **MP** 7

$4x^4$ $2x$

Ⓐ $8x^3$ cubes

Ⓑ $8x^9$ cubes

Ⓒ $64x^8$ cubes

Ⓓ $64x^{12}$ cubes

2 The table gives the area of a square and volume of a cube with side lengths as shown. Complete the table. 8.EE.1, **MP** 7

	Side Length x	Side Length $3y^2$	Double the Side Length of $3y^2$
Area of a square	x^2		
Volume of a cube	x^3		

3 One cube has side length of $3x^6$ and another has side length $2x^7$. Which cube has the greater volume when $x = 3$? 8.EE.1, **MP** 7

_____

_____

4 ✋**H.O.T. Problem** A rock is dropped from the top of the bleachers. The expression $4.9x^2$ gives the distance in meters the rock has fallen in x seconds. Mrs. Malone's class wants to know how many meters the rock has fallen in x^2 seconds. One group says the answer is $24.01x^4$ meters. Is their answer correct? Support your answer. 8.EE.1, **MP** 3

_____

_____

_____

_____

Lesson 5 **Multi-Step** Problem Solving

Multi-Step Example

The table shows the hair lengths of five samples taken for a laboratory study. Which of the following shows the order of these hair lengths from least to greatest? **8.EE.1, MP 2**

Ⓐ $2^2, 2^{-2}, 2^0, 2^{-1}, 2^{-3}$

Ⓑ $2^0, 2^{-3}, 2^{-2}, 2^{-1}, 2^2$

Ⓒ $2^2, 2^0, 2^{-1}, 2^{-2}, 2^{-3}$

Ⓓ $2^{-3}, 2^{-2}, 2^{-1}, 2^0, 2^2$

Sample	Hair Length (in.)
1	2^2
2	2^{-2}
3	2^0
4	2^{-1}
5	2^{-3}

Use a problem-solving model to solve this problem.

1 Understand

Read the problem. Circle the information you know.
Underline what the problem is asking you to find.

2 Plan

What will you need to do to solve the problem? Write your plan in steps.

Step 1 Evaluate _____.

Step 2 _____ and _____ the values.

Read to Succeed!

Be careful when evaluating negative exponents. For example, $2^{-3} = \frac{1}{2^3}$.

3 Solve

Use your plan to solve the problem. Show your steps.

$2^2 =$ _____ $2^{-2} =$ _____ $2^0 =$ _____

$2^{-1} =$ _____ $2^{-3} =$ _____

Since _____ < _____ < _____ < _____ < _____ , choice

_____ is the answer. Fill in that answer choice.

4 Check

How do you know your solution is accurate?

_____

_____

_____

_____

Lesson 5 *(continued)*

Use a problem-solving model to solve each problem.

1 On the number line shown below, the coordinate of point X is 3^{-3} and the coordinate of point Y is 3^{-2}. Which of the following is the coordinate of a point between X and Y? **8.EE.1, MP 2**

      Ⓐ 2^{-5}

      Ⓑ 4^{-1}

      Ⓒ 5^{-2}

      Ⓓ 6^{-1}

2 The table shows the dimensions in feet of four rectangles. What is the difference in area of the rectangle with the greatest area and the rectangle with the least area? **8.EE.1, MP 2**

Rectangle	Width (ft)	Length (ft)
A	2^{-1}	2^7
B	2^6	2^{-3}
C	2^{-2}	2^6
D	2^5	2^{-5}

3 What is the total surface area of the rectangular prism shown below? **8.EE.1, MP 1**

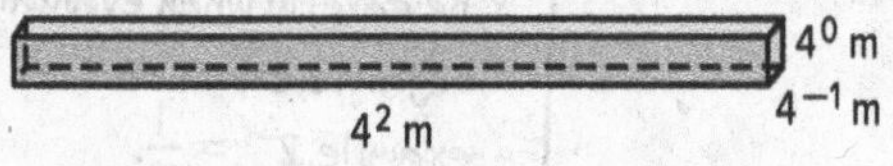

$$4^0 \text{ m}$$
$$4^{-1} \text{ m}$$
$$4^2 \text{ m}$$

4 ✋**H.O.T. Problem** If a, b, and c are different negative integers less than -1 and $2^a \cdot 2^b \cdot 2^c = \dfrac{1}{512}$, what is the absolute value of abc? Explain your answer. **8.EE.1, MP 7**

Lesson 6 **Multi-Step** Problem Solving

Multi-Step Example

The attendance records at games for four professional football teams for a recent year are shown in the table. Which of the following lists the teams from greatest attendance to least attendance? 8.EE.4, **MP** 1

Team	Attendance
W	5.58×10^4
X	5.49×10^5
Y	5.51×10^4
Z	5.53×10^5

Ⓐ W, Z, Y, X

Ⓑ Y, W, X, Z

Ⓒ Z, X, W, Y

Ⓓ X, Y, Z, W

Use a problem-solving model to solve this problem.

Understand

Read the problem. ⟨Circle⟩ the information you know.
Underline what the problem is asking you to find.

Plan

What will you need to do to solve the problem? Write your plan in steps.

Step 1 Express each value in standard decimal notation.

Step 2 Order the numbers from _____.

Solve

Use your plan to solve the problem. Show your steps.

W: 5.58×10^4 = _____   **X:** 5.49×10^5 = _____

Y: 5.51×10^4 = _____   **Z:** 5.53×10^5 = _____

Since _____ > _____ > _____ > _____ , the teams, in

order of greatest to least attendance, are ____, ____, ____, and ____.

So, the correct answer is C. Fill in that answer choice.

> **Read to Succeed!**
> When comparing numbers with the same number of decimal places, start at the right and compare digits until you come to the digits that are different.

Check

How do you know your solution is accurate?

_____

_____

_____

Lesson 6 (continued)

Use a problem-solving model to solve each problem.

1 The table shows the mass of one atom of each of several elements. Which element has the greatest mass per atom? 8.EE.4, ⓂⓅ 1

Element	Mass per Atom
argon	6.64×10^{-23} g
helium	6.65×10^{-24} g
iodine	2.11×10^{-22} g
mercury	3.33×10^{-22} g

Ⓐ argon

Ⓑ helium

Ⓒ iodine

Ⓓ mercury

2 The volume the rectangular prism shown below is 4.8×10^9 cubic meters. What is the height h of the prism expressed in standard decimal notation? 8.EE.4, ⓂⓅ 2

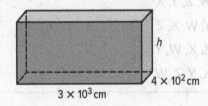

3×10^3 cm

4×10^2 cm

3 The table shows three numerical expressions. Suppose each expression is evaluated and the result is written in scientific notation. What will be the power of 10 of the expression with the greatest value? 8.EE.4, ⓂⓅ 2

Calculation Number	Expression
1	$\dfrac{(28,000)(6,000)}{400}$
2	$\dfrac{(7,000)(600,000)}{3,000}$
3	$\dfrac{(350,000)(900,000)}{14,000}$

4 ✋ **H.O.T. Problem** Light travels at approximately 186,000 miles per second. A light year is the distance that light can travel in one year. How many miles is a light year? Express your answer in scientific notation and explain your work. 8.EE.4, ⓂⓅ 1

_____

_____

_____

_____

_____

Lesson 7   Multi-Step Problem Solving

Multi-Step Example

In 2010, the population of China was 1,370,000,000 and the population of the U.S. was 3×10^8. Which of the following statements is true? **8.EE.4, MP 2**

Ⓐ The population of China was approximately 100% greater than the population of the U.S.

Ⓑ The ratio of the population of China to the population of the U.S. was 1:3.

Ⓒ The population of China was about 46 times as great as the population of the U.S.

Ⓓ The total combined population of China and the U.S. was 1.67×10^9 people.

Use a problem-solving model to solve this problem.

1 Understand

Read the problem. Circle the information you know.
Underline what the problem is asking you to find.

2 Plan

What will you need to do to solve the problem? Write your plan in steps.

Step 1   Write China's population in _____ and

adjust to the _____ power of 10 as U.S. population.

Step 2   _____the whole numbers to determine the
relationship between the two populations.

Read to Succeed!

You can add numbers written in scientific notation if they have the same power of 10.

3 Solve

Use your plan to solve the problem. Show your steps.

China's population in _____ = _____

U.S. population = 3×10^8 China's population = _____ $\times 10^8$

Compare the whole numbers.   _____ $\times 10^8$ ÷ _____ $\times 10^8$ ≈ _____

This means that the population of China was about _____ times as great as the

population of the U.S. which is _____ percent and a ratio of _____:1.

_____ $\times 10^8$ + _____ $\times 10^8$ = _____ $\times 10^8$ This means that the total

combined population in scientific notation is _____. The answer is _____.

4 Check

How do you know your solution is reasonable?

_____

_____

Lesson 7 (continued)

Use a problem-solving model to solve each problem.

1 An internet company averages 7.3×10^7 spam E-mails and 1,300,000,000 regular E-mails per year. How many total E-mails does the internet company average per year? Express the answer in scientific notation. **8.EE.4, MP 2**

Ⓐ 1.373×10^7

Ⓑ 1.373×10^9

Ⓒ 13.73×10^7

Ⓓ 137.3×10^9

2 A music download company averages 3×10^9 music downloads and has 4×10^7 customers. How many songs does the average customer download? **8.EE.4, MP 1**

_____

3 The table shows the amount of mail delivered through three different courier services per year. How many times more per year does Mike's Mail deliver than Send It? **8.EE.3, MP 2**

Courier Service	Amount of Mail per Year
Mike's Mail	5×10^9
Fast Package	4,560,000
Send It	5,000,000

4 ✋ **H.O.T. Problem** Which expression does not belong? Explain your reasoning. **8.EE.4, MP 1**

21.17×10^{11}
2.117×10^{11}
$(2.9)(7.3) \times 10^{4+7}$
$(2.9 \times 10^4)(7.3 \times 10^7)$

_____

_____

_____

_____

_____

Lesson 8 Multi-Step Problem Solving

Multi-Step Example

A bulletin board consists of four equal-sized cork squares arranged in a row to form a rectangle. If the total area of all four cork squares is 100 square feet, what is the length in feet of the bulletin board? 8.EE.2, 1

Use a problem-solving model to solve this problem.

 Understand

Read the problem. Circle the information you know.
Underline what the problem is asking you to find.

 Plan

What will you need to do to solve the problem?
Write your plan in steps.

Step 1 Determine the _____ of the area of one square.

Step 2 Multiply the answer to Step 1 by _____ .

 Solve

Use your plan to solve the problem. Show your steps.

$100 \div 4 =$ _____   area of one square in square feet

$\sqrt{25} =$ _____   length in feet of one side of one square

$4 \cdot$ _____ = _____   length in feet of entire bulletin board

The answer is _____ feet.

Read to Succeed!

Since distance cannot be negative, use only the positive square root.

 Check

How do you know your solution is accurate?

_____

_____

_____

_____

_____

Lesson 8 *(continued)*

Use a problem-solving model to solve each problem.

1 What is the difference in side length of the cubes shown below? **8.EE.2, MP 1**

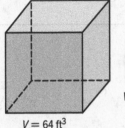

$V = 64\ ft^3$

$V = 27\ ft^3$

_____

2 The area of the figure below is 300 square centimeters. What is the perimeter of the figure? **8.EE.2, MP 2**

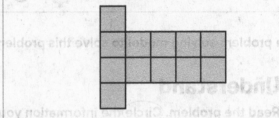

3 The volume of the rectangular prism shown is 4,320 cubic centimeters. What is the surface area of the whole prism? Explain. **8.EE.2, MP 3**

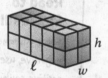

h

ℓ

w

_____

_____

_____

4 ✋ **H.O.T. Problem** Dario wants to buy paper to wrap a birthday present in the cube-shaped box shown below. If an 8.3-square-foot package of wrapping paper costs $1.25, how much will Dario spend on the wrapping paper? Explain. **8.EE.2, MP 7**

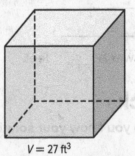

$V = 27\ ft^3$

_____

_____

_____

_____

_____

_____

Lesson 9 **Multi-Step** Problem Solving

Multi-Step Example

The table shows the area of four square photos. Which of the following is the order of the photos from greatest area to least area? 8.NS.2, **MP** 1

Ⓐ B, C, A, D

Ⓑ C, B, A, D

Ⓒ B, A, C, D

Ⓓ D, A, C, B

Photos	Area (cm²)
A	$\sqrt{130}$
B	$\sqrt{172}$
C	13
D	11

Use a problem-solving model to solve this problem.

1 Understand

Read the problem. (Circle) the information you know.
Underline what the problem is asking you to find.

2 Plan

What will you need to do to solve the problem? Write your plan in steps.

Step 1 Estimate the _____ of photos A and B.

Step 2 Compare and order the photos from _____ according to their _____ .

3 Solve

Use your plan to solve the problem. Show your steps.

Since $\sqrt{130}$ is a little less than halfway between _____ and

_____ , _____ is a good estimate for $\sqrt{130}$.

Since $\sqrt{172}$ is much closer to _____ than _____ , _____ is a

good estimate for $\sqrt{172}$.

Since 13.1 > 13 > 11.4 > 11, choice A is correct. Fill in that answer choice.

Read to Succeed!

When there is no number, or index, in front of the radical sign, you are finding a square root.

4 Check

How do you know your solution is accurate?

_____

_____

_____

Lesson 9 *(continued)*

Use a problem-solving model to solve each problem.

1 The table shows the volume of four cubes. Which is the order of the volumes from least to greatest? **8.NS.2,** **1**

Cube	Volume (cm³)
A	$\sqrt[3]{74}$
B	3
C	$\sqrt[3]{110}$
D	5

Ⓐ $\sqrt[3]{74}$, $\sqrt[3]{110}$, 3, 5

Ⓑ 3, 5, $\sqrt[3]{74}$, $\sqrt[3]{110}$

Ⓒ 3, $\sqrt[3]{74}$, $\sqrt[3]{110}$, 5

Ⓓ 5, $\sqrt[3]{110}$, $\sqrt[3]{74}$, 3

2 Roger made a square sign to place in front of the school shown below in the sketch. What is the approximate perimeter, in inches, of his sign? (*Hint:* 1 m ≈ 39.37 in.) **8.NS.2,** **2**

138 m²

Ⓐ B, C, A, D

Ⓑ C, B, A, D

Ⓒ B, A, C, D

Ⓓ D, A, C, B

_____

3 The diagonal of a box d with length ℓ, width w, and height h is given by the formula $d = \sqrt{\ell^2 + w^2 + h^2}$. What is the length of the diagonal of the box shown below to the nearest whole meter? **8.NS.2,** **2**

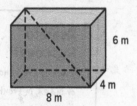

6 m

4 m

8 m

_____

4 ✋ **H.O.T. Problem** A circle of radius r has an area A of 214 square centimeters. Estimate the radius of the circle to the nearest whole centimeter. Use 3 as an estimate for π. Explain how you found your answer. **8.NS.2,** **7**

$A = 214$ cm²

_____

_____

_____

_____

Lesson 10 Multi-Step Problem Solving

Multi-Step Example

Which number line shows {350%, π, 3.$\overline{3}$, $\sqrt{14}$}? 8.NS.1, MP 6

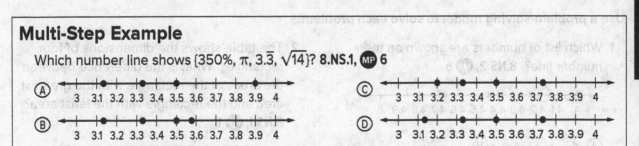

Use a problem-solving model to solve this problem.

1 Understand

Read the problem. Circle the information you know.
Underline what the problem is asking you to find.

2 Plan

What will you need to do to solve the problem? Write your plan in steps.

Step 1 Express each number in _____ , rounding

to _____ if necessary.

Step 2 Determine which number line shows {_____, _____, _____, _____}.

3 Solve

Use your plan to solve the problem. Show your steps.

350% = _____   π ≈ _____

3.$\overline{3}$ ≈ _____ $\sqrt{14}$ ≈ _____

The correct answer is _____. Fill in that answer choice.

 Read to Succeed!

Consider the intervals on the number line and the locations of the points when deciding which decimal place to use in rounding.

4 Check

How do you know your solution is accurate?

_____

_____

Lesson 10 (continued)

Use a problem-solving model to solve each problem.

1 Which list of numbers are shown on the number line? **8.NS.2, MP 6**

4 4.1 4.2 4.3 4.4 4.5 4.6 4.7 4.8 4.9 5

Ⓐ $4\frac{5}{11}$, $\sqrt{23}$, $4.\overline{6}$, $\sqrt{18}$

Ⓑ $4\frac{5}{9}$, $\sqrt{23}$, $4\frac{4}{11}$, $\sqrt{18}$

Ⓒ $4.\overline{6}$, $\sqrt{20}$, $4\frac{4}{11}$, $\sqrt{18}$

Ⓓ $4\frac{5}{9}$, $\sqrt{23}$, $4\frac{4}{9}$, $\sqrt{18}$

2 The table shows the dimensions of four rectangles. What is the difference between the areas of the rectangle with the greatest area and the rectangle with the least area? **8.NS.1, MP 1**

Rectangle	Width (cm)	Length (cm)
A	4	4
B	3.1	5
C	7	2.5
D	6	2.7

3 The areas of two squares are shown below. To the nearest whole meter, what is the difference between the side lengths of these squares? **8.EE.2, MP 2**

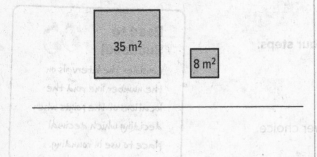

35 m²   8 m²

4 🔥 **H.O.T. Problem** Label the Venn diagram with the five subsets of real numbers and examples of each subset. Then give a brief description of the set of real numbers. **8.NS.1, MP 3**

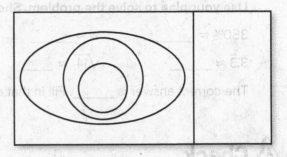

Lesson 1 **Multi-Step** Problem Solving

Multi-Step Example

The Jackson family drove 175 miles on their road trip. This distance is $2\frac{1}{2}$ times the distance they drove on the first day. How many miles did the Jackson family drive on the first day? **8.EE.7b, 1**

Ⓐ 70 mi   Ⓒ 350 mi

Ⓑ 175 mi   Ⓓ 437.5 mi

Use a problem-solving model to solve this problem.

Understand

Read the problem. ⓒircle the information you know.
Underline what the problem is asking you to find.

2 Plan

What will you need to do to solve the problem? Write your plan in steps.

Step 1 Define the _____ and write an _____ that represents the situation.

Step 2 _____ the equation.

> **Read to Succeed!**
> Remember the multiplicative inverse of a number is the value that you multiply by to make the number equal 1.

3 Solve

Use your plan to solve the problem. Show your steps.

Define the variables and write an equation.

Let *d* equal the distance traveled on the first day.

$\frac{5}{2}d =$ _____

Solve the equation. _____ each side by the multiplicative inverse.

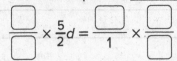

$d =$ _____

The correct answer is _____ miles. Choice _____ is correct. Fill in that answer choice.

4 Check

How do you know your solution is accurate?

_____

_____

Lesson 1 (continued)

Use a problem-solving model to solve each problem.

1 Yer has read 85% of her new employee manual. She has read 306 pages. How many pages are in the employee manual? 8.EE.7, (MP) 1

Ⓐ 26 pages

Ⓑ 36 pages

Ⓒ 260 pages

Ⓓ 360 pages

2 A bakery is keeping track of different baked goods in a table. Complete the table. 8.EE.7b, (MP) 1

Type of Baked Good	Portion of Total Baked Goods	Number of the Type of Baked Good	Total Baked Goods
Sesame bagels	$\frac{1}{5}$		175
Raisin cookies	$\frac{9}{20}$	27	

3 Jonah makes deposits in his account based on his paycheck total. Complete the table of deposits Jonah has made this month. 8.EE.7, (MP) 7

Percent of Deposit	Deposit into Account	Paycheck Total
60%		$675.00
75%	$337.50	

4 🔥**H.O.T. Problem** Write a real-world problem that could be represented by the equation, $\frac{2}{3}b = 24$ and then solve the problem. 8.EE.7a, (MP) 4

_____

_____

_____

_____

_____

Lesson 2　Multi-Step Problem Solving

Multi-Step Example

Fahrenheit and Kelvin temperatures are related by the formula $F = \frac{9}{5}K - 460$, where F is degrees Fahrenheit and K is degrees Kelvin. The highest temperature ever recorded in Texas is 120° Fahrenheit. To the nearest whole number, what is the Kelvin equivalent of 120° Fahrenheit? **8.EE.7b,** **MP 2**

- Ⓐ 64° Kelvin
- Ⓑ 189° Kelvin
- Ⓒ 322° Kelvin
- Ⓓ 1,044° Kelvin

Use a problem-solving model to solve this problem.

Understand

Read the problem. Ⓒircle the information you know.
Underline what the problem is asking you to find.

Plan

What will you need to do to solve the problem? Write your plan in steps.

Step 1　Replace ____ with ____ in $F = \frac{9}{5}K - 460$.

Step 2　Solve for __.

Read to Succeed!

When solving for K, remember to multiply each side of the equation by the multiplicative inverse.

Solve

Use your plan to solve the problem. Show your steps.

Replacing F with 120 results in the equation $120 = \frac{9}{5}K - 460$.

To solve the equation, I _____ 460 to each side and _____ each side by $\frac{5}{9}$.

So, 120° Fahrenheit is equal to _____. The correct answer is ____.

Fill in that answer choice.

Check

How do you know your solution is accurate?

_____

_____

_____

Lesson 2 (continued)

Use a problem-solving model to solve each problem.

1 The lowest temperature ever recorded in Texas is −31° Celsius. Celsius and Rankine temperatures are related by the formula $C = \frac{5}{9}R - 273$, where C is degrees Celsius and R is degrees Rankine. To the nearest whole number, what is the Rankine equivalent of −31° Celsius? **8.EE.7b, MP 2**

- Ⓐ 547° Rankine
- Ⓑ 436° Rankine
- Ⓒ 134° Rankine
- Ⓓ 48° Rankine

2 The Baker family is driving on a highway. The equation $y = 14 - \frac{1}{32}x$ shows the relationship between y, the number of gallons of fuel in the tank, and x, the number of miles the family has driven since Mrs. Baker filled the tank. How many miles has the Baker family driven when the tank contains $8\frac{1}{2}$ gallons of fuel? **8.EE.7b, MP 2**

_____

3 ✋**H.O.T. Problem** Riley wants to take a 10-week martial arts course at one of three schools. School B is offering 50% off the regular membership fee. School C is offering 15% off its regular per-class fee.

	Regular Cost ($)		Total Discounted Cost ($)
	Membership Fee	Per Class Fee ($)	
A	40.00	a	152.50
B	20.00	13.50	b
C	20.00	16.00	c

Which school offers the lowest total cost? Justify your answer. **8.EE.7, MP 1**

_____

_____

_____

_____

Lesson 3   Multi-Step Problem Solving

Multi-Step Example

Brian, Natalie, and Lakita have raised $49.30 for improvements to the science lab. The table shows information about the amount raised. Which equation can be solved to find the amount Brian has raised? **8.EE.7b, MP 4**

Ⓐ $2.3x + 3.50 = 49.30$ Ⓒ $3.3x + 3.50 = 49.30$

Ⓑ $3x + 3.80 = 49.30$ Ⓓ $5.5x + 0.30 = 49.30$

Science Lab Fundraising	
Student	Amount ($)
Brian	x
Natalie	3.50 more than Brian
Lakita	30% more than Brian

Use a problem-solving model to solve this problem.

1 Understand

Read the problem. Circle the information you know.
Underline what the problem is asking you to find.

2 Plan

What will you need to do to solve the problem? Write your plan in steps.

Step 1   Use the information _____ to write an equation.

Step 2   Collect _____ to write an _____ equation.

> **Read to Succeed!**
>
> When collecting like terms, remember the x equals 1x.

3 Solve

Use your plan to solve the problem. Show your steps.

X represents the amount of money raised by _____. Write expressions

to represent the amounts raised by _____ and _____. The equation

_____ + _____ + _____ = _____ represents the total amount

raised by all three students.

Since the equation can be written as _____ + _____ = _____,

the correct answer is ____. Fill in that answer choice.

4 Check

How do you know your solution is accurate?

_____

_____

_____

Lesson 3 (continued)

Use a problem-solving model to solve each problem.

1 The total land area of the three largest states in the United States is approximately 9.9×10^5 square miles.

Approximate Land Areas	
State	**Land Area (sq mi)**
Alaska	3.1×10^5 more than Texas
Texas	t
California	40% less than Texas

Which equation can be solved to find the approximate land area of Texas? **8.EE.7b, MP 2**

Ⓐ $2.4t + 310{,}000 = 990{,}000$

Ⓑ $2.6t + 310{,}000 = 990{,}000$

Ⓒ $2.6t + 3{,}100{,}000 = 9{,}900{,}000$

Ⓓ $3.6t + 3{,}100{,}000 = 9{,}900{,}000$

2 The diagram shown below represents three streets on a map. The measure of angle 2 is twice the measure of angle 1. The measure of angle 3 is 20° more than the measure of angle 2. What is the measure of angle 4 in degrees? **8.EE.7, MP 1**

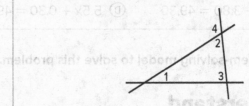

_____

_____

3 An engineer drew this cross-section view of a concrete highway support. The cross-section area is 200 square units.

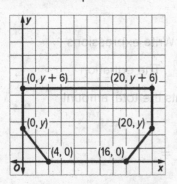

What is the value of y? **8.EE.7b, MP 7**

_____

4 **H.O.T. Problem** Tia wants a window like the one shown below. If the outside perimeter of the window is 170 inches, what is its width w? Use $\frac{22}{7}$ for π. Defend your answer. **8.EE.7b, MP 3**

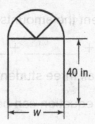

_____

_____

_____

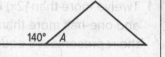

Lesson 4 Multi-Step Problem Solving

Multi-Step Example

The sum of the measure of angle A and 15x is 10x less than the sum of the measures of all three of the interior angles of a triangle shown at the right. Which of the following equations could represent this relationship? 8.EE.7, MP 4

(A) $40 + 15x = 180 - 10x$

(B) $40 - 15x = 180 + 10x$

(C) $40 - 15x = 180 - 10x$

(D) $40 + 15x = 180 + 10x$

Use a problem-solving model to solve this problem.

1 Understand

Read the problem. (Circle) the information you know.
Underline what the problem is asking you to find.

2 Plan

What will you need to do to solve the problem? Write your plan in steps.

Step 1 Translate the _____ sentence to a mathematical _____.

Step 2 Determine which _____ listed above represents the situation.

3 Solve

Use your plan to solve the problem. Show your steps.

The measure of angle A is 180 − _____ or_____.

The mathematical expressions _____ and _____ represent the verbal expressions.

So, the equation _____ = _____ can be used to represent

the relationship. The correct answer is ____. Fill in that answer choice.

> **Read to Succeed!**
> Remember that the sum of the interior angles of a triangle is 180°.

4 Check

How do you know your solution is accurate?

_____

_____

Lesson 4 *(continued)*

Use a problem-solving model to solve each problem.

1 Twelve more than $(2x)$ is x. One-half y is two and one-half more than $(3y)$. Which shows the representative equations and the directions to plot a point with the resulting coordinate values? **8.EE.7b,** **MP** 4

Ⓐ $2x + 12 = x$; $0.5y = 2.5 + 3y$; From the origin, move 12 units right and 1 unit up.

Ⓑ $2x + 12 = x$; $0.5y = 2.5 + 3y$; From the origin, move 12 units left and 1 unit down.

Ⓒ $x + 12 = 2x$; $0.5y + 2.5 = 3y$; From the origin, move 12 units right and 1 unit up.

Ⓓ $x + 12 = 2x$; $0.5y + 2.5 = 3y$; From the origin, move 12 units left and 1 unit down.

2 The circumference of a circle with diameter $(6a - 1)$ feet equals the circumference of the circle below. What is the diameter of the circle below in inches? **8.EE.7,** **MP** 1

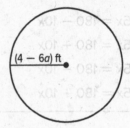

(4 − 6a) ft

3 Rectangle A is similar to rectangle B by scale factor r. The length of rectangle A is $1.5r + 2.25$ units. The length of rectangle B is 3 units. What is the scale factor? **8.EE.7b,** **MP** 7

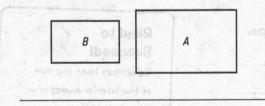

4 🔥 **H.O.T. Problem** The total area of the composite figure shown below is twice the area of one of its two shapes. What is the value of x? **8.EE.7,** **MP** 7

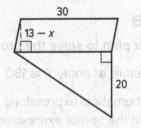

30

13 − x

20

Lesson 5   **Multi-Step** Problem Solving

Multi-Step Example

The table shows the hours worked by employees at a coffee shop last month. What is the ratio of Jaime's hours worked to Mai's hours worked if the total hours worked for all employees is $7m + 19$? Write your answer as a decimal. **8.EE.7b,** **1**

Employee	Hours Worked
Shantel	48
Lorenzo	$2m + 7$
Jaime	$3.5(m - 6)$
Mai	m

Use a problem-solving model to solve this problem.

 Understand

Read the problem. Circle the information you know.
Underline what the problem is asking you to find.

 Plan

What will you need to do to solve the problem? Write your plan in steps.

Step 1 Write and solve an _____ that represents

the total number of _____.

Step 2 Write the _____ of _____ hours worked

to _____ hours worked as a decimal.

> **Read to Succeed!**
> Remember that a ratio can be written in a variety of forms, including as a decimal.

3 Solve

Use your plan to solve the problem. Show your steps.

The equation $48 +$ _____ $+$ _____ $+ m =$ _____ represents

the total number of hours worked, so $m =$ ____.

Since $m =$ ____, Jaime worked ____ hours and Mai worked ____ hours.

So, the ratio of Jaime's hours to Mai's hours is ____:____ or ____.

4 Check

How do you know your solution is accurate? _____

_____

_____

_____

Lesson 5 *(continued)*

Use a problem-solving model to solve each problem.

1 The area of Rectangle *B* is 2*x* square units less than the area of Rectangle *A*. What is the value of *x*? 8.EE.7b, **MP** 4

Rectangle A:

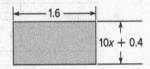

Rectangle B:

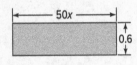

2 The graph shows the number of coins Pascual has in a jar. How much money, in dollars, does he have if the total number of coins is twice the number of pennies? 8.EE.7a, **MP** 2

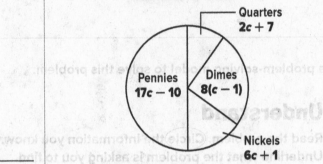

3 ✋ **H.O.T. Problem** Calvin bought the items described below. Determine the total cost of his purchase. Explain. 8.EE.7a, **MP** 1

- The price of the shirt is triple the price of the socks.
- The price of the wallet is $6 more than the price of the umbrella.
- The price of the umbrella is 150% of the price of the socks.
- There was no sales tax on the clothing. There was 6% sales tax on the umbrella and wallet.
- The pre-tax price of the wallet and umbrella equals the price of the clothing.

Lesson 1 Multi-Step Problem Solving

Multi-Step Example

The graph shows the relationship between the length of the side of a square and the perimeter of the square. Which statement describes the relationship? *Preparation for* **8.EE.5,** **7**

Ⓐ It is a proportional linear relationship with a unit rate of 8.

Ⓑ It is a proportional linear relationship with a unit rate of 4.

Ⓒ It is a non-proportional linear relationship.

Ⓓ It is a non-linear relationship.

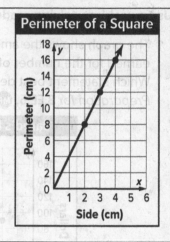

Perimeter of a Square

Side (cm)

Use a problem-solving model to solve this problem.

1 Understand

Read the problem. Circle the information you know.
Underline what the problem is asking you to find.

2 Plan

What will you need to do to solve the problem? Write your plan in steps.

Step 1 Connect the points to see if they form a _____ passing through the _____.

Step 2 If the relationship is linear, determine if the _____ of the pairs of points equal ____ or ____.

3 Solve

Use your plan to solve the problem. Show your steps.

The points form a _____ that passes through the _____.

Since there is a vertical distance of ____ units and a horizontal

distance of ____ unit between points, the unit rate is _____ or ___.

So, the relationship is a _____ with

a unit rate of ____. The correct answer is ____.

> **Read to Succeed!**
> When finding a unit rate from a graph, count the units up or down and then the right or left.

4 Check

How do you know your solution is accurate?

_____

_____

Lesson 1 *(continued)*

Use a problem-solving model to solve each problem.

1 The graph shows the amount of pay Jared earned for the number of hours he worked. Which statement best describes the graph?
Preparation for **8.EE.5,** **MP** 4

Jared's Pay

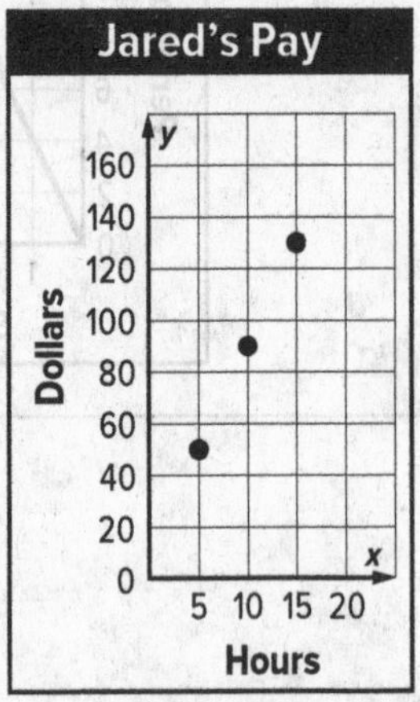

Ⓐ The graph shows a proportional linear relationship with a unit rate of 8.

Ⓑ The graph shows a proportional linear relationship with a unit rate of 10.

Ⓒ The graph shows a non-proportional linear relationship.

Ⓓ The graph shows a non-linear relationship.

2 The table below shows the print speed for color paper of an office computer. How many pages can the printer print in one hour?
Preparation for **8.EE.5,** **MP** 4

Minutes	Pages per Minute
2	32
3	48
4	64

3 The table below shows the amount of dog food needed each day based on a dog's weight. How many pounds of dog food are needed to feed a 28-pound dog for 1 week? Round your answer to the nearest pound.
Preparation for **8.EE.5,** **MP** 4

Weight (lb)	Daily Amount of Food (oz)
5	1.6
15	4.8
20	6.4

4 🔥**H.O.T. Problem** The table below shows a linear relationship. What is the value of k? Support your answer.
Preparation for **8.EE.5,** **MP** 3

x	y
3	9
7	k
9	21

_____

_____

_____

Lesson 2 Multi-Step Problem Solving

Multi-Step Example

The table shows the coordinates of two points on a line. If the slope of the line is $-\frac{3}{4}$, what is the value of k? *Preparation for* **8.EE.5,** **MP** 7

x	2	6
y	5	k

(A) -8 (C) 2

(B) -2 (D) 8

Use a problem-solving model to solve this problem.

1 Understand

Read the problem. (Circle) the information you know.
Underline what the problem is asking you to find.

2 Plan

What will you need to do to solve the problem? Write your plan in steps.

Step 1 Replace known values for the variables in the slope formula.

Step 2 Solve the equation for k.

3 Solve

Use your plan to solve the problem. Show your steps.

Replace m with $-\frac{3}{4}$, y_2 with _____, y_1 with _____, x_2 with _____,

and x_1 with _____.

Solve for k.

$$\frac{\boxed{}}{\boxed{}} = \frac{\boxed{} - \boxed{}}{\boxed{} - \boxed{}}$$

Since $k = $ _____, the correct answer is _____.

Read to Succeed!

Remember to subtract the y-coordinates and the x-coordinates in the same order.

4 Check

How do you know your solution is accurate?

_____

_____

_____

Lesson 2 (continued)

Use a problem-solving model to solve each problem.

1 The slope of a line is $-\frac{2}{3}$. One point on the line is (4, 3). Which of the following is another point on the line? *Preparation for* **8.EE.5,** (MP) **1**

Ⓐ (10, 7)

Ⓑ (10, −1)

Ⓒ (0, 9)

Ⓓ (8, 9)

2 The graph shows the times, called split times, for each mile in a 5-mile race. Which rate of change in minutes per mile is greater: the rate of change between miles 1 and 2 or between miles 4 and 5? Explain. *Preparation for* **8.EE.5,** (MP) **4**

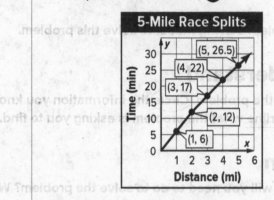

_____

_____

_____

3 The points in the table below lie on a line. What is the value of *y* when *x* is 10? *Preparation for* **8.EE.5,** (MP) **7**

x	−1	1	3
y	−87	3	93

_____

4 🔥 **H.O.T. Problem** The vertices of parallelogram *ABCD* are *A*(11, 5), *B*(8, 1), *C*(2, 3), and *D*(x, 7). What is the value of *x*? Justify your answer. *Preparation for* **8.EE.5,** (MP) **3**

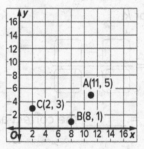

_____

_____

_____

_____

Lesson 3   **Multi-Step** Problem Solving

Multi-Step Example

Trevor burns 40 Calories when he cycles for 5 minutes and 80 Calories when he cycles for 10 minutes. The equation $y = 3.25x$ represents the number of Calories he burns when walking. How many more Calories does Trevor burn by cycling for 20 minutes than by walking for 20 minutes? **8.F.2,** **MP** **2**

Use a problem-solving model to solve this problem.

 Understand

Read the problem. (Circle) the information you know.
Underline what the problem is asking you to find.

 Plan

What will you need to do to solve the problem? Write your plan in steps.

Step 1   Write an equation to represent the Calories burned when _____.

Step 2   Replace _____ in both equations with _____ and determine the number of Calories burned by _____ each of cycling and walking.

Read to Succeed!

When writing an equation for Calories burned by cycling, find the unit rate of Calories burned per minute.

 Solve

Use your plan to solve the problem. Show your steps.

The equation _____ represents the Calories burned

when _____.

Trevor burns ____(____) or ____ Calories when cycling

and ____(____) or ____ Calories when walking. Since

____ − ____ = ____, ____ more Calories are burned by cycling.

 Check

How do you know your solution is accurate?

_____

_____

Lesson 3 *(continued)*

Use a problem-solving model to solve each problem.

1 The table below shows the number of words Luz types over different periods of time. Deepak's typing speed is represented by the equation $w = 34t$. If each student types for 5 minutes at a constant rate, who types more words? how many more? **8.F.2, MP 2**

Number of Words (w)	Time in Minutes (t)
84	3
168	6
224	8

2 The table below shows the number of rectangular tiles needed to cover square-shaped floors with certain side lengths. If the number of tiles is proportional to the area of the floor, how many tiles would be needed for a square-shaped floor with a side length of 9 feet? **8.F.4, MP 4**

Number of Tiles	Side Length of Floor (ft)
147	7
432	12
675	15

3 Denzel and Maria played a game and recorded their scores after each turn as ordered pairs. Denzel's ordered pairs included (1, 4), (3, 12), and (4, 16). Maria's ordered pairs included (1, 5), (5, 25), and (6, 30). Each player made a graph using the ordered pairs. Assuming each player's score is proportional, what is the difference between the slope of Denzel's graph and the slope of Maria's graph? **8.F.4, MP 2**

4 🔥**H.O.T. Problem** Refer to the graph below. What is the value of x when $y = 125$? Explain **8.EE.5, MP 4**

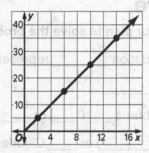

Lesson 4   Multi-Step Problem Solving

Multi-Step Example

The table shown at the right represents the online cost of a specific number of tickets, including a \$2 handling fee, at a movie theater last week. Next week, the movie theater will increase the online ticket price by \$1 each. Which equation represents the new online cost of movie theater tickets, including the \$2 handling fee? **8.F.4, MP 2**

Number of Tickets	Cost (\$)
0	2
1	11
2	20
3	29

Ⓐ $y = 9x$ Ⓒ $y = 10x$

Ⓑ $y = 9x + 2$ Ⓓ $y = 10x + 2$

Use a problem-solving model to solve this problem.

Understand

Read the problem. ⟨Circle⟩ the information you know.
Underline what the problem is asking you to find.

Plan

What will you need to do to solve the problem? Write your plan in steps.

⟨ **Step 1** ⟩   Write an _____ that represents _____.

⟨ **Step 2** ⟩   Revise the _____ to represent _____.

Solve

Use your plan to solve the problem. Show your steps.

Last week, the cost per ticket was $\dfrac{\boxed{} - \boxed{}}{\boxed{} - \boxed{}} = \$\boxed{}$.

The equation _____ represents the cost of x number of

tickets last week. So, the equation _____ represents the

new cost. The correct answer is _____.

> **Read to Succeed!**
>
> When writing an equation in slope-intercept form, ask yourself what the slope will represent and what the y-intercept will represent.

Check

How do you know your solution is accurate?

_____

_____

_____

Lesson 4 *(continued)*

Use a problem-solving model to solve each problem.

1 The table shown below shows the number of pizzas ordered from a local pizza shop and the total cost in dollars. The cost includes a $2 delivery fee. Next week, the shop is going to decrease the price of a pizza by $1.50. Which equation represents the new relationship? **8.F.4,** **MP** **2**

Number of Pizzas	Total Cost ($)
1	13
2	24
3	35
4	46

Ⓐ $y = 9.50x + 2$

Ⓑ $y = 9.50x$

Ⓒ $y = 12.50x + 2$

Ⓓ $y = 12.50x$

2 Davina is comparing cell phone plans. The first plan has a flat fee of $10 per month plus $0.04 per text message. The second plan has a flat fee of $5 per month plus $0.12 per text message. What is the difference in dollars of the two plans for sending 15 text messages each month for six months? **8.F.4,** **MP** **2**

3 A puppy grows at a constant rate of 1.25 pounds per week. After 4 weeks, he weighs 8 pounds. How many pounds will he weigh after 6 weeks if he continues to grow at the same rate? **8.F.4,** **MP** **2**

_____

4 ✋ **H.O.T. Problem** If the given line is slid right 4 and up 2 grid spaces, what will be the equation of the line? **8.F.4,** **MP** **4**

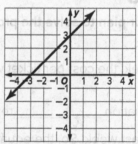

_____

Lesson 5   Multi-Step Problem Solving

Multi-Step Example

Concession sales for *x* number of hot dogs and *y* number of pizza slices at a football game are represented by the equation $2x + 3y = 1{,}728$. Which statement is true?
Preparation for **8.EE.8c,** **MP** **2**

Ⓐ Each hot dog cost $3.

Ⓑ Each pizza slice cost $2.

Ⓒ If 0 hot dogs were sold, then 576 pizza sliced were sold.

Ⓓ If 0 hot dogs were sold, then 864 pizza slices were sold.

Use a problem-solving model to solve this problem.

1 Understand

Read the problem. Circle **the information you know.**
Underline what the problem is asking you to find.

2 Plan

What will you need to do to solve the problem? Write your plan in steps.

Step 1   Write the equation in _____ form.

Step 2   Interpret the meaning of the _____.

3 Solve

Use your plan to solve the problem. Show your steps.

The equation can be written as $y =$ _____, which means

that _____ pizza slices are sold when _____ hot dogs are sold. Since

each hot dog costs _____ and each pizza slice costs _____, the correct

answer is _____. Fill in that answer choice.

Read to Succeed!

Remember the *y*-intercept occurs when the *x*-value is 0.

4 Check

How do you know your solution is accurate?

_____

_____

Lesson 5 (continued)

Use a problem-solving model to solve each problem.

1 Play ticket sales for x number of Friday evening tickets and y number of Saturday evening tickets are represented by the equation $14x + 21y = 12{,}579$. Which statement is *not* true?
Preparation for **8.EE.8c**, 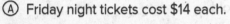 2

  Ⓐ Friday night tickets cost $14 each.

  Ⓑ Saturday night tickets cost $21 each.

  Ⓒ If nobody attended Saturday night, 599 people attended Friday night.

  Ⓓ If nobody attended Friday night, 599 people attended Saturday night.

2 Line ℓ shown in the graph below. What is the x-intercept of the line that has the same y-intercept as, but one-half the slope of, ℓ?
Preparation for **8.EE.8c**, 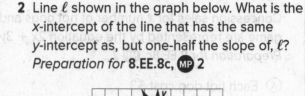 2

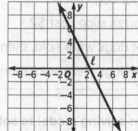

3 The table shows the cost of paint and paint brushes at a local art store. The art store spent $2,400 on the most recent shipment. What is the sum of the slope and y-intercept of the line that represents this shipment?
Preparation for **8.EE.8c**, MP 2

	Paint (gal)	Paint Brushes
Cost ($)	14	8
Amount Ordered	x	y

4 🖐 **H.O.T. Problem** Two rectangles are shown below. The perimeter of the smaller rectangle is 130 units. The perimeter of the larger rectangle is 190 units. Write an equation in standard form for each rectangle. What do you know about the y-intercepts of the graphs of the equations? Support your answer. *Preparation for* **8.EE.8c**, MP 4

$x\;\boxed{}$ $x\;\boxed{}$
$\quad\;\; y_1 \qquad\qquad\quad\; y_2$

Lesson 6 Multi-Step Problem Solving

Multi-Step Example

The graph shows the height in inches i of a candle at h number of hours. Which equation represents this relationship?
Preparation for **8.EE.8c,**  **2**

Ⓐ $h - 2i = 12$

Ⓑ $h + 2i = 12$

Ⓒ $-h - 2i = 12$

Ⓓ $-h + 2i = 12$

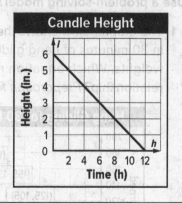

Candle Height

Height (in.) / Time (h)

Use a problem-solving model to solve this problem.

1 Understand

Read the problem. Circle the information you know.
Underline what the problem is asking you to find.

2 Plan

What will you need to do to solve the problem? Write your plan in steps.

Step 1 Use the _____ to write an _____ in slope-intercept form.

Step 2 Write my _____ in standard form.

> **Read to Succeed!**
> When determining the slope, be sure to check the scale on each axis.

3 Solve

Use your plan to solve the problem. Show your steps.

The equation _____ represents the relationship. An

equivalent equation is _____. So, the correct answer is _____.

Fill in that answer choice.

4 Check

How do you know your solution is accurate?

_____

_____

_____

Lesson 6 *(continued)*

Use a problem-solving model to solve each problem.

1 The graph below shows the Calories burned in 30 minutes of hang gliding at various weights. Which equation represents this relationship? *Preparation for* **8.EE.8c, MP 2**

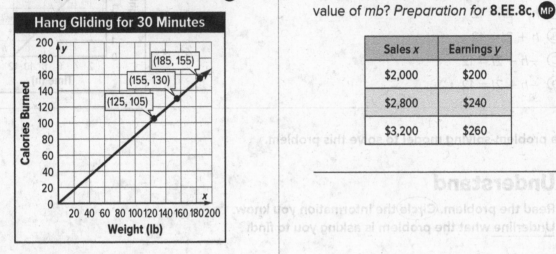

Hang Gliding for 30 Minutes

(185, 155)
(155, 130)
(125, 105)

Calories Burned
Weight (lb)

Ⓐ $y = \frac{6}{5}x - \frac{6}{5}$ Ⓒ $y = \frac{5}{6}x + \frac{5}{6}$

Ⓑ $y = \frac{6}{5}x + \frac{6}{5}$ Ⓓ $y = \frac{5}{6}x$

2 A salesperson is paid a daily salary plus commission as shown in the table below. If the equation that represents this relationship is written in slope-intercept form, what is the value of *mb*? *Preparation for* **8.EE.8c, MP 2**

Sales *x*	Earnings *y*
$2,000	$200
$2,800	$240
$3,200	$260

_____

3 The table below shows the cost *C* for a taxi ride of *m* miles. If the equation that represents this relationship is written in slope-intercept form, what is the value of *m* + *b*? *Preparation for* **8.EE.8c, MP 2**

Miles	1	2	3
Cost ($)	6.50	10.00	13.50

_____

4 🔥 **H.O.T. Problem** The rate of water flowing from a hose is shown in the table below. A 30,000-gallon swimming pool starts out with 4,000 gallons. About how many days does it take to fill it to capacity? Support your answer. *Preparation for* **8.EE.8c, MP 4**

Gallons	18	36	45
Minutes	2	4	5

_____

_____

_____

_____

Lesson 7 Multi-Step Problem Solving

Multi-Step Example

Cody is participating in a walk-a-thon for charity. Cody wants to determine when his uncle's donation will equal the combined total of his sister's and cousin's donations. Which pair of equations and point of intersection represents the situation? **8.EE.8c,** Ⓜ **4**

Family Member	Pledge
Sister	One-time of $30
Uncle	$2.00 per mile
Cousin	50 cents per mile

Ⓐ $y = 2 + x$ and $y = 0.5 + 30x$; (20, 40)

Ⓑ $y = 2 + x$ and $y = 0.5 + 30x$; (0.05, 2.05)

Ⓒ $y = 2x$ and $y = 30 + 0.5x$; (0.05, 2.05)

Ⓓ $y = 2x$ and $y = 30 + 0.5x$; (20, 40)

Use a problem-solving model to solve this problem.

1 Understand

Read the problem. Ⓒircle the information you know.
<u>Underline</u> what the problem is asking you to find.

2 Plan

What will you need to do to solve the problem? Write your plan in steps.

Step 1 Determine the _____ that represents the situation.

Step 2 Determine the _____ that satisfies _____ equations.

3 Solve

Use your plan to solve the problem. Show your steps.

Let x represent the _____. His uncle's donation can

be represented by $y =$ ____. The sum of his sister's and cousin's donations can be

represented by $y =$ _____. So, either __ or __ is the correct answer.

Since 40 = 2(___) and 40 = _____ are true statements, the correct answer is ___.

Read to Succeed!

The phrase $2 per mile can be represented as two times x or 2x.

4 Check

How do you know your solution is accurate?

_____

_____

_____

Lesson 7 *(continued)*

Use a problem-solving model to solve each problem.

1 The table below shows two price packages for gymnastics classes.

Package	Monthly Price
1	$50 plus $8 per class
2	$15 plus $15 per class

Suppose each session is 2 hours, what is the solution and interpretation of the simultaneous equations that represent the two packages? **8.EE.8c, MP 4**

Ⓐ (5, 90); The monthly cost for 10 hours is the same for both packages.

Ⓑ (90, 5); The monthly cost for 5 hours is the same for both packages.

Ⓒ (5, 90); The monthly cost for 10 sessions is the same for both packages.

Ⓓ (90, 5); The monthly cost for 90 sessions is the same for both packages.

3 In Week 1, a department store had a store-wide sale of a percentage off the regular price of any item. In Week 2, the store offered a rebate off any regular-priced item. The graph shows a set of simultaneous equations that represents the sales during both weeks. What is the difference between the regular price and sale price of the item that sold for the same price each week? **8.EE.8b, MP 7**

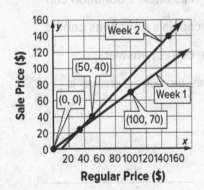

2 A pair of linear equations is graphed to show where the perimeters of the two shapes shown below are equal. The lines intersect at (5, 40). What is the value of a? **8.EE.8a, MP 7**

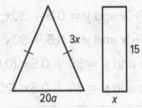

_____

4 🔥 **H.O.T. Problem** Miguel orders pizza from two pizza shops. The first shop charges $7 for a cheese pizza and $1.60 per topping. The second shop charges $10 for a cheese pizza and $0.80 per topping. Miguel paid $13.20 for a 4-topping pizza at the second shop. Define a variable, x, and write a pair of linear equations that could help Miguel determine which pizza shop offers the better deal. **8.EE.8c, MP 4**

_____

_____

_____

_____

_____

_____

_____

Lesson 8 Multi-Step Problem Solving

Multi-Step Example

A total of 85 tickets were sold for the school play. Sixteen times as many adult tickets as children's tickets were sold. How many children's tickets were sold? **8.EE.8c, MP** 4

Ⓐ 5   Ⓑ 16   Ⓒ 17   Ⓓ 80

Use a problem-solving model to solve this problem.

1 Understand

Read the problem. Circle the information you know.
Underline what the problem is asking you to find.

2 Plan

What will you need to do to solve the problem? Write your plan in steps.

Step 1 Define the _____ and write a system of _____ to represent the situation.

Step 2 _____ the system algebraically.

Step 3 Interpret the _____.

> **Read to Succeed!**
> Remember to define the variables so that you can interpret the answer correctly.

3 Solve

Use your plan to solve the problem. Show your steps.

Let x equal the number of children's tickets sold. Let y equal the number of adult tickets sold. Write an equation to represent the total number of tickets sold.
$x + y =$ _____

Write an equation to represent the number of children's tickets sold compared to the number of adult tickets sold. ____ $= 16 \cdot$ ____

Use substitution to solve the system of equations.

$x + y =$ _____ $x +$ _____ $= 85$ _____ $= 85$ $x =$ _____

Next solve for y. $y =$ _____ $y = 16 \cdot$ _____ $y =$ _____

Since x is the number of children's tickets sold and y is the number of adult tickets sold we know that there were _____ adult tickets sold and _____ children's

tickets sold. The correct answer is _____. Fill in that answer.

4 Check

How do you know your solution is accurate?

_____

_____

Lesson 8   (continued)

Use a problem-solving model to solve each problem.

1 Marjorie bought a total of 9 articles of clothing that included shirts and pants. She bought 3 more shirts than pants. How many of each did she buy? **8.EE.8c,** (MP) **4**

Ⓐ 6 pants; 3 shirts

Ⓑ 5 pants; 4 shirts

Ⓒ 4 pants; 5 shirts

Ⓓ 3 pants; 6 shirts

2 The table shows the rate at which two motorcycles are racing in an endurance race. Motorcycle A starts 75 miles ahead of motorcycle B. How long will it take for motorcycle B to catch up to motorcycle A, and how far will motorcycle B have traveled? **8.EE.8c,** (MP) **4**

Motorcycle	Rate (mph)
A	20
B	80

_____

_____

_____

3 The bar diagram represents the sales of popcorn and hot dogs at a baseball game. How many boxes of popcorn and hot dogs were sold at the game? **8.EE.8c,** (MP) **4**

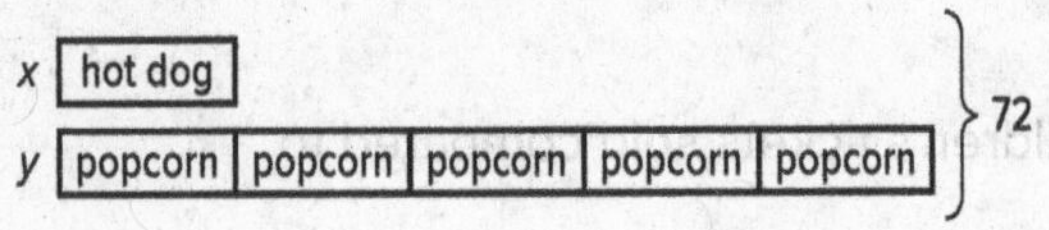

x	hot dog				
y	popcorn	popcorn	popcorn	popcorn	popcorn

} 72

_____

_____

_____

4 ✋**H.O.T. Problem** What is the solution to the system $-2x + y = 6$ and $y = 2x - 3$? Explain your answer. **8.EE.8b,** (MP) **1**

_____

_____

_____

_____

_____

Lesson 1 Multi-Step Problem Solving

Multi-Step Example

Bruno and Mía joined yoga classes. The amount Bruno pays is represented by the equation $y = 5x$, where x represents the number of classes and y represents the total cost. The table shows the amount Mía pays for her yoga classes. What is the difference between the costs of each plan for 10 classes? 8.F.4, MP 1

Classes	Cost ($)
1	22
2	24
3	26
4	28

Use a problem-solving model to solve this problem.

1 Understand

Read the problem. Circle the information you know.
Underline what the problem is asking you to find.

2 Plan

What will you need to do to solve the problem? Write your plan in steps.

Step 1 Determine the _____ of each plan for 10 classes.

Step 2 Determine the _____ in the cost for 10 classes.

3 Solve

Use your plan to solve the problem. Show your steps.

Bruno pays _____(_____) or _____ for 10 classes.

Mía's cost increases by _____ per class. So, she pays _____ for 10 classes.

Since _____ – _____ is _____, the difference in cost between

the two plans is _____.

Read to Succeed!

Notice that the table does not give the y-intercept.

4 Check

How do you know your solution is accurate?

_____

_____

_____

Lesson 1 *(continued)*

Use a problem-solving model to solve each problem.

1 The cost of renting a bike using Plan A is given by $y = 5x + 25$, where x represents the number of days and y represents the total cost in dollars. The graph shows the cost for Plan B. What is the difference between the cost of Plan A and Plan B for renting a bike for 8 days? **8.F.4, MP 4**

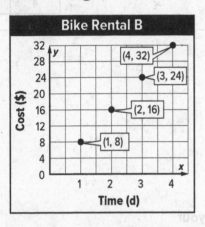

Bike Rental B

(4, 32)
(3, 24)
(2, 16)
(1, 8)

Cost ($) vs Time (d)

_____

2 Jun recorded the times and distances she rode her bike this weekend. At the rate shown in the table, how long will it take her to ride $71\frac{1}{4}$ miles? **8.F.4, MP 4**

Minutes	Miles
90	22.5
150	37.5
210	52.5
330	82.5

3 The graph shows the amount, in dollars, in Thiago's savings account each week for several weeks. If the pattern continues, in how many weeks will Thiago have $125 in his savings account? **8.F.4, MP 4**

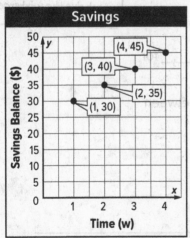

Savings

(4, 45)
(3, 40)
(2, 35)
(1, 30)

Savings Balance ($) vs Time (w)

_____

4 ✋H.O.T. Problem Games R Us offers two plans for renting video games. Plan A charges a one-time membership fee of $24 plus $1 for each game rental. Plan B charges $3 per game rental. For what number of games is the cost of both plans the same? Justify your answer. **8.F.4, MP 1**

_____

_____

_____

_____

Lesson 2 **Multi-Step** Problem Solving

Multi-Step Example

The relations in the graph at the right show the distances driven by Denzel and Mei on the second day of a two-day road trip. Which statement is true when the time equals 5 hours? *Preparation for* **8.F.1, MP 2**

Ⓐ Mei is driving at a faster speed than Denzel.

Ⓑ Denzel is driving at a faster speed than Mei.

Ⓒ Mei and Denzel are driving at the same speed.

Ⓓ The speeds of Mei and Denzel cannot be determined.

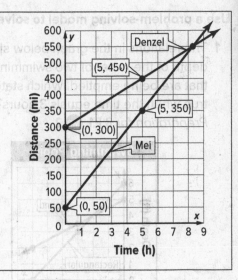

Use a problem-solving model to solve this problem.

1 Understand

Read the problem. Circle the information you know.
Underline what the problem is asking you to find.

2 Plan

What will you need to do to solve the problem? Write your plan in steps.

Step 1 Determine the _____ of each driver.

Step 2 Compare the _____ of the two drivers.

3 Solve

Use your plan to solve the problem. Show your steps.

Denzel's speed is ————— or ____ miles per hour.

Mei's speed is ————— or ____ miles per hour.

Since ____ > ____, _____'s speed is faster than _____'s speed.

So, the correct answer is ____. Fill in that answer choice.

> **Read to Succeed!**
>
> When finding slope, remember to subtract the x-coordinates in the same order that you subtracted the y-coordinates.

4 Check

How do you know your solution is accurate?

_____

_____

Lesson 2 *(continued)*

Use a problem-solving model to solve each problem.

1 The relations in the graph below show the depth of the water of two swimming pools that are being emptied. Which statement is true when the time equals 3 hours?
Preparation for 8.F.1, **MP** 2

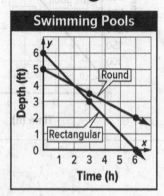

Ⓐ The rectangular pool is being emptied at a slower rate than the round pool.

Ⓑ The round pool is being emptied at a slower rate than the rectangular pool.

Ⓒ The pools are being emptied at the same rate.

Ⓓ The rates at which the pools are being emptied cannot be determined.

2 The table below shows the pressure in pounds per square foot that an object would be under if it were submerged to various depths. What would be the approximate pressure in pounds per square inch of an object submerged to a depth of 20 feet?
Preparation for 8.F.1, **MP** 4

Depth (ft)	Pressure (lb/ft²)
0	2,117
4	2,367
8	2,617
10	2,742

_____

_____

3 The relation shown below shows the cost of downloading songs from an online music Web site. Suppose you spent $36.75 on downloads from this site. How many songs did you download? *Preparation for 8.F.1,* **MP** 2

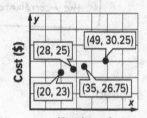

_____

4 🖐 **H.O.T. Problem** A concession stand at a high school football game sells a hot dog meal that includes a drink for $3.50. Write a relation consisting of five ordered pairs where the domain represents the number of meals and the range represents the total cost. Then write an equation that represents your relation. Interpret the slope and *y*-intercept. **8.F.4,** **MP** 4

_____

_____

_____

Lesson 3   **Multi-Step** Problem Solving

Multi-Step Example

A store is having a sale on T-shirts. Customers receive one free T-shirt for every three T-shirts purchased. If T-shirts sell for $10 each and a customer selects 6 T-shirts, which of the following statements about the customer's purchase is true? **8.F.1, MP 2**

Ⓐ The relation is a function and has a range of {1, 2, 3, 4, 5, 6}.

Ⓑ The relation is a function and has a range of {10, 20, 30, 40, 50}.

Ⓒ The relation is not a function and has a range of {1, 2, 3, 4, 5, 6}.

Ⓓ The relation is not a function and has a range of {10, 20, 30, 40, 50}.

Use a problem-solving model to solve this problem.

Understand

Read the problem. ⟨Circle⟩ the information you know.
Underline what the problem is asking you to find.

2 Plan

What will you need to do to solve the problem? Write your plan in steps.

Step 1   Write a set of _____ that represents the customer's purchase.

Step 2   Determine if the relation is a _____, and determine its _____.

Solve

Use your plan to solve the problem. Show your steps.

The customer's purchase can be represented as the set of ordered pairs (number of T-shirts, total cost).

{(1, 10), (2, 20), (3, _____), (4, _____), (5, _____), (6, _____)}

Since each member of the domain is mapped to

_____, the relation is a function. The range is

{_____}. So, the correct answer is _____. Fill in that choice.

> **Read to Succeed!**
> When writing your ordered pairs, remember that every 4th T-shirt is free.

4 Check

How do you know your solution is accurate?

_____

_____

_____

Lesson 3 *(continued)*

Use a problem-solving model to solve each problem.

1 As shown in the table below, Fav Pizza offers half off of each additional topping. Which ordered pair represents the cost of a pizza with 6 toppings? **8.F.1,** **MP** **2**

Number of Toppings	Fav Pizza Cost ($)
1	11.60
2	12.40
3	12.80
4	13.00

    Ⓐ (6, 13.15)   Ⓒ (13.4, 6)

    Ⓑ (6, 13.4)   Ⓓ (13.5, 6)

2 In the mapping below, A maps onto B, and B maps onto C. Assume the function mapping A onto B and B onto C are linear. If the input value for A equals 6, what would the output value for C equal? **8.F.1,** **MP** **2**

$$A \longrightarrow B \longrightarrow C$$

A	B	C
1	4	7
3	6	11
−2	1	1

3 The table shows the cost of purchasing and profit from various numbers of backpacks. What is cost of purchasing 20 backpacks? What is the profit based on purchasing 20 backpacks? **8.F.1,** **MP** **4**

Number of Backpacks	Cost ($)	Profit ($)
6	120	10
7	135	15
8	150	20
9	165	25

_____

4 🔥 **H.O.T. Problem** The table shows two relations, A and B. Which relation is not a function? Which single value of x or y could be changed to make the relation a function? Justify your answers. **8.F.1,** **MP** **2**

A		B	
x	y	x	y
−4	5	−3	−3
0	−4	3	3
−4	−2	0	3

_____

_____

_____

Lesson 4   Multi-Step Problem Solving

Multi-Step Example

Which statement is true about the relationships involving a circle shown at the right? **8.F.4, MP 7**

Ⓐ Only Relationships 1 and 2 are linear functions.

Ⓑ Only Relationship 3 is a linear function.

Ⓒ All three of the relationships are linear functions.

Ⓓ None of the relationships are linear functions.

Relationship	
1.	(radius, diameter)
2.	(radius, circumference)
3.	(radius, area)

Use a problem-solving model to solve this problem.

1 Understand

Read the problem. Circle the information you know. Underline what the problem is asking you to find.

2 Plan

What will you need to do to solve the problem? Write your plan in steps.

Step 1   Determine the _____, _____, and _____ for various radii.

Step 2   Determine which relations, if any, represent _____.

3 Solve

Use your plan to solve the problem. Show your steps.

Write ordered pairs using radii of 1, 2, 3, 4, and 5.

(radius, diameter): {(1, _____), (2, _____), (3, _____), (4, _____), (5, _____)}

(radius, circumference): {(1, _____), (2, _____), (3, _____),

(4, _____), (5, _____)}

(radius, area): {(1, _____), (2, _____), (3, _____), (4, _____),

(5, _____)}

All three relations are _____, but the third relation does not have

a constant _____. So, the correct answer is _____.

> **Read to Succeed!**
> Since the circumference and area formulas involve pi, round your calculations to the nearest tenth.

4 Check

How do you know your solution is accurate?

_____

_____

Lesson 4 (continued)

Use a problem-solving model to solve each problem.

1 Which statement is true about the relations shown in the tables below? 8.F.4, **MP** 7

Table 1	
x	y
−4	−4
1	2
5	5

Table 2	
x	y
−1	1
3	5
5	7

Ⓐ Neither table represents a linear function.

Ⓑ Only Table 1 represents a linear function.

Ⓒ Only Table 2 represents a linear function.

Ⓓ Both tables represent linear functions.

2 The table below shows the number of net Calories Silvia burns swimming for various numbers of minutes. Based on Silvia's metabolism, she must burn 3,500 net Calories to lose 16 ounces of fat. If Silvia swims 30 minutes a day, about how many days will it take her to lose at least 5 pounds? 8.F.4, **MP** 1

Minutes	Net Calories Burned
2	28
4	56
6	84
8	112

_____

3 Pablo bought tickets at the state fair to play arcade games. Expressions for the number of tickets he used to play three arcade games are shown in the table below. After playing the third game, he had 6 tickets left. How many total tickets did Pablo buy? 8.F.4, **MP** 1

Game	Expressions
1	$\frac{1}{2}$(tickets bought − 2)
2	$\frac{1}{4}$ tickets remaining
3	$\frac{1}{3}$ tickets remaining

_____

4 🔥 **H.O.T. Problem** A faucet is dripping at a constant rate of 400 cubic millimeters per minute. A 6 fluid ounce cup is set under the faucet to collect water. How long will it take for the dripping water to fill the cup? Justify your response. (*Hint*: 6 fl oz ≈ 177.67 cm³) 8.F.4, **MP** 7

_____

_____

_____

_____

_____

_____

_____

_____

Lesson 5   **Multi-Step** Problem Solving

Multi-Step Example

A librarian is considering two options for calculating overdue late fees. The first option uses $L = 0.30d + 0.50$, where L is the late fee in dollars and d is the number of days late. The second option is shown in the table. Which statement describes how the late fees compare for a book that is 8 days late? **8.F.2, MP 2**

Option 2				
Days Late	1	2	3	4
Late Fee ($)	0.40	0.80	1.20	1.60

Ⓐ The late fee in the proportional option is $0.30 more.

Ⓑ The late fee in the non-proportional plan is $0.30 more.

Ⓒ The late fee in the proportional plan is $0.90 more.

Ⓓ The late fee in the non-proportional plan is $0.90 more.

Use a problem-solving model to solve this problem.

1 Understand

Read the problem. Circle the information you know.
Underline what the problem is asking you to find.

2 Plan

What will you need to do to solve the problem? Write your plan in steps.

Step 1   Determine which option is _____. For each option, determine

the late fee for a book that is _____.

Step 2   Determine which statement is correct.

3 Solve

Use your plan to solve the problem. Show your steps.

Option 1: $L = \$$_____(____) + $\$$_____ = $\$$_____

Option 2: $\$$_____(____) = $\$$_____

The fee for a book that is 8 days late is _____ under

Option ____, which is the _____ option. So, the correct answer is ____.

> **Read to Succeed!**
>
> Recall that the quantities in proportional relationships have equal ratios. Equations of proportional relationships can be written in $y = mx$ form.

4 Check

How do you know your solution is accurate?

_____

_____

_____

Lesson 5 *(continued)*

Use a problem-solving model to solve each problem.

1 Sonia's profits from mowing lawns is given by $y = 5.50x$, where y is the profit in dollars and x is the number of hours worked. Victor's profits are shown in the table.

Victor's Profits				
Hours Worked	1	2	3	4
Profit ($)	1.50	8.00	14.50	21.00

Which option describes how the profits compare for 7 hours of work? **8.F.2, MP 2**

Ⓐ The profit of the proportional function is $2.00 more.

Ⓑ The profit of the non-proportional function is $2.00 more.

Ⓒ The profit of the proportional function is $7.00 more.

Ⓓ The profit of the non-proportional function is $7.00 more.

2 Leto is considering buying books on display at four different tables. Each table has one of the following signs.

Each Book $10

Each Book $8 for Club Members (One-Time Membership Fee: $15)

Each Book 50% Off

What will be the total cost if Leto buys 6 books from the table whose sign indicates a non-proportional relationship? **8.F.4, MP 4**

_____

3 Hugo's elevation as he drives his car is represented by $y = 175x$, where y is elevation in feet and x is the number of minutes he has driven. Irene's elevation is shown in the graph.

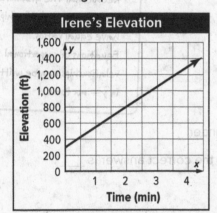

Irene's Elevation

What is the rate of change of the elevation in the non-proportional function? **8.F.2, MP 2**

_____

4 👆 **H.O.T. Problem** Ed and Rayna are cycling in the same direction on the same straight road. Ed's distance from a roadside rest area is given by $d = 6t$. Rayna's distance from the same rest area is given by $d = 4.5t + 12$. In each function, d is distance in miles and t is time in hours. Determine which function(s) is proportional or non-proportional. When are Ed and Rayna the same distance from the rest area? Defend your answers. **8.F.4, MP 3**

_____

_____

_____

_____

Lesson 6   **Multi-Step** Problem Solving

Multi-Step Example

Felicia wants to fence in a rectangular region whose length will be twice its width. She also wants to fence in a rectangular dog pen that will share a length of fence, as shown in the diagram at the right. Which equation represents the amount of fencing Felicia needs? 8.F.4, 1

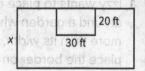

Ⓐ $y = 3x + 70$ Ⓒ $y = 3x + 100$

Ⓑ $y = 6x + 70$ Ⓓ $y = 6x + 100$

Use a problem-solving model to solve this problem.

1 Understand

Read the problem. Circle the information you know.
Underline what the problem is asking you to find.

2 Plan

What will you need to do to solve the problem? Write your plan in steps.

Step 1   Determine the sum of the perimeters of the _____

and the _____.

Step 2   Subtract the _____ length of fencing.

3 Solve

Use your plan to solve the problem. Show your steps.

The perimeter of the rectangular region is 2(_____) + 2(_____)

or _____ feet.

The perimeter of the dog pen is 2(_____) + 2(_____) or _____ feet.

So, the total amount of fencing, less the shared length, is ____ + ____ − ____

or ____ + ____ feet. The correct answer is ____. Fill in that answer.

> **Read to Succeed!**
>
> Remember even though coefficients are added or subtracted when combining like terms, the variables remain the same.

4 Check

How do you know your solution is accurate?

_____

_____

_____

Lesson 6 (continued)

Use a problem-solving model to solve each problem.

1 Izzy wants to place a landscape border around a garden whose length will be 50% more than its width, *x*. He also wants to place the border on two edges of the patio, as shown in the diagram below.

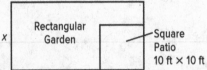

Which equation represents the amount of border Izzy will need? **8.F.4,** (MP) **1**

Ⓐ $y = 2.5x + 20$

Ⓑ $y = 3x + 20$

Ⓒ $y = 5x + 20$

Ⓓ $y = 5x + 40$

2 Rosa wants to buy a motor scooter. The graph shows information about two different scooters.

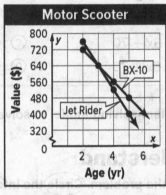

Assuming that the patterns continue, what will be the difference in values of the two scooters when they are 8 years old? **8.F.4,** (MP) **4**

_____

3 The population of a city has grown according to the pattern shown in the table, where *x* represents the number of years since the year 2000. **8.F.4,** (MP) **4**

Years, *x*	City Population, *y*
3	$3.5 \times 10^5 + 3(5 \times 10^5)$
4	$3.5 \times 10^5 + 4(5 \times 10^5)$
5	$3.5 \times 10^5 + 5(5 \times 10^5)$

Using the pattern in the table, what is the value of $\dfrac{\text{population in 2000}}{\text{rate of increase in population}}$?

_____

4 ✋**H.O.T. Problem** Jack and Ryan save at the rates shown in the graph below. In about how many weeks will the boys have a combined savings of $500? **8.F.4,** (MP) **4**

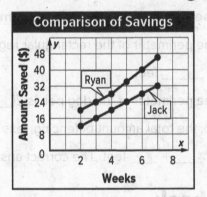

Lesson 7 Multi-Step Problem Solving

Multi-Step Example

The table shows the rate at which a mountain climber is climbing up a mountain. Does the information in the table represent a linear function? Explain your answer. 8.F.3, **MP** 2

Time (h)	2	4	6	8	10
Distance (mi)	10	20	30	40	50

Ⓐ No; because the rate of change is constant.

Ⓑ No; because the rate of change is not constant.

Ⓒ Yes; because the rate of change is constant.

Ⓓ Yes; because the rate of change is not constant.

Use a problem-solving model to solve this problem.

 Understand

Read the problem. Circle the information you know.
Underline what the problem is asking you to find.

> **Read to Succeed!**
>
> Remember, linear functions increase or decrease the same amount between any two points.

 Plan

What will you need to do to solve the problem? Write your plan in steps.

Step 1 Determine the _____ in time.

Step 2 Determine the _____ in distance.

Step 3 Decide whether the _____ is _____.

 Solve

Use your plan to solve the problem. Show your steps.

The differences in the times are _____ hours. The differences in the distances

are _____ miles. The rate of change is _____. The correct answer

is _____; the table represents a linear function because

_____.

The correct answer choice is _____. Fill in that answer choice.

Check

How do you know your solution is accurate?

_____

_____

_____

Lesson 7 *(continued)*

Use a problem-solving model to solve each problem.

1 The volume of a cube is a function of its side length. Does this situation represent a linear function? Explain your answer. **8.F.3, MP 2**

Side Length (cm)	1	2	3	4	5
Volume (cubic cm)	1	8	27	64	125

Ⓐ Yes; because the rate of change is constant.

Ⓑ Yes; because the rate of change is not constant.

Ⓒ No; because the rate of change is constant.

Ⓓ No; because the rate of change is not constant.

2 Jocelyn drove from Seattle to San Francisco. The table shows the distance driven as a linear function of the hours traveled. Complete the table. **8.F.3, MP 2**

Time (h)	1	2	3	6		x
Distance (mi)	75		225		750	

3 Determine whether each function represents a linear or nonlinear situation. Complete the table by filling in the word *linear* or *nonlinear*. **8.F.3, MP 2**

Function	Linear/Nonlinear
$y = \dfrac{3}{x}$	
$x = 3y$	
$y = x + 2$	
$y = x^2 - 3$	

4 🔥 **H.O.T. Problem** Give an example of a real-world situation that can be represented by a nonlinear function. **8.F.3, MP 4**

_____

_____

_____

Lesson 8 Multi-Step Problem Solving

Multi-Step Example

Graph the quadratic function $h = -4.9t^2 + 15t$ which gives the height h of a projectile in meters after t seconds. Use the graph to estimate how many seconds it will take for the projectile to reach its maximum height.

8.F.5, 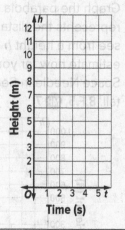 7

Ⓐ 1 second

Ⓑ 1.5 seconds

Ⓒ 2 seconds

Ⓓ 2.5 seconds

Use a problem-solving model to solve this problem.

 Understand

Read the problem. ⟨Circle⟩ the information you know.
Underline what the problem is asking you to find.

Read to Succeed!

Remember, quadratic functions have a variable with the power of 2.

 Plan

What will you need to do to solve the problem? Write your plan in steps.

Step 1   Graph the _____ function.

Step 2   Look along the _____ to determine the maximum _____ then

look along the _____ to determine the _____ in seconds.

 Solve

Use your plan to solve the problem. Show your steps.

The maximum height occurs at about _____ feet. It takes the projectile about

_____ seconds to reach its maximum height. The correct answer is _____.
Fill in that answer choice.

 Check

How do you know your solution is accurate?

_____

_____

_____

Lesson 8 (continued)

Use a problem-solving model to solve each problem.

1 Graph the parabola $h = 0.66d^2$, which represents the distance d in miles you can see from a height h in feet. Use the graph to estimate how far you can see from the Space Needle in Seattle, which is 605 feet tall. **8.F.5,** **MP 7**

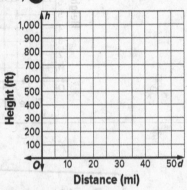

Ⓐ 30 miles

Ⓑ 35 miles

Ⓒ 50 miles

Ⓓ 65 miles

2 A tennis ball is dropped from a height of 300 feet. The function $d = -16t^2 + 300$ models the distance d in feet the tennis ball is from the ground at time t seconds. Graph the function and then use the graph to estimate the time it will take for the tennis ball to reach the ground. **8.F.5,** **MP 7**

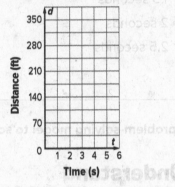

3 Graph the quadratic function $y = x^2 - 5$. Does the graph have a maximum or minimum? What is the coordinate of the maximum or minimum? **8.F.5,** **MP 7**

4 ✋**H.O.T. Problem** Write an equation of a quadratic function that opens downward and has its maximum at (0, 7.5). **8.F.5,** **MP 4**

_____

_____

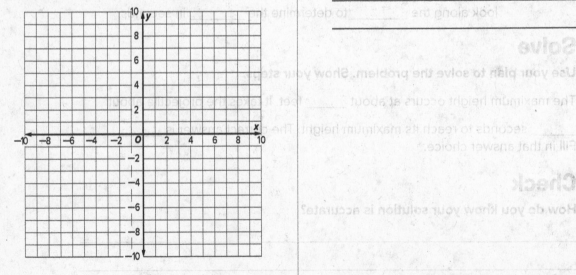

_____

_____

Lesson 9 Multi-Step Problem Solving

Multi-Step Example

The graph displays the speed of an airplane. Describe the change in speed over time. 8.F.5, MP 4

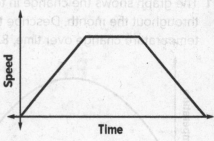

Ⓐ The airplane increases speed at a varied rate, then stops flying, and then decreases speed at a varied rate.

Ⓑ The airplane decreases speed at a varied rate, then stops flying, and then increases speed at a varied rate.

Ⓒ The airplane decreases speed at a constant rate, then maintains a constant speed, and then increases speed at a constant rate.

Ⓓ The airplane increases speed at a constant rate, then maintains a constant speed, and then decreases speed at a constant rate.

Use a problem-solving model to solve this problem.

 Understand

Read the problem. Circle the information you know. Underline what the problem is asking you to find.

 Plan

What will you need to do to solve the problem? Write your plan in steps.

Step 1   Look along the _____ to determine the speed.

Step 2   Look along the _____ to determine the _____.

3 Solve

Use your plan to solve the problem. Show your steps.

The speed _____ at a constant rate. The speed then remains the same

because the line becomes _____. Finally, the speed _____ at a

constant rate. The correct answer is ____.

4 Check

How do you know your solution is accurate?

_____

_____

> **Read to Succeed!**
>
> Remember, linear functions increase or decrease at the same rate. Nonlinear functions increase or decrease at varied rates.

Lesson 9 (continued)

Use a problem-solving model to solve each problem.

1 The graph shows the change in temperature throughout the month. Describe the temperature change over time. 8.F.5, **MP** 4

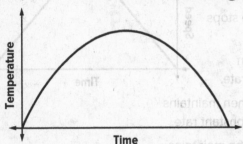

Time

Ⓐ The temperature increases at a varied rate, reaches a maximum, and then decreases at a varied rate.

Ⓑ The temperature decreases at a steady rate, then maintains a constant temperature, and then increases at a steady rate.

Ⓒ The temperature increases at a steady rate, then maintains a constant temperature, and then decreases at a steady rate.

Ⓓ The temperature decreases at a varied rate, reaches a maximum, and then increases at a varied rate.

2 The graph displays a student's distance from school during the school day. Describe the change in distance from the school over time. 8.F.5, **MP** 4

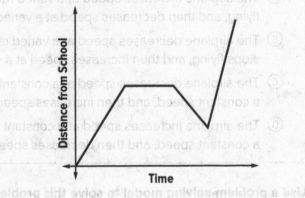

Time

_____

_____

_____

_____

3 The graph shows a cyclist's speed. Describe a situation that would produce this graph. 8.F.5, **MP** 4

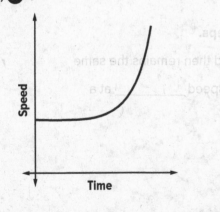

Time

_____

_____

_____

4 🔥**H.O.T. Problem** A man enters an elevator in the lobby and pushes the button for the 11th floor. The elevator malfunctions and does not stop at the 11th floor when it gets there, but it immediately returns to the lobby. Draw a graph of the height of the elevator over time. 8.F.5, **MP** 4

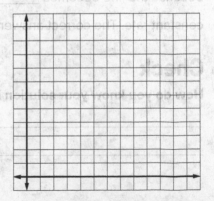

Lesson 1 Multi-Step Problem Solving

Multi-Step Example

What is the value of y in the diagram at the right? 8.G.5, MP 7

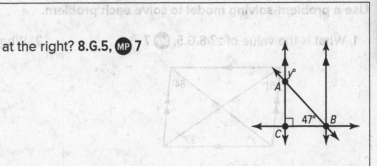

Ⓐ 43

Ⓑ 47

Ⓒ 137

Ⓓ 157

Use a problem-solving model to solve this problem.

1 Understand

Read the problem. Ⓒircle the information you know.
Underline what the problem is asking you to find.

2 Plan

What will you need to do to solve the problem? Write your plan in steps.

Step 1   Use the _____ relationship of a triangle to determine the

measure of angle _____.

Step 2   Determine the value of _____.

3 Solve

Use your plan to solve the problem. Show your steps.

Since m∠_____ + 47 + 90 = _____, m∠_____ = _____.

Since ∠_____ and the angle with the missing measure are

straight angles, y = _____ − _____ or _____ degrees.

The correct answer is ____.

Read to Succeed!

When identifying the third angle of the triangle in the diagram using its vertices, use A as the middle letter.

4 Check

How do you know your solution is accurate?

_____

_____

_____

Lesson 1 (continued)

Use a problem-solving model to solve each problem.

1 What is the value of z? 8.G.5, **MP** 7

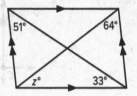

Ⓐ 32

Ⓑ 51

Ⓒ 64

Ⓓ 116

2 What is the value of x? 8.G.5, **MP** 7

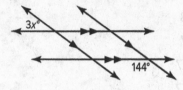

_____

3 If $m\angle 1 = 11x$ and $m\angle 2 = 7x$, what is $m\angle 3$? 8.G.5, **MP** 7

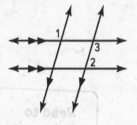

_____

_____

4 👍 **H.O.T. Problem** What is $m\angle 1$? Defend your answer. 8.G.5, **MP** 3

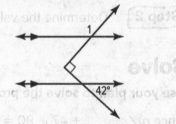

_____

_____

_____

_____

NAME ______________________________ DATE ______________ PERIOD ________

Lesson 2 Multi-Step Problem Solving

Multi-Step Example

Given: $AC = 20$ and the length of BC is triple the length of AB.
Prove: $BC = 15$.
Preparation for **8.G.6, MP 3**

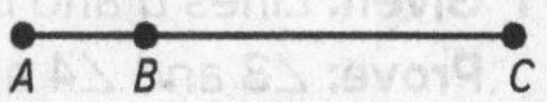

Use a problem-solving model to solve this problem.

> **Read to Succeed!**
> A proof is just a plan to solve a problem with justifications for each step.

1 Understand

Read the problem. Circle the information you know.
Underline what the problem is asking you to find.

2 Plan

What will you need to do to solve the problem? Write your plan in steps.

Step 1 Determine the ________ information.

Step 2 Form a ________ to ________ the given statement.

Step 3 Write a ________ explaining how you solved the problem.

3 Solve

Use your plan to solve the problem. Show your steps.

You know that $AC = 20$ and $BC =$ ________ because of the ________ statements.

You can state that $AB + BC = AC$ because of the ______________________ Property.

By substitution, ____________ = ________.

By solving the equation you find that segment ______ = ______.

By ____________ you prove that $BC = 15$ because $BC = 3AB = 3 \cdot$ ______.

4 Check

How do you know your solution is accurate?

____

____

____

Lesson 2 *(continued)*

Use a problem-solving model to solve each problem.

1 Given: Lines *a* and *b* are perpendicular.
Prove: ∠3 and ∠4 are complementary.
Fill in the blanks of the proof.
Preparation for 8.G.6, **MP** 3

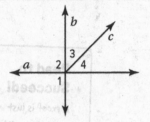

Given: Lines *a* and *b* are _____.

Prove: ∠3 and ∠4 are _____.

Proof: Since lines *a* and *b* are perpendicular,

$m\angle 1 = $ _____.

Because of the definition of vertical angles,

∠1 is congruent to _____ + _____.

Using substitution, _____ = _____.

Therefore, ∠3 and ∠4 are _____
because complementary angles add

together to equal _____.

2 Given that lines
a and *b* are
parallel and are
intersected by
transversal *c*,
$m\angle 1 = 5x + 20$,
and $m\angle 5 =$
$18x - 58$, prove
that $x = 6$. Fill in the blanks of the two-
column proof. *Preparation for 8.G.6,* **MP** 3

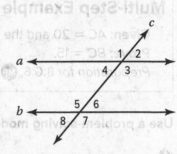
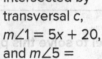

Statements	Reasons
Lines *a* and *b* are parallel and are intersected by transversal *c*. $m\angle 1 = 5x + 20$ $m\angle 5 = 18x - 58$	
$m\angle 1 = m\angle 5$	
	Substitution Property
$13x - 58 = 20$	
	Addition Property of Equality

3 👍 **H.O.T. Problem**
Given: lines *a* and *b* intersect;
$m\angle 1 = 2x - 75$ and
$m\angle 3 = 5x - 150$
Prove: $x = 25$
Explain why this cannot be proven. *Preparation for 8.G.6,* **MP** 3

_____

_____

_____

Lesson 3 Multi-Step Problem Solving

Multi-Step Example

What are the values of x and y? 8.G.5, 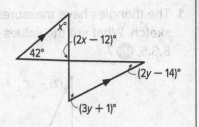 7

Ⓐ $x = 42$, $y = 24.2$

Ⓑ $x = 50$, $y = 21$

Ⓒ $x = 50$, $y = 28.6$

Ⓓ $x = 70$, $y = 13$

Use a problem-solving model to solve this problem.

① Understand

Read the problem. Circle the information you know.
Underline what the problem is asking you to find.

② Plan

What will you need to do to solve the problem? Write your plan in steps.

Step 1 Write an equation to determine the value of x.

Step 2 Write an equation to determine the value of y.

③ Solve

Use your plan to solve the problem. Show your steps.

Since the sum of the interior angles of a triangle is _____,

$x + (2x - 12) +$ ____ = _____ and $x =$ ____. So, the value

of $2x - 12$ is $2($____$) - 12$ or ____. Since the two triangles

form a pair of vertical angles, solve the equation

____ $+ (2y - 14) + (3y + 1) =$ _____ to determine the value of y.

Since the value of y is ____, the correct answer is __. Fill in that
answer choice.

> **Read to Succeed!**
> Remember to simplify the expressions on the left side of the equation by combining like terms.

④ Check

How do you know your solution is accurate?

_____

_____

_____

Lesson 3 *(continued)*

Use a problem-solving model to solve each problem.

1 The triangles have measures shown in the sketch. What are the values of x and y? 8.G.5, MP 7

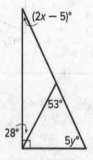

$(2x - 5)°$

$53°$

$28°$

$5y°$

Ⓐ $x = 25, y = 65$

Ⓑ $x = 65, y = 25$

Ⓒ $x = 15, y = 13$

Ⓓ $x = 13, y = 15$

2 In the diagram below, the two vertical lines are parallel. What is the value of y? 8.G.5, MP 7

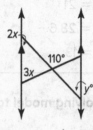

$2x°$

$110°$

$3x°$

$y°$

_____

_____

3 The measures of the angles of a triangle have ratio 3:4:5. What is the measure of the exterior angle formed at the vertex of the angle with the greatest measure? 8.G.5, MP 1

4 ✋ **H.O.T. Problem** The parallelogram has angle measures as shown. If $a = 100°$ and $e = 50°$, what is the value of $a + b + e + f$? Justify your answer. 8.G.5, MP 3

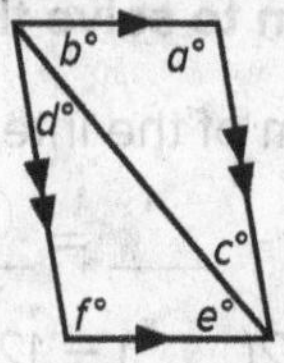

$b°$ $a°$

$d°$

$c°$

$f°$ $e°$

_____

_____

_____

_____

_____

_____

_____

Lesson 4 Multi-Step Problem Solving

Multi-Step Example

Hiro wants to build a birdhouse with a floor, two walls, and a peaked roof. If the shape is a regular pentagon, what angle will Hiro need to make each interior angle of his birdhouse? *Extension of* **8.G.5, MP 4**

Ⓐ 90° Ⓑ 108° Ⓒ 360° Ⓓ 540°

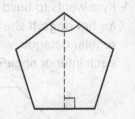

Use a problem-solving model to solve this problem.

1 Understand

Read the problem. Circle the information you know. Underline what the problem is asking you to find.

2 Plan

What will you need to do to solve the problem? Write your plan in steps.

Step 1 Find the number of _____ in the pentagon if all the diagonals are drawn from one vertex.

Step 2 Multiply the number of triangles by _____ to determine the sum of the interior angles in the birdhouse.

Step 3 _____ the _____ _____ by the number of _____ in a pentagon. The angles will all be equal because the pentagon is _____.

3 Solve

Use your plan to solve the problem. Show your steps.

The pentagon can be divided into _____ triangles. Multiply 3 by _____.

The sum of the interior angles is _____ in a pentagon.

By dividing the total number of degrees by _____, you find that each angle should be _____. Fill in answer choice _____.

4 Check

How do you know your solution is accurate?

_____

_____

_____

> **Read to Succeed!**
>
> To find the total sum of the interior angles of a polygon, subtract 2 from the number of sides and multiply by 180. The sum of the measure of the exterior angles of a polygon is always 360°.

Lesson 4 *(continued)*

Use a problem-solving model to solve each problem.

1 Kyra wants to build an octagon-shaped pen for her dogs. If she wants the pen to be a regular octagon, what will be the measure of each interior angle? *Extension of* **8.G.5, MP 4**

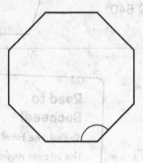

Ⓐ 1080°

Ⓑ 540°

Ⓒ 135°

Ⓓ 90°

2 Find the missing measures of the angles of this irregular hexagon. *Extension of* **8.G.5, MP 4**

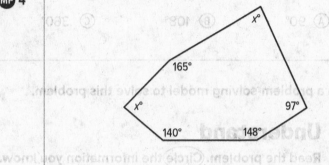

3 Find the measures of the exterior angles of the polygon. *Extension of* **8.G.5, MP 4**

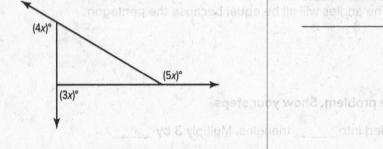

_____

_____

4 🔥 **H.O.T. Problem** How many sides does a regular polygon have if each interior angle measures 162°? *Extension of* **8.G.5, MP 4**

_____

Lesson 5   Multi-Step Problem Solving

Multi-Step Example

Alma has a motor boat that averages 3 miles per gallon of gasoline, and the tank holds 15 gallons of gasoline. At 9 A.M., Alma left the dock in her boat. At 10 A.M., she was 3 miles west and 4 miles north of the dock. If she continues at this rate, in how many more hours will the tank be out of gasoline? 8.G.7, MP 4

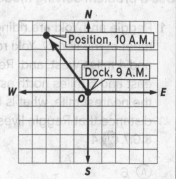

Ⓐ 45

Ⓒ 8

Ⓑ 25

Ⓓ 5

Use a problem-solving model to solve this problem.

 Understand

Read the problem. Circle the information you know.
Underline what the problem is asking you to find.

 Plan

What will you need to do to solve the problem? Write your plan in steps.

Step 1   Determine the number of _____ possible on one tank of gasoline.

Step 2   Determine the number of _____ Alma traveled in one _____.

Then determine the number of _____ before the motor boat's tank is out of gasoline.

 Solve

Use your plan to solve the problem. Show your steps.

The tank holds _____ of gasoline, and the boat averages

_____. So, the boat can travel _____(_____) or

_____ miles on 1 tank of gasoline

In 1 hour, Alma traveled $\sqrt{\underline{} + \underline{}}$ or _____ miles. At this rate,

there will be enough gasoline for _____ ÷ _____ or _____ hours. Since Alma has

already traveled for 1 hour, the correct answer is _____. Fill in that answer choice.

> **Read to Succeed!**
> Remember distance has to be positive, so only the positive square root will be used.

 Check

How do you know your solution is accurate?

_____

_____

Lesson 5 *(continued)*

Use a problem-solving model to solve each problem.

1 Reggie and Yoki are riding their bikes to meet at the library. Yoki rode 4 miles south and 4 miles west, and Reggie rode 8 miles east and 5 miles north as shown below. To the nearest mile, what is the straight-line distance that Reggie lives from Yoki? **8.G.7,** **MP** 4

Ⓐ 6

Ⓒ 15

Ⓑ 9

Ⓓ 225

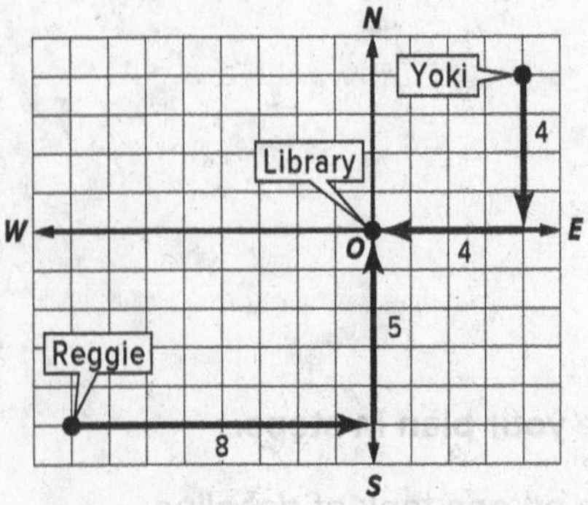

2 Triangle A has side lengths of 10 units, 24 units, and 26 units. Ryan cut out two copies of triangle A and joined them together to form a rectangle. What is the perimeter of the rectangle formed when the two triangles are joined? **8.G.7,** **MP** 1

_____

3 Felix hits three croquet balls from the same spot as shown in the diagram below. Starting at point *F*, he picks up each ball. What is the shortest distance Felix can travel to pick up all three croquet balls, ending at the point where he picks up the third ball? **8.G.7,** **MP** 4

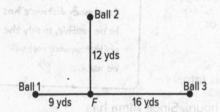

_____

4 🖐 **H.O.T. Problem** What is the perimeter of parallelogram *PTRU* shown in the diagram below? Explain. **8.G.7,** **MP** 4

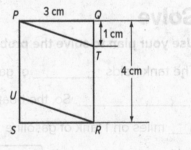

_____

_____

_____

_____

Lesson 6   Multi-Step Problem Solving

Multi-Step Example

Olivia walks at a steady rate of 4 miles per hour. She walks east for 24 minutes, north for 15 minutes, east for 24 minutes, and north for 20 minutes. What is the approximate straight-line distance in miles between Olivia's starting point and ending point? 8.EE.2, **MP** 4

Use a problem-solving model to solve this problem.

1 Understand

Read the problem. Circle the information you know.
Underline what the problem is asking you to find.

2 Plan

What will you need to do to solve the problem? Write your plan in steps.

Step 1   Determine the _____ distance between Olivia's starting point and ending point in minutes.

Step 2   Express Olivia's distance in _____.

Read to Succeed!
You may wish to draw a diagram that shows the route Olivia walks.

3 Solve

Use your plan to solve the problem. Show your steps.

Use the Pythagorean Theorem to determine Olivia's distance in minutes;

$$\text{distance}_{min} = \sqrt{\underline{\quad}^2 + \underline{\quad}^2} + \sqrt{\underline{\quad}^2 + \underline{\quad}^2} \approx \underline{\quad} + \underline{\quad} \approx \underline{\quad}.$$

So, Olivia walks for about ____ minutes.

Since there are 60 minutes in _____ and Olivia walks

at a rate of _____ per hour, the _____ distance

is about _____.

4 Check

How do you know your solution is accurate?

_____

_____

_____

Lesson 6 (continued)

Use a problem-solving model to solve each problem.

1 Pablo walks west for 16 minutes, north for 4 minutes, west for 8 minutes, and north for 6 minutes. If Pablo walks at a steady rate of 3 miles per hour, what is the straight-line distance in miles that Pablo walks? 8.EE.2, **MP** 4

_____

2 A shipping container with bases that are isosceles triangles is shown below

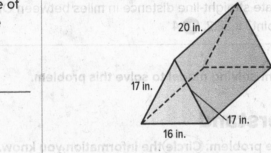

What is the volume of the container? 8.G.7, **MP** 4

_____

3 In the scale drawing shown below, polygon *ABCD* represents a plot of land. The scale is 1 inch: 10 feet.

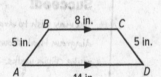

What is the actual area of the plot of land, in square feet? 8.G.7, **MP** 4

_____

4 👆 **H.O.T. Problem** The diagram of a kite is shown below.

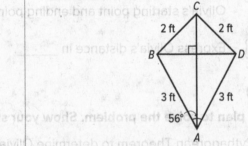

If $BD = \sqrt{8}$ ft, what are the measures of $\angle BCD$, $\angle ABC$, and $\angle ADC$? Justify your answers. 8.G.7, **MP** 7

_____
_____
_____
_____
_____
_____
_____
_____
_____

Chapter 5

Lesson 7 Multi-Step Problem Solving

Multi-Step Example

The map at the right shows two walking trails in a park.
Both paths end at the picnic area, located at $C(6, 1)$.
Trail A starts at $A(-6, 6)$, and Trail B starts at $B(-10, -11)$.
If each unit on the map represents 0.5 mile, how many
miles longer is Trail B than Trail A? **8.EE.2, MP 4**

(A) 3.5

(C) 16.5

(B) 13

(D) 20

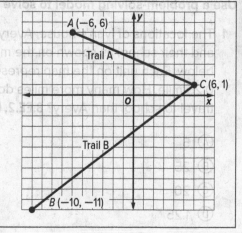

Use a problem-solving model to solve this problem.

1 Understand

Read the problem. Circle the information you know.
Underline what the problem is asking you to find.

2 Plan

Read to Succeed!

Since the diagram does not include the scale, refer back to the problem to find the scale of the map.

What will you need to do to solve the problem? Write your plan in steps.

Step 1 Use the _____ to determine the length in _____
of both trails.

Step 2 Determine how much longer _____ is than _____ in _____.

3 Solve

Use your plan to solve the problem. Show your steps.

Trail B is $\sqrt{(\_\_\_ - \_\_\_)^2 + (\_\_\_ - \_\_\_)^2}$ or ____ units long. Trail A is

$\sqrt{(\_\_\_ - \_\_\_)^2 + (\_\_\_ - \_\_\_)^2}$ or ____ units long. Trail B is ___ − ___ or ____

units longer than Trail A.

Since one unit represents ____ mile, Trail B is ____(__) or ____ miles longer than

Trail A. Fill in answer choice _____.

4 Check

How do you know your solution is accurate?

_____

_____

_____

Lesson 7 (continued)

Use a problem-solving model to solve each problem.

1 The locations of Ivan's house, Avery's house, and their school as shown on the map below. Each unit on the map represents 0.25 mile. How many more miles does Ivan travel to school than Avery? **8.EE.2,** MP **4**

ⓐ 5

ⓑ 25

ⓒ 20

ⓓ 1.25

2 The map shows a bike trail in a park. Emilio rides from point *A* to point *B* and then rides back to point *A*. He rides at an average rate of 15 miles per hour. If each unit on the map represents 0.5 mile, how many minutes does Emilio's ride take? **8.G.8,** MP **4**

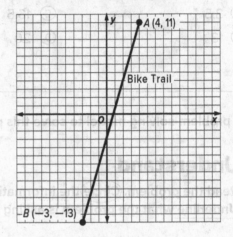

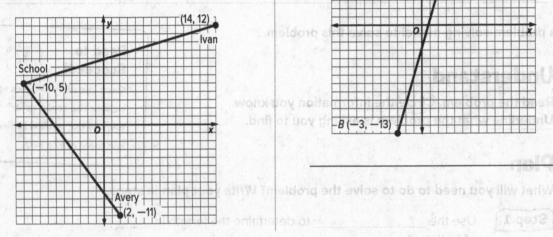

3 A rectangle is drawn on a coordinate grid and has vertices at (−10, 4), (5, 4), (5, −4), and (−10, −4). If each unit on the grid represents 6 inches, what is the approximate length of the diagonal of the rectangle in feet? Round your answer to the nearest tenth. **8.G.8,** MP **4**

4 🔥 **H.O.T. Problem** A circle with center *C*(2, −2) passes through *A*(5, 2). Determine the area of the circle. Use 3.14 for π. Justify your response. **8.EE.2,** MP **4**

_____

_____

_____

_____

_____

_____

_____

Lesson 1 Multi-Step Problem Solving

Multi-Step Example

$\triangle ABC$ is translated to $\triangle A'B'C'$. Then $\triangle A'B'C'$ is translated 2 units to the right and 1 unit up to form $\triangle A''B''C''$. Which of the following describes the translation of $\triangle ABC$ to $\triangle A''B''C''$? **8.G.3, MP 2**

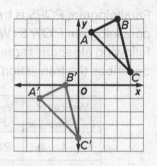

Ⓐ $(x, y) \rightarrow (x + 2, y + 1)$

Ⓑ $(x, y) \rightarrow (x - 2, y - 4)$

Ⓒ $(x, y) \rightarrow (x - 4, y - 5)$

Ⓓ $(x, y) \rightarrow (x + 2, y + 4)$

Use a problem-solving model to solve this problem.

1 Understand

Read the problem. Circle the information you know.
Underline what the problem is asking you to find.

2 Plan

What will you need to do to solve the problem? Write your plan in steps.

Step 1 Graph _____ to determine its coordinates.

Step 2 Count the number of units from _____ to _____.

3 Solve

Use your plan to solve the problem. Show your steps.

Vertex A'' is (____, ____), vertex B'' is (____, ____), and

vertex C'' is (____, ____).

So, $\triangle ABC$ is translated _____ and _____.

The correct answer is ____. Fill in that answer choice.

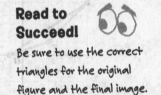

Read to Succeed!

Be sure to use the correct triangles for the original figure and the final image.

4 Check

How do you know your solution is accurate?

_____

_____

_____

Lesson 1 *(continued)*

Use a problem-solving model to solve each problem.

1 Parallelogram *PQRS* is translated to parallelogram *P'Q'R'S'*. Which of the following algebraic representations describes the translation? **8.G.3, MP 2**

Vertices of *PQRS*	Vertices of *P'Q'R'S'*
$P(-4, -4)$	$P'(-1, -5)$
$Q(-3, -1)$	$Q'(0, -2)$
$R(-1, -1)$	$R'(2, -2)$
$S(-2, -4)$	$S'(1, -5)$

- Ⓐ $(x, y) \rightarrow (x + 3, y - 1)$
- Ⓑ $(x, y) \rightarrow (x - 3, y + 1)$
- Ⓒ $(x, y) \rightarrow (x - 1, y + 3)$
- Ⓓ $(x, y) \rightarrow (x + 1, y - 3)$

2 The vertices of a rectangle are $A(-3, 2)$, $B(1, 2)$, $C(1, -1)$, and $D(-3, -1)$. Rectangle *ABCD* is translated 2 units right and 4 units down to rectangle *A'B'C'D'*. What is the quotient of diagonal *AC* and diagonal *A'C'*? **8.G.3, MP 2**

_____

_____

_____

3 $\triangle XYZ$ is translated 4 units right and 2 units down to $\triangle X'Y'Z'$. What is the sum of all of the *x*-coordinates and *y*-coordinates of the vertices of $\triangle X'Y'Z'$? **8.G.3, MP 2**

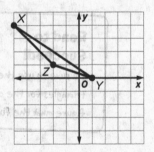

_____

_____

_____

4 ✋ **H.O.T. Problem** $\triangle ABC$ is translated to $\triangle A'B'C'$, and $\triangle A'B'C'$ is then translated to $\triangle A''B''C''$. Use algebraic notation to explain the effect of both translations. Then use algebraic notation to explain the effect of translating $\triangle ABC$ to $\triangle A''B''C''$. **8.G.3, MP 6**

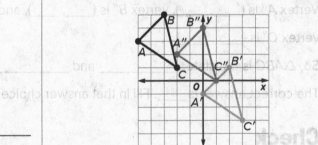

_____

_____

_____

Lesson 2 Multi-Step Problem Solving

Multi-Step Example

△ABC is reflected over the x-axis and then translated 4 units left and 5 units down to △DEF. Which algebraic representation explains the effect of the transformation of △ABC to △DEF? 8.G.3, 4

Ⓐ $(x, y) \rightarrow (-x - 4, y - 5)$

Ⓑ $(x, y) \rightarrow (-x + 4, y + 5)$

Ⓒ $(x, y) \rightarrow (x + 4, -y - 5)$

Ⓓ $(x, y) \rightarrow (x - 4, -y - 5)$

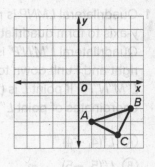

Use a problem-solving model to solve this problem.

1 Understand

Read the problem. (Circle) the information you know.
Underline what the problem is asking you to find.

2 Plan

What will you need to do to solve the problem? Write your plan in steps.

Step 1 Reflect △ABC over _____. Then translate the image
and _____ and _____ to form △DEF.

Step 2 Use the _____ of a pair of corresponding _____ to
evaluate the statements above.

3 Solve

Use your plan to solve the problem. Show your steps.

Vertex A is (____, ____) and vertex D is (____, ____).

Since $1 - 4 =$ ____ and $-(-3) - 5 =$ ____, $(x, y) \rightarrow$ _____.

explains the effect of the transformation. So, ____ is the correct
answer. Fill in that answer choice.

4 Check

How do you know your solution is accurate?

_____

_____

_____

Read to Succeed!

Since the algebraic representation explains the effect of a reflection followed by a translation, it will be necessary to multiply one of the coordinates by −1.

Lesson 2 (continued)

Use a problem-solving model to solve each problem.

1 Quadrilateral *LMNP* is reflected over the *y*-axis to form quadrilateral *L'M'N'P'*. Quadrilateral *L'M'N'P'* is then translated 1 unit right and 1 unit down to form quadrilateral *L"M"N"P"*. If point *L* is (−4, −4), what are the coordinates of point *L"*? **8.G.3, MP 4**

Ⓐ *L"*(4, −4)

Ⓑ *L"*(5, −5)

Ⓒ *L"*(−3, −5)

Ⓓ *L"*(−3, 3)

2 Quin is playing an online puzzle game, moving puzzle pieces from Quadrant III to Quadrant I. The puzzle pieces can be moved with three different transformations: a reflection over the *x*-axis, a reflection over the *y*-axis, or a translation. Each transformation counts as one move. Quin has one more piece to move to complete the puzzle. What are the fewest number of moves he can use to move the puzzle piece shown below into its appropriate place? **8.G.1, MP 7**

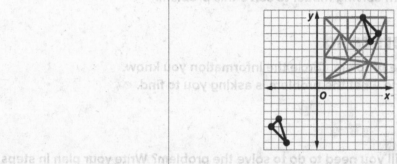

_____

_____

3 △*ABC* is reflected over the *x*-axis, reflected over the *y*-axis, and then translated. Point *A'''* is the image of point *A* after the three transformations. What are the coordinates of *B'''*? **8.G.3, MP 4**

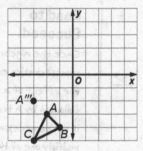

_____

4 ✋ **H.O.T. Problem** A triangle is reflected and then translated. Will the image of this triangle be the same if the translation is applied first followed by the reflection? Defend your answer. **8.G.3, MP 7**

_____

_____

_____

_____

_____

_____

Lesson 3   **Multi-Step** Problem Solving

Multi-Step Example

Before moving furniture in her bedroom, Jasmine made a diagram of the current arrangement. She drew rectangle *ABCD* to represent her desk with vertices at (2, 4), (6, 4), (6, 1), and (2, 1), respectively. She moved the desk twice, first translating it 3 units left and 2 units down, and then rotating it 90° counterclockwise about the image of vertex *D*. What is the *y*-coordinate of vertex *C* after these transformations are applied? 8.G.3, **MP** 4

Use a problem-solving model to solve this problem.

1 Understand

Read the problem. Circle the information you know.
Underline what the problem is asking you to find.

2 Plan

What will you need to do to solve the problem? Write your plan in steps.

Step 1   Determine the coordinates of rectangle *A'B'C'D'*
following a translation _____ and _____.

Step 2   Determine the *y*-coordinate of __ following a
_____ rotation about ____.

Read to Succeed!

Be sure to use the correct angle of rotation and center of rotation.

3 Solve

Use your plan to solve the problem. Show your steps.

A' is (____, ____), *B'* is (____, ____), *C'* is (____, ____), and *D'* is

(____, ____). Since there are 4 horizontal units between *C'* and *D'*,
there will be 4 vertical units between *C"* and *D"* following a

_____ rotation.

Since −1 + 4 = ____, the *y*-coordinate of *D"* is ____.

4 Check

How do you know your solution is accurate?

_____

_____

_____

Lesson 3 *(continued)*

Use a problem-solving model to solve each problem.

1 A planter in Vincent's office is represented by △*JKL* on the coordinate plane below. He moves the planter by a translation of 4 units left and 3 units up, followed by a rotation of 180° clockwise about the image of vertex *K*. Which ordered pair represents vertex *J* after these transformations? **8.G.3, MP 4**

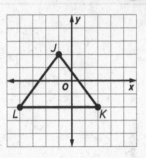

Ⓐ (−5, 5)

Ⓑ (4, 1)

Ⓒ (1, −3)

Ⓓ (3, 5)

2 Kendra made a sun with rotational symmetry out of mosaic tiles as shown below. She then placed the sun on a coordinate plane so that the center of the sun was the origin. What is the smallest angle of clockwise rotation in degrees that the sun can be rotated about the origin and match the original orientation of Kendra's sun? **8.G.1, MP 4**

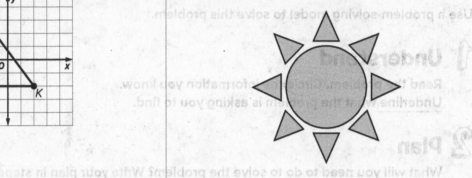

3 Belinda drew triangle *TUV* on graph paper. Then, she rotated the triangle 90° clockwise about vertex *U*. Finally, she translated the triangle 2 units down and 1 unit to the left. How many vertical units away from the preimage *V* is the image of vertex *V*? **8.G.3, MP 4**

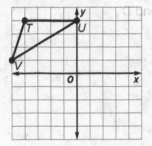

4 ♨**H.O.T. Problem** Rectangle *PQRS* has vertices *P*(−3, −1), *Q*(−1, −1), *R*(−1, −4), and *S*(−3, −4). The rectangle is rotated 90° counterclockwise about the origin. It is then reflected over the *x*-axis. What are the coordinates of the vertices of rectangle *P″Q″R″S″*? **8.G.3, MP 4**

Lesson 4 **Multi-Step** Problem Solving

Multi-Step Example

Malik uses a dilation in a perspective drawing. Using the origin as the center of the dilation, he dilates Rectangle I to obtain Rectangle II. Which option describes the change in perimeter, using the following variables? 8.G.3, **MP** 4

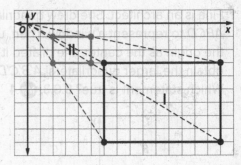

P_I = perimeter of Rectangle I

P_{II} = perimeter of Rectangle II

SF = scale factor of the dilation

Ⓐ $P_I = SF \times P_{II}$ Ⓒ $P_{II} = SF \times P_I$

Ⓑ $P_I = (SF)^2 \times P_{II}$ Ⓓ $P_{II} = (SF)^2 \times P_I$

Use a problem-solving model to solve this problem.

1 Understand

Read the problem. Circle **the information you know.**
Underline what the problem is asking you to find.

2 Plan

What will you need to do to solve the problem? Write your plan in steps.

Step 1 Determine which equations model the relationship between
scale factor and _____ when dilating a figure.

Step 2 Determine which equation models the dilation of _____
to obtain _____.

3 Solve

Use your plan to solve the problem. Show your steps.

Answer choices ____ and ____ show the relationship between
scale factor and perimeter.

Of these two choices, ____ shows the dilation of _____ to

obtain _____. So, the correct answer is ____ . Fill in that answer choice.

Read to Succeed!

Remember that perimeter uses linear units of measure, while area uses square units of measure.

4 Check

How do you know your solution is accurate?

_____

_____

Lesson 4 *(continued)*

Use a problem-solving model to solve each problem.

1 Fina is an architect. She drew quadrilateral *ABCD* to represent a window. Then, using the origin as the center, she dilated it to obtain the larger quadrilateral *A′B′C′D′*. Which statement is true? **8.G.3,** **MP** **4**

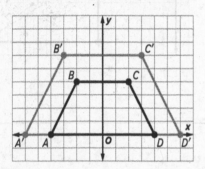

ⓐ $m\angle A' = 1.5 \times m\angle A$

ⓑ $m\angle A' = 2.25 \times m\angle A$

ⓒ area of *A′B′C′D′* = 1.5 × area of *ABCD*

ⓓ area of *A′B′C′D′* = 2.25 × area of *ABCD*

2 Aponi is a structural engineer. She drew △*PQR* to represent a roof truss. Using point *P* as the center, she dilated △*PQR* by a scale factor of 2 and then dilated the resulting image by a scale factor of 1.1 to obtain a final image. The area of the final image, *A″*, is related to the original area *A* by the equation $A'' = x \cdot A$. What is the value of *x*? **8.G.3,** **MP** **4**

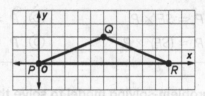

_____

_____

3 The rectangle below is dilated, increasing both dimensions by 20%. Then the image is dilated, decreasing both dimensions by 20%. The origin is the center of both dilations. The perimeter of the final image, *P″*, is related to the original perimeter *P* by the equation $P' = x \cdot P$. What is the value of *x*? **8.G.3,** **MP** **4**

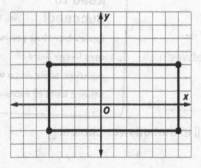

4 ♨ **H.O.T. Problem** Polygon *PQRS* has vertices *P*(−4, −2), *Q*(3, −2), *R*(3, 6), and *S*(−4, 6). Polygon *PQRS* is dilated, using the origin as the center of the dilation. The image is polygon *P′Q′R′S′*, and *P′* has coordinates (−10, −5). What is the perimeter of polygon *P′Q′R′S′*? Support your answer. **8.G.3,** **MP** **6**

_____

_____

_____

_____

_____

_____

_____

Lesson 1 Multi-Step Problem Solving

Multi-Step Example

Serena arranged sixteen floor tiles into patterns A and B as shown. Are Serena's two designs congruent? If so, describe the transformation or series of transformations that map pattern A to pattern B. 8.G.2, MP 3

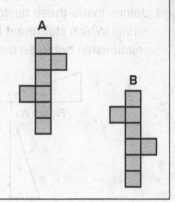

(A) Design A is translated to make design B.

(B) Design A is translated and rotated to make design B.

(C) Design A is reflected and translated to make design B.

(D) The designs are not congruent.

Use a problem-solving model to solve this problem.

1 Understand

Read the problem. (Circle) the information you know.
Underline what the problem is asking you to find.

2 Plan

What will you need to do to solve the problem? Write your plan in steps.

Step 1 Trace design A on a separate sheet of paper.

Step 2 _____ and _____ design A as described above to determine if the designs are _____.

3 Solve

Use your plan to solve the problem. Show your steps.

No matter how design A is transformed, it is _____ to design B.

So, the correct answer is ___. Fill in that answer choice.

Read to Succeed!
When checking for congruency, pay close attention to the position of the squares located to the left and right of the center squares.

4 Check

How do you know your solution is accurate?

_____

_____

_____

Lesson 1 *(continued)*

Use a problem-solving model to solve each problem.

1 James made these designs with pieces of string. Which statement best describes the relationship between the figures? 8.G.2, **MP** 3

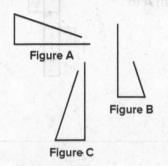

Figure A

Figure B

Figure C

Ⓐ *A* is rotated and translated to make *B*, and is not congruent to *C*.

Ⓑ *A* is rotated and translated to make *C*, and is not congruent to *B*.

Ⓒ *A* is rotated and reflected to make *B*, and rotated and translated to make *C*.

Ⓓ *A* is rotated and reflected to make *C*, and and rotated and translated to make *B*.

2 Beth used $\triangle JKL$ as a preimage for a series of transformations such that $\triangle J'K'L'$ and $\triangle JKL$ are congruent. If her resulting image has coordinates $L'(4, -1)$ and $K'(1, -3)$, what whole number is a possible x-coordinate of J'? 8.G.2, **MP** 4

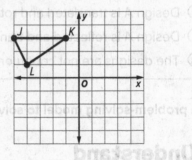

3 A line segment has endpoints $A(-2, 2)$ and $B(7, 2)$. Segment *AB* is first reflected across the y-axis, then reflected across the x-axis, and finally rotated counterclockwise about the origin to create segment $A'B'$. If B' has coordinates $(2, -7)$, how many degrees counterclockwise was segment *AB* rotated? 8.G.1a, **MP** 4

4 👆 **H.O.T. Problem** Miranda drew the design shown below. She translated the design 6 units right and 6 units down. Then she dilated the image using a scale factor of 2. Which transformation(s) produced congruent figures? Support your answer. 8.G.1, **MP** 3

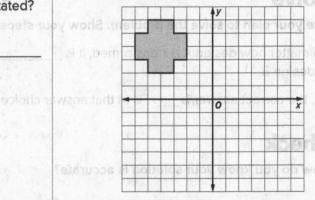

Lesson 2   **Multi-Step** Problem Solving

Multi-Step Example

Which composition of transformations will map $\triangle DEF$ to $\triangle LMN$ so that the two triangles coincide? **8.G.2, MP 2**

Ⓐ reflection over the *x*-axis followed by a translation 6 units down

Ⓑ reflection over the *y*-axis followed by a translation 6 units down

Ⓒ a 90° clockwise rotation about the origin followed by a reflection over the *y*-axis

Ⓓ a 90° clockwise rotation about the origin followed by a reflection over the *x*-axis

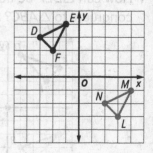

Use a problem-solving model to solve this problem.

 Understand

Read the problem. (Circle) the information you know.
Underline what the problem is asking you to find.

2 Plan

What will you need to do to solve the problem? Write your plan in steps.

Step 1   Trace $\triangle DEF$ on a separate sheet of paper.

Step 2   _____, _____, and _____ $\triangle DEF$ to determine

which _____ maps $\triangle DEF$ onto _____.

3 Solve

Use your plan to solve the problem. Show your steps.

A _____ about the origin followed by a

reflection _____, maps $\triangle DEF$ onto $\triangle LMN$. So, the

correct answer is _____. Fill in that answer choice.

> **Read to Succeed!**
>
> Be sure that corresponding sides and angles match up when you are determining the correct series of transformations.

 Check

How do you know your solution is accurate?

_____

_____

_____

Lesson 2 (continued)

Use a problem-solving model to solve each problem.

1 How can △DEF be transformed to show it is congruent to △ABC? 8.G.2, **MP** 2

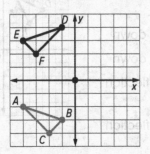

Ⓐ reflection over the *y*-axis followed by a translation 5 left and 6 down

Ⓑ reflection over the *x*-axis followed by a translation 5 left and 6 up

Ⓒ rotation 270° counterclockwise about the origin

Ⓓ rotation 270° clockwise about the origin

2 △ABC is translated 2 units right and 3 units up. △A′B′C′ is then reflected over the *y*-axis. What are the lengths of $\overline{A''B''}$, $\overline{B''C''}$, and $\overline{A''C''}$? 8.G.1a, **MP** 4

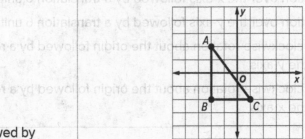

$A''B'' = $ _____, $B''C'' = $ _____, $A''C'' = $ _____

3 △ABC ≅ △RST. What is the measure in degrees of ∠T? 8.G.1b, **MP** 2

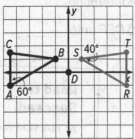

_____

4 ✋ **H.O.T. Problem** △PQR is reflected over the *x*-axis and then rotated 90° counterclockwise about the origin to form △P″Q″R″. List all of the corresponding parts of the two triangles. What are the coordinates of △P″Q″R″? What is the length P″R″? 8.G.2, **MP** 7

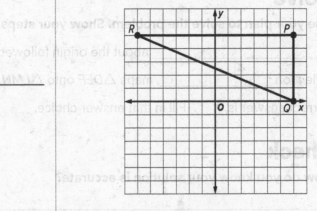

_____

_____

_____

Lesson 3 Multi-Step Problem Solving

Multi-Step Example

A website developer enlarges an image with a length of 6 centimeters and width of 9 centimeters by a scale factor of 3. The developer decides that the enlarged image is too large and reduces it by a scale factor of 0.5. Will the final image fit into a space that has an area of 121 square centimeters? Explain your answer. 8.G.4, MP 4

(A) Yes, the area of the image is 54 square centimeters.

(B) Yes, because the area of the image is 121 square centimeters.

(C) No, because the area of the image is 486 square centimeters.

(D) No, because the area of the image is 121.5 square centimeters.

Use a problem-solving model to solve this problem.

1 Understand

Read the problem. Circle the information you know.
Underline what the problem is asking you to find.

2 Plan

What will you need to do to solve the problem? Write your plan in steps.

Step 1 Determine the dimensions of the enlargement and then determine the dimensions of the _____.

Step 2 Determine the _____ of the final image.

Read to Succeed!

Similar figures are the same shape but not the same size.

3 Solve

Use your plan to solve the problem. Show your steps.

To find the dimensions of the _____, multiply the dimensions by _____.

So, _____ and _____. Multiply these dimensions by _____ to find

the dimensions of the _____. The final dimensions of the image are

_____ centimeters and _____ centimeters. The area of the image would be

_____ square centimeters. This makes the correct answer _____.

4 Check

How do you know your solution is accurate?

_____

_____

_____

Lesson 3 (continued)

Use a problem-solving model to solve each problem.

1 A fashion designer needs to reduce the pattern she has made for a rectangular decal she plans to use on her garment. The original dimensions of the decal are 5 inches by 10 inches. She reduces the decal by a scale factor of $\frac{2}{5}$. After placing it on the garment, she decides the decal is now too small. She enlarges the decal by a scale factor of $\frac{3}{2}$. Will the decal fit in a space that has an area of 12 square inches? Explain your answer. **8.G.4, (MP) 4**

(A) Yes, because the area of the image is 8 square inches.

(B) Yes, because the area of the image is 5 square inches.

(C) No, because the area of the image is 18 square inches.

(D) No, because the area of the image is 12.5 square inches.

3 Are the two figures similar? Explain your reasoning. **8.G.4, (MP) 7**

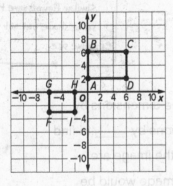

_____

_____

_____

_____

2 A gardener drew plans for a rectangular garden. The original drawing was 1.5 inches by 4 inches. Before he showed the drawing to the client, he enlarged it to show more detail. His enlarged drawing was 2 feet 6 inches by 7 feet 5 inches. The client points out to him that something does not look right. Explain the error. **8.G.4, (MP) 2**

_____

_____

_____

4 ✋ **H.O.T. Problem** Describe the differences between congruent figures and similar figures. Make sure to compare the side lengths, the angle measures, and the transformations that can be used in your description. **8.G.4, (MP) 3**

_____

_____

_____

_____

_____

_____

_____

Lesson 4   **Multi-Step** Problem Solving

Multi-Step Example

Alex used reflective tape to make the design shown on a jacket. First, he made the small polygon. Then he enlarged the small polygon to make the large polygon, using a scale factor that extended the 8-centimeter side by 2 centimeters. What total length of reflective tape did Alex use to create the entire design? **8.G.4, MP 4**

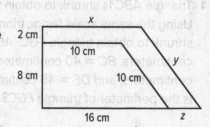

- Ⓐ 44 cm
- Ⓑ 55 cm
- Ⓒ 75 cm
- Ⓓ 99 cm

Use a problem-solving model to solve this problem.

1 Understand

Read the problem. Circle the information you know.
Underline what the problem is asking you to find.

2 Plan

What will you need to do to solve the problem? Write your plan in steps.

Step 1   Determine the scale factor from the small polygon to the large polygon.

Step 2   Use the scale factor to determine the measures needed to find the total length of tape used.

3 Solve

Read to Succeed!
When determining the total amount of tape used, remember to add the two 10-centimeter lengths.

Use your plan to solve the problem. Show your steps.

Multiply ____ and ____ by the scale factor ____ to determine the missing measures x, y, and z. Remember that the length of the large polygon is $16 + z$.

Add $8 + 10 + 10 + 16 + 2 +$ ____ $+$ ____ $+$ ____.

Alex used _____ of tape. So, the correct answer is ____.
Fill in that answer choice.

4 Check

How do you know your solution is accurate?

_____

_____

_____

_____

Lesson 4 (continued)

Use a problem-solving model to solve each problem.

1 Triangle *ABC* is shrunk to obtain triangle *DEC*. Using the same scale factor, triangle *DEC* is shrunk to obtain triangle *FGC*. *AB* = 50 centimeters, *BC* = 40 centimeters, *CA* = 40 centimeters, and *DE* = 45 centimeters. What is the perimeter of triangle *FGC*? **8.G.4,** **MP** 4

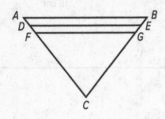

- Ⓐ 87.2 cm
- Ⓑ 100 cm
- Ⓒ 105.3 cm
- Ⓓ 117 cm

2 The rectangle shown below was used in a magazine advertisement for a digital camera. It represents the image sensor region of the camera. The actual image sensor region in the camera is a dilation of the rectangle by a scale factor of 4×10^{-2}. What is the area of the actual image sensor region, in square centimeters, rounded to the nearest hundredth? **8.G.4,** **MP** 2

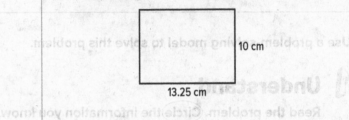

3 Abril drew the scale drawing shown below to represent the front of a garage she plans to build. The scale is 1 inch:2.5 feet. The equation $A_2 = A_1 x$, where A_2 is the actual area in square feet and A_1 is the area of the drawing, represents the relationship between the areas. What is the value of *x*? **8.G.4,** **MP** 2

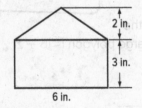

_____

4 ✋**H.O.T. Problem** Triangle *ABC* is shown on the graph. Triangle *XYZ* is similar to triangle *ABC* and has the same orientation. The *x*-coordinate of *Y* in triangle *XYZ* is 12.

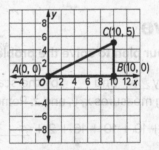

What are the coordinates of *Z*? Justify your answer. **8.G.4,** **MP** 3

_____

_____

_____

_____

Lesson 5   Multi-Step Problem Solving

Multi-Step Example

Emilio is creating designs for a stained glass window. In his design, points Q and R lie on line segment PS and point K lies on line segment JS. Which option shows all of the similar triangles in the design, and only similar triangles? **8.G.5, MP 2**

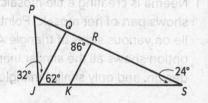

Ⓐ △SKR, △SJQ

Ⓑ △JPQ, △SKR

Ⓒ △SKR, △SJQ, △SPJ

Ⓓ △JPQ, △SJQ, △SPJ

Use a problem-solving model to solve this problem.

1 Understand

Read the problem. Ⓒircleⓣhe information you know.
Underline what the problem is asking you to find.

2 Plan

What will you need to do to solve the problem? Write your plan in steps.

Step 1 Determine the measures of the interior angles of △SKR, △SJQ, △JPQ, and △SPJ.

Step 2 Identify all of the triangles that have equal angle measures.

3 Solve

Use your plan to solve the problem. Show your steps.

Since the sum of the interior angles of a triangle is _____ and the

sum of two supplementary angles is _____, ∠SKR = _____,

∠SRK = _____, and ∠JPQ = _____.

Since the measures of the interior angles of triangles SKR, SJQ, and SPJ are 24°, 94°, and 62°, the triangles are similar. So, the correct answer is _____. Fill in that answer choice.

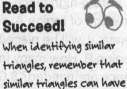

Read to Succeed!

When identifying similar triangles, remember that similar triangles can have different sizes and orientations.

4 Check

How do you know your solution is accurate?

_____

_____

_____

Lesson 5 *(continued)*

Use a problem-solving model to solve each problem.

1 Neema is creating a tile mosaic. The diagram shows part of her mosaic. Points B, D, and F lie on various sides of triangle ACE. Which option shows all the similar triangles in the design, and only similar triangles? **8.G.5, MP 2**

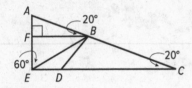

Ⓐ △AFB, △AEC

Ⓑ △AFB, △BDC

Ⓒ △AFB, △AEC, △BDC

Ⓓ △AFB, △BDC, △ABE

2 The diagram shows a municipal park formed by two triangular lots. A sidewalk is planned from point P to point R and from point R to point S. The shaded section from points P and Q has been paved. What is the remaining length in meters that needs to be paved? **8.G.5, MP 4**

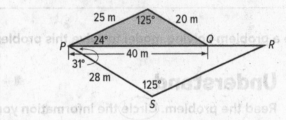

3 A triangular plot in a zoo is separated into regions A and B as shown in the diagram. A 10-foot-high fence, x, will be placed along an edge of region A, and a 12-foot-high fence, y, will be placed along an edge of region B. How many feet of 12-foot-high fence are needed? **8.G.5, MP 4**

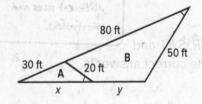

4 🔥 **H.O.T. Problem** The length of segment JP is indicated by x. What is the value of x to the nearest whole number? Justify your answer. **8.G.5, MP 3**

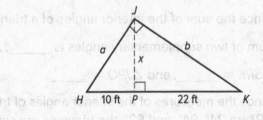

_____

_____

_____

_____

_____

_____

_____

Lesson 6 Multi-Step Problem Solving

Multi-Step Example

The graph shows a line and a slope triangle *RST* for the line.
Which of the following are the coordinates of another slope
triangle for the line? 8.EE.6, **MP** 7

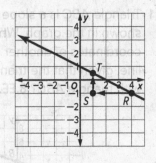

Ⓐ *X*(2, 0), *Y*(−5, 0), and *Z*(−5, 3)

Ⓑ *X*(2, 1), *Y*(−4, 1), and *Z*(−4, 3)

Ⓒ *X*(2, −1), *Y*(−5, −1), and *Z*(−5, 3)

Ⓓ *X*(2, 0), *Y*(−4, 0), and *Z*(−4, 3)

Use a problem-solving model to solve this problem.

 Understand

Read the problem. Circle the information you know.
Underline what the problem is asking you to find.

Plan

What will you need to do to solve the problem? Write your plan in steps.

Step 1 | Graph each set of vertices. Determine which triangles have two
_____ that lie on ____.

Step 2 | Determine the slopes of the triangles with two _____ on line ____.

Solve

Use your plan to solve the problem. Show your steps.

The vertices of choices ____ and ____ form triangles with two

_____ that lie on line ____.

The slope of *RT* is _____. Count units to determine that only the

line *XZ* formed by the triangle with vertices at (__, __), (____, __),

and (____, __) has the same slope. Fill in that answer choice ____.

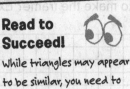

Read to Succeed!

While triangles may appear to be similar, you need to determine slopes to establish similarity.

Check

How do you know your solution is accurate?

_____

_____

_____

Lesson 6 (continued)

Use a problem-solving model to solve each problem.

1 Triangle *ABC* is a slope triangle for the line shown in the graph. What are the coordinates of another slope triangle for the line, given that the triangle shares a vertex with triangle *ABC*? 8.EE.6, MP 7

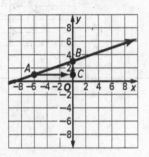

Ⓐ D(6, 5), E(6,3), and *A*

Ⓑ D(6, 5), E(6, 1), and *C*

Ⓒ D(6, 5), E(6, 3), and *B*

Ⓓ D(6, 5), E(6, 1), and *B*

2 The tables show the coordinates of two slope triangles for a line. What is the slope of the line? 8.EE.6, MP 4

Point	R	S	T
x	−3	−1	−1
y	−10	−10	−4

Point	U	V	W
x	1	2	2
y	2	2	5

_____

_____

3 ♻ **H.O.T. Problem** Xavier is making a wooden box frame formed by an 8-inch square and two connecting triangles. What is the total amount of wood, in inches, needed to make the frame? Explain. 8.EE.6, MP 3

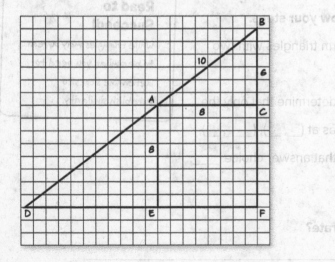

_____

_____

_____

_____

_____

_____

Lesson 7 **Multi-Step** Problem Solving

Multi-Step Example

Ella is painting two walls that have the shape of the figure at the right. The first wall has an area of 720 square feet. The second wall is a dilation of the first wall with a scale factor of 1.2. One gallon of paint will cover 300 square feet. If paint costs $25.00 per gallon, how much will Ella spend to paint both walls? *Extension of* **8.G.4,** **4**

Use a problem-solving model to solve this problem.

1 Understand

Read the problem. (Circle) the information you know.
Underline what the problem is asking you to find.

2 Plan

What will you need to do to solve the problem? Write your plan in steps.

Step 1 Determine the total area of both walls.

Step 2 Determine the cost of the total number of gallons needed to paint both walls.

> **Read to Succeed!**
> Remember that perimeter uses linear units of measure, while area uses square units of measure.

3 Solve

Use your plan to solve the problem. Show your steps.

The area of the larger wall is _____ square feet. So, the total

area is 720 + _____ or _____ square feet.

To find the number of gallons needed, divide _____ by _____

_____ and round to the nearest whole number. To find the

total cost, multiply ___ gallons by _____.

Ella will spend _____ to paint both walls.

4 Check

How do you know your solution is accurate?

_____

_____

_____

Lesson 7 *(continued)*

Use a problem-solving model to solve each problem.

1 A rectangular wall with an area of 300 square feet is covered with cedar shingles. Hugo needs to buy shingles to cover another wall that is larger than the first wall by a scale factor of 1.5. Suppose each bundle of shingles costs $120, and one bundle covers 100 square feet. How much will Hugo spend on shingles to cover the second wall if he must buy whole bundles of shingles? *Extension of* **8.G.4,** **MP** 4

2 The "T" shape is a target on a square board at a carnival game. It is formed by two rectangles that are each 40 centimeters long and 10 centimeters wide. The game operator wants to make the target smaller. He dilates the target by a scale factor of $\frac{1}{2}$ and replaces the target on the square board. What is the area of the new target? *Extension of* **8.G.4,** **MP** 4

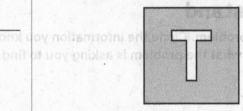

3 The diagram shown below represents a rectangular painting. The artist wants to create another painting of the same shape by dilating the rectangle by a scale factor of 1.4. She needs to buy canvas for the painting surface and molding for the frame. Suppose canvas costs $1.00 per square foot and molding costs $4.10 per foot. If molding is sold by the foot and canvas is sold by the square foot, what will be the total cost of the materials for the new painting? *Extension of* **8.G.4,** **MP** 4

2 ft

2 ft 6 in.

4 🖐 **H.O.T. Problem** The table provides information about three shapes and their dilated images. Which shape was dilated by the greatest scale factor? Support your answer. *Extension of* **8.G.4,** **MP** 1

Shapes and Dilated Images
A rectangle has a width of 10 cm and an area of 200 cm². The perimeter of the dilated figure is 90 cm.
A circle has a radius of 10 cm. The area of the dilated figure is 628 cm².
A trapezoid has an area of 150 cm² and parallel side lengths of 10 cm and 20 cm. The height of the dilated figure is 20 cm.

Lesson 1   **Multi-Step** Problem Solving

Multi-Step Example

A pool with dimensions as shown is filling with water at a rate of 20 gallons per minute. About how many hours will it take to fill the pool? (*Hint:* 1 cubic foot ≈ 7.5 gallons) **8.G.9, MP 4**

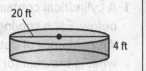
20 ft   4 ft

Ⓐ 471   Ⓒ 31

Ⓑ 56   Ⓓ 8

Use a problem-solving model to solve this problem.

 Understand

Read the problem. ⟨Circle⟩ the information you know.
Underline what the problem is asking you to find.

2 Plan

What will you need to do to solve the problem? Write your plan in steps.

[Step 1]   Determine the number of _____ of water needed to fill the pool.

[Step 2]   Determine the number of _____ it will take to fill the pool.

3 Solve

Use your plan to solve the problem. Show your steps.

Replace *r* with ____ and *h* with __ in the formula $V =$ ____, and multiply

the product by ____ to determine the number of gallons needed.

Divide the number of gallons by ____ to determine the number

of minutes and then by ____ to determine the number of hours.

About _____ hours are needed to fill the pool. So, the correct

answer is ____. Fill in that answer.

Read to Succeed!

Notice that the pool is filling at a rate of 20 gallons per minute, but the question asks for the number of hours needed to fill the pool.

 Check

How do you know your solution is accurate?

_____

_____

_____

Lesson 1 (continued)

Use a problem-solving model to solve each problem.

1 A cylindrical container of oats is shown below. Each serving of oats is 8 cubic inches. If a container of oats this size costs $2.20, what is the cost for each serving of oats? 8.G.9, **MP** 4

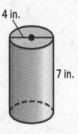

4 in.

7 in.

_____

2 A triangular prism has a cylindrical hole cut through it as shown below. What is the volume of the resulting solid to the nearest tenth of a cubic foot? 8.G.9, **MP** 4

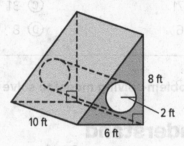

8 ft

2 ft

10 ft

6 ft

3 A cylinder-shaped glass with a base area of 7.07 square inches and a height of 6 inches weighs 1.06 ounces when empty. The glass is then filled with water to one inch from the top. If 1 cubic inch of water weighs 0.6 ounce, how many ounces does the glass of water weigh, including the weight of the glass? Round to the nearest hundredth. 8.G.9, **MP** 1

4 ☝ **H.O.T. Problem** Refer to the cylinder shown below. By what factor is the volume increased if both the radius and height are doubled? Explain your answer. 8.G.9, **MP** 3

r

h

_____

_____

_____

_____

_____

Lesson 2   **Multi-Step** Problem Solving

Multi-Step Example

A movie theater offers popcorn in two sizes as shown. The cost of the smaller container is $1.00. The cost per cubic inch of the larger container is the same as the cost per cubic inch of the smaller container. What is the ratio of the cost of the smaller container to the cost of the larger container? 8.G.9, **MP** 4

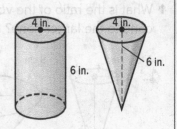

Ⓐ 1:3

Ⓒ 3:2

Ⓑ 2:3

Ⓓ 3:1

Use a problem-solving model to solve this problem.

1 Understand

Read the problem. (Circle) **the information you know.**
Underline what the problem is asking you to find.

2 Plan

What will you need to do to solve the problem? Write your plan in steps.

Step 1 Determine the _____ of each solid.

Step 2 Determine the ratio of the cost of the _____ container

to the _____ container.

3 Solve

Use your plan to solve the problem. Show your steps.

Replace *r* with 2 and *h* with 6 in the formulas for the volume of a cylinder and the volume of a cone. Then determine the ratio of the volume of the cone to the volume of the cylinder. $\dfrac{\text{cubic inches}}{\text{cubic inches}}$

> **Read to Succeed!**
> When finding the ratio, round the values for each volume to the same place value.

4 Check

How do you know your solution is accurate?

_____

_____

_____

_____

Lesson 2 *(continued)*

Use a problem-solving model to solve each problem.

1 What is the ratio of the volume of the smaller cone to the larger cone? 8.G.9, **MP** 7

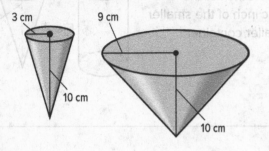

3 cm

9 cm

10 cm

10 cm

Ⓐ 1:3

Ⓑ 1:9

Ⓒ 3:1

Ⓓ 9:1

2 Cone A and Cone B are shown in the figure. The volume of Cone A is 942 cm³. The volume of Cone B is $\frac{1}{4}$ the volume of Cone A. How many *times* longer is the diameter of Cone A than the diameter of Cone B? 8.G.9, **MP** 2

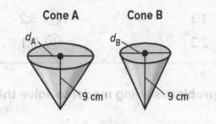

Cone A   Cone B

d_A d_B

9 cm   9 cm

3 What is the volume of the solid figure made up of two congruent cones and a cylinder as shown below? Round to the nearest whole number. 8.G.9, **MP** 4

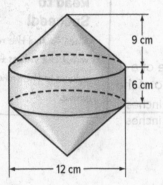

9 cm

6 cm

12 cm

4 🔥 **H.O.T. Problem** A conical paper cup has a diameter of 3 inches and a height of 3 inches. A cylindrical paper cup has a radius of 1.5 inches and a height of 3 inches. Suppose both cups are filled with water. If 1 cubic inch of water weighs 0.6 ounce, how much more does the water in the cylindrical cup weigh, to the nearest tenth of an ounce? Defend your answer. 8.G.9, **MP** 3

Lesson 3 Multi-Step Problem Solving

Multi-Step Example

Brad is packing 3 bouncy balls in a cylindrical container. The radius of each bouncy ball is 10 centimeters. The cylinder has a base area of 314 square centimeters and a height of 65 centimeters. What is the volume of empty space in the container rounded to the nearest whole number? 8.G.9, **MP** 4

(A) 4,189 cm³   (C) 12,566 cm³

(B) 7,844 cm³   (D) 20,410 cm³

Use a problem-solving model to solve this problem.

1 Understand

Read the problem. Circle the information you know.
Underline what the problem is asking you to find.

2 Plan

What will you need to do to solve the problem? Write your plan in steps.

Step 1 Determine the volumes of the _____ and the

three _____.

Step 2 _____ to find the volume of _____.

> **Read to Succeed!**
> Remember to multiply the value you find for the volume of one bouncy ball by 3 since Brad is packing 3 bouncy balls.

3 Solve

Use your plan to solve the problem. Show your steps.

The volume of the container is _____ cubic centimeters, and the

volume of the three bouncy balls is about _____ cubic centimeters.

The volume of the empty space is _____ − _____, or _____,

cubic centimeters. The correct answer is _____.

4 Check

How do you know your solution is accurate?

_____

_____

_____

Lesson 3 *(continued)*

Use a problem-solving model to solve each problem.

1 The radius of a tennis table ball is 2 centimeters. Olivia is packing 30 tennis table balls in a box with a length of 24 centimeters, a width of 20 centimeters, and a height of 4 centimeters. What is the approximate volume of empty space? **8.G.9, MP 4**

Ⓐ 1,920 cm³

Ⓑ 1,005 cm³

Ⓒ 915 cm³

Ⓓ 335 cm³

2 Trevor is creating a concrete sculpture of an ice cream cone. His sculpture consists of a hemisphere on top of a cone as shown below. Trevor needs to order a whole number of cubic yards of concrete. How many cubic yards of concrete should Trevor order so that the amount left over is minimized? **8.G.9, MP 4**

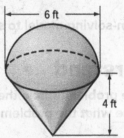

_____

3 A spherical water tank has a 20-foot diameter and is completely filled. How many hours will it take to empty the tank at the rate of 100 gallons per minute? Round your answer to the nearest hour. (*Hint*: 1 cubic foot ≈ $7\frac{1}{2}$ gallons) **8.G.9, MP 4**

_____

4 ✋**H.O.T. Problem** A cylinder and a sphere have the same radius, and the height of the cylinder equals that radius. The equation $V_{sphere} = k \times V_{cylinder}$ shows the relationship between the volumes of the two solids. What is the value of k? Justify your answer. **8.G.9, MP 3**

_____

_____

_____

_____

Lesson 4 Multi-Step Problem Solving

Multi-Step Example

To the nearest whole square centimeter, what is the total surface area of all three cylinders described in the table? *Extension of* **8.G.9,** **4**

Cylinder	Diameter (cm)	Height (cm)
A	6	5
B	4	2
C	12	3

Use a problem-solving model to solve this problem.

 Understand

Read the problem. Circle the information you know. Underline what the problem is asking you to find.

Plan

What will you need to do to solve the problem? Write your plan in steps.

Step 1   Determine the _____ of each _____.

Step 2   Determine the _____ of all three _____.

> **Read to Succeed!**
> Remember to use the radius when determining the surface area of each cylinder.

 Solve

Use your plan to solve the problem. Show your steps.

Use the formula $S =$ _____ determine the _____ for each cylinder: $S_{Cylinder\ A} \approx$ _____cm², $S_{Cylinder\ B} \approx$ _____cm²,

$S_{Cylinder\ C} \approx$ _____cm².

So, the _____ of all three cylinders is about _____ square centimeters.

Check

How do you know your solution is accurate?

_____

_____

_____

Lesson 4 *(continued)*

Use a problem-solving model to solve each problem.

1 To the nearest whole square foot, what is the total surface area of all three cylinders described in the table below?
Extension of **8.G.9, MP 4**

Cylinder	Height (ft)	Radius (ft)
R	2.5	1
S	10	4
T	3	9

2 A painter paints the two circular bases of figure A, and paints just the lateral area of figure B. How many square yards are painted in all? Round your answer to the nearest whole square yard.
Extension of **8.G.9, MP 4**

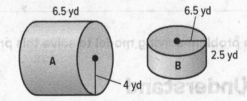

6.5 yd   6.5 yd
A   B
2.5 yd
4 yd

3 Miguel is wrapping cylindrical cans with colored paper for an art project. Two cylinders have a height of 20 inches and diameter of 16 inches. One cylinder has a height of 10 inches and diameter of 6 inches. How much colored paper will Miguel need to wrap all three cans? Round your answer to the nearest whole square inch.
Extension of **8.G.9, MP 4**

4 ✋**H.O.T. Problem** If all the exposed surfaces of the figure are painted, including the bottom of the figure, how many square inches will be painted? Justify your response. Round your answer to the nearest whole square inch.
Extension of **8.G.9, MP 4**

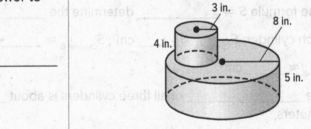

3 in.
8 in.
4 in.
5 in.

Lesson 5 **Multi-Step** Problem Solving

Multi-Step Example

Campers would like to make a cone-shaped tent with a covered floor with the dimensions shown. How much fabric would be used to cover the tent and the floor? (Use 3.14 for π.) *Extension of* **8.G.9,** **MP** 4

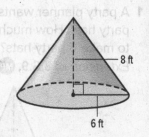

8 ft

6 ft

Use a problem-solving model to solve this problem.

Understand

Read the problem. Circle the information you know.
Underline what the problem is asking you to find.

Plan

What will you need to do to solve the problem? Write your plan in steps.

Step 1 Use the _____ to find the _____ of the cone.

Step 2 Use the _____ to find the _____ of the tent.

Solve

Use your plan to solve the problem. Show your steps.

Using the _____, you find the _____ is

10 feet. By using the formula for the _____ of a cone *S.A.* = $\pi r \ell + \pi r^2$,

you find that the campers need _____ of fabric to cover the tent.

Check

How do you know your solution is accurate?

_____

_____

_____

_____

_____

Lesson 5 *(continued)*

Use a problem-solving model to solve each problem.

1 A party planner wants to make her own party hats. How much paper will it take to make 6 party hats? (Use 3.14 for π.) *Extension of* **8.G.9,** (MP) **4**

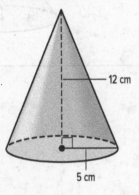

12 cm

5 cm

Ⓐ 1,130.4 cm²

Ⓑ 1,224.6 cm²

Ⓒ 1,601.4 cm²

Ⓓ 1,695.6 cm²

2 A cone has a surface area of 75.36 square centimeters and a radius of 3 centimeters. What is the height of the cone? (Use 3.14 for π.) *Extension of* **8.G.9,** (MP) **4**

_____

3 A cone has a surface area of 113.04 square centimeters and a diameter that is two thirds the length of the slant height. What is the slant height of the cone? (Use 3.14 for π). *Extension of* **8.G.9,** (MP) **1**

_____

4 ✋**H.O.T. Problem** Jamal is finding the lateral area of a waffle cone with a height of 24 centimeters and radius of 10 centimeters. Are the steps he used to solve the problem correct? (He used 3.14 for π.) Explain your answer.

L.A. = (24)(10)π

L.A. ≈ 753.6 cm²

Extension of **8.G.9,** (MP) **3**

_____

_____

_____

_____

Lesson 6   Multi-Step Problem Solving

Multi-Step Example

Mika is making dollhouse furniture out of cardboard to match the actual furniture in his house. His television has a total surface area of 14 square feet. It sits on a cube-shaped chest with sides measuring 3 feet. Using a scale factor of $\frac{1}{10}$, how many square inches of cardboard will Mika use for the dollhouse's television and chest? 8.G.9, MP 4

Ⓐ 8.3   Ⓒ 97.92

Ⓑ 47.2   Ⓓ 979.2

Use a problem-solving model to solve this problem.

1 Understand

Read the problem. Circle the information you know.
Underline what the problem is asking you to find.

2 Plan

What will you need to do to solve the problem? Write your plan in steps.

Step 1 Determine the _____ of the _____ television and chest in square inches.

Step 2 Use the _____ to determine the _____ of the _____ television and chest .

3 Solve

Use your plan to solve the problem. Show your steps.
The total surface area of the actual television and chest is

____ + ____(____)² or ____ square feet, or _____ square inches.
The total surface area of the dollhouse television and chest is

_____ __ or _____ square inches. So, the correct

answer is ____. Fill in that answer choice.

> **Read to Succeed!**
> Remember to convert the total surface area of the actual items to square inches.

4 Check

How do you know your solution is accurate?

_____

_____

_____

Lesson 6 *(continued)*

Use a problem-solving model to solve each problem.

1 Carlos makes geometrical artworks out of sheet metal for public parks. The dimensions of a full-size sculpture will be 6 times the dimensions of the model shown below. He will not use any metal for the bottom base of the cylinder. How many square feet of sheet metal will Carlos use for the full-size sculpture? 8.G.9, **MP** 4

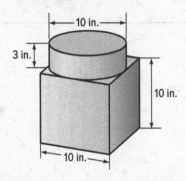

(A) 172.8

(C) 772.8

(B) 193.2

(D) 27,820.8

2 Bethany is filling two conical containers with water. The larger container has dimensions twice those of the smaller container. If there is 0.6 fluid ounce per cubic inch of water, how many ounces of water are in the larger container? Round your answer to the nearest whole number. 8.G.9, **MP** 4

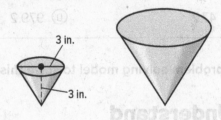

3 Kurt made burrito filling for a scout troop and now he is making the same recipe at home. At home, he is using a can of beans that has dimensions one-half the dimensions of the can of beans he used for the troop. If a serving is 7.3 cubic inches, how many servings are in the smaller can? Round your answer to the nearest whole number. 8.G.9, **MP** 2

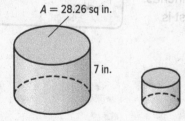

$A = 28.26$ sq in.

7 in.

4 **H.O.T. Problem** Trisha made a giant cereal box for the scenery of a play about nutrition. The original box is 30 centimeters long, 5 centimeters wide, and 20 centimeters tall. She enlarged the box by a scale factor of 8. Trisha says that the surface area of the giant box is 870,400 cm². Explain her mistake and show the correct calculations. 8.G.9, **MP** 3

_____

_____

_____

_____

Lesson 1 Multi-Step Problem Solving

Multi-Step Example

The table shows the 40-yard dash times in seconds for athletes at varying weights in pounds. Which describes the association between speed and weight as shown by a scatter plot of the data? 8.SP.1, MP 7

Ⓐ negative linear association

Ⓑ positive linear association

Ⓒ non-linear association

Ⓓ no association

Speed (s)	Weight (lb)
4.24	178
4.28	176
4.29	155
4.29	186
4.24	197
4.29	188
4.29	193
4.28	181
4.29	184
4.29	200

Use a problem-solving model to solve this problem.

1 Understand

Read the problem. Circle the information you know.
Underline what the problem is asking you to find.

2 Plan

What will you need to do to solve the problem? Write your plan in steps.

Step 1 Construct a _____ of the data on a separate sheet of grid paper.

Step 2 Determine the _____, if any, among the observed data.

3 Solve

Use your plan to solve the problem. Show your steps.

The graph shows that weights for specific speeds vary greatly. For example, the weights for a speed of 4.29 seconds range from

____ to ____. Since there is no obvious _____, the correct answer is ___.

Read to Succeed!

A graph's scales can change its appearance. Choose scales for the x- and y-axes that will accurately show relationships among sets of data.

4 Check

How do you know your solution is accurate?

_____

_____

Lesson 1 (continued)

Use a problem-solving model to solve each problem.

1 The tables below show the average monthly temperatures in degrees Fahrenheit for a certain city for one year, with January representing month 1 and December representing month 12. Which describes the association among the data? **8.SP.1,** MP **7**

Month	1	2	3	4	5	6
°F	31	37	39	49	60	74

Month	7	8	9	10	11	12
°F	78	80	73	58	50	35

Ⓐ negative linear association

Ⓑ positive linear association

Ⓒ non-linear association

Ⓓ no association

2 The table shows the number of gallons in thousands of water in a swimming pool after each hour. What conjecture can be made from the data about the number of gallons of water in the pool after 9 hours? **8.F.5,** MP **2**

Time (h)	Water (1,000 gal)
1	27
2	24
3	22
4	18
5	15
6	13

_____

_____

3 🔥**H.O.T. Problem** The table shows Dario's savings for seven months. Construct a scatterplot of the data. Analyze the scatterplot for patterns of association, outliers, and clusters. If a relationship exists, make a conjecture about how much money Dario will have saved after 10 months. **8.SP.1,** MP **7**

Dario's Savings							
Month	1	2	3	4	5	6	7
Total Savings (dollars)	20	45	75	78	80	121	145

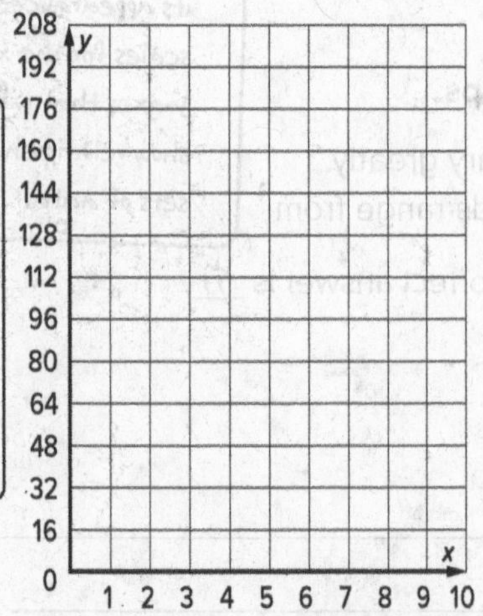

_____

_____

_____

_____

_____

Lesson 2 **Multi-Step** Problem Solving

Multi-Step Example

The scatterplot at the right shows the cost per pound of potatoes from 2000 to 2007. Use a trend line to determine the best estimate for the cost of a pound of potatoes in 2016. **8.SP.1,** **4**

Ⓐ 62 cents

Ⓑ 72 cents

Ⓒ 82 cents

Ⓓ 92 cents

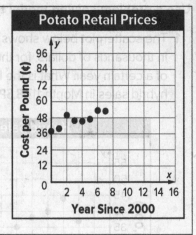

Potato Retail Prices

Cost per Pound (¢) vs Year Since 2000

Use a problem-solving model to solve this problem.

1 Understand

Read the problem. ⟨Circle⟩ the information you know.
Underline what the problem is asking you to find.

2 Plan

What will you need to do to solve the problem? Write your plan in steps.

Step 1 ▸ Draw a _____ that represents the data.

Step 2 ▸ Write an equation for the _____. Then use the equation to make a prediction of the _____.

> **Read to Succeed!**
> Pay close attention to the scale when determining the slope and y-intercept.

3 Solve

Use your plan to solve the problem. Show your steps.

From my trend line, I found potatoes cost about _____ cents

per pound in 2000 and increased about ____ cents per pound in

following years. I then replaced x with ____ in the equation y = ____x + ____.

Potatoes will cost about ___ cents per pound in 2016. So, ___ is the correct answer.

4 Check

How do you know your solution is accurate?

_____

_____

Lesson 2   (continued)

Use a problem-solving model to solve each problem.

1 The scatterplot below shows hybrid car sales, in thousands of dollars, for the first 9 months of a certain year. What is the best estimate of hybrid sales in Month 11? **8.SP.1, MP 4**

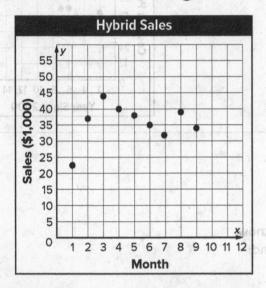

Ⓐ $32,000   Ⓒ $44,000

Ⓑ $38,000   Ⓓ $50,000

2 The scatterplot below shows the length and width of clams obtained in a sample from a certain body of water. Write an equation of a trend line that represents the data. **8.SP.3, MP 2**

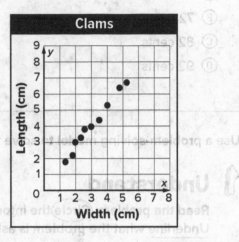

3 The scatterplot below shows the height of a young lady at various ages. Write an equation of a trend line that represents the data. **8.SP.2, MP 2**

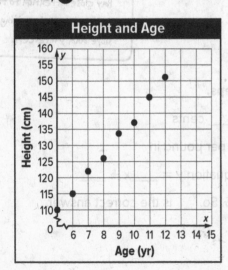

4 ✋ **H.O.T. Problem** The table below shows the progress of a typing student. Construct a scatterplot and draw a trend line. Predict the number of words per minute typed after the 9th week. **8.SP.3, MP 7**

Week	1	2	3	4	5	6
Words Per Minute	15	20	38	42	50	60

Lesson 3   Multi-Step Problem Solving

Multi-Step Example

A group of males and females were surveyed about what color of car they owned. The data are shown in the two-way table. Which statement is true about males and females who own a black car? **8.SP.4, MP 7**

Car Color	Males	Females
Red	14	15
Black	12	12
White	15	12

Ⓐ The same percentage of males and females own black cars.

Ⓑ A larger percentage of males than females own black cars.

Ⓒ A larger percentage of females than males own black cars.

Ⓓ There is not enough information in this table to make a comparison.

Use a problem-solving model to solve this problem.

1 Understand

Read the problem. Circle the information you know. Underline what the problem is asking you to find.

Read to Succeed!

A two-way table shows data of one sample group as it relates to two different categories.

2 Plan

What will you need to do to solve the problem? Write your plan in steps.

Step 1   Find the total number of _____ and the total number of _____.

Step 2   Use the totals to find the relative frequencies of _____ who own black cars.

Step 3   Compare the percentages and choose the correct statement.

3 Solve

Use your plan to solve the problem. Show your steps.

Total males: _____   Total females: _____

The _____ of a male who owns a black car is _____, and the

_____ of a female who owns a black car is _____.

The percentage of females who own black cars is _____ than the percentage of males who own black cars.

The correct answer is _____. Fill in that answer choice.

4 Check

How do you know your solution is accurate?

_____

_____

_____

Lesson 3 (continued)

Use a problem-solving model to solve each problem.

1 A group of 21-year-olds were surveyed about whether they live with their parents and if they are in college. The results are shown in the two-way table. Which statement is true about the 21-year-olds? 8.SP.4, **MP** 7

	Attends College	Does Not Attend College
Lives with Parents	30	30
Does Not Live with Parents	55	60

Ⓐ The percentage of students who attend college is the same for those who do and do not live at home.

Ⓑ A larger percentage of those who attend college live with their parents than those who do not attend college.

Ⓒ A larger percentage of those who do not attend college live with their parents than those who do attend college.

Ⓓ There is not enough information in this table to make a comparison.

2 There are 203 male and 175 female students at Nathan Middle School. A survey showed that 117 males and 97 females ride the bus. What is the difference between the relative frequency of males who ride the bus and the relative frequency of females who do not ride the bus, rounded to the nearest hundredth? 8.SP.4, **MP** 1

	Rides Bus	Does Not Ride Bus	Total
Males	117	86	203
Females	97	78	175
Total	214	164	378

3 Martin surveyed 150 tenth-grade students to find out if they have a part-time job. There are 94 students who have a part-time job, including 57 honor roll students. Half of the students who do not have a job are on the honor roll. Complete the two-way table. What is the relative frequency of an honor roll student with no job rounded to the nearest hundredth? 8.SP.4, **MP** 2

	Honor Roll	No Honor Roll	Total
Job	57		94
No Job			
Total			150

4 🔥 **H.O.T. Problem** Grace is interpreting survey data about people who own a truck. Out of 100 females surveyed, 37 own a truck. Grace makes the statement that of the people who own a truck, 37% are female. Is her statement accurate? Why or why not? 8.SP.4, **MP** 3

_____

_____

_____

Lesson 4   Multi-Step Problem Solving

Multi-Step Example

The box plot shows the number of books read by students during the summer. How much greater is the range than the interquartile range?
Preparation for S.ID.1, MP 4

Summer Reading

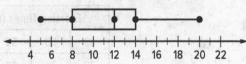

Use a problem-solving model to solve this problem.

1 Understand

Read the problem. Circle the information you know.
Underline what the problem is asking you to find.

2 Plan

What will you need to do to solve the problem? Write your plan in steps.

Step 1   Use the box plot to determine the _____ between the range and interquartile range.

Step 2   _____ the lesser value from the greater value.

3 Solve

Use your plan to solve the problem. Show your steps.

The range is ____ − ____, or ____. The interquartile range is

____ − ____, or ____. The range is ____ − ____ or ____ units

greater.

The answer is ____.

Read to Succeed!

Remember the range is the difference between the maximum and minimum values and the interquartile range is the difference between the third and first quartiles.

4 Check

How do you know your solution is accurate?

_____

_____

_____

Lesson 4 *(continued)*

Use a problem-solving model to solve each problem.

1 The heights of the girls on a basketball team are shown in the table below. How many inches greater is the range than the interquartile range? *Preparation for* **S.ID.1,** (MP) **4**

Heights (in.)				
65	70	66	73	67
71	65	68	70	69

_____

2 The table below shows the amount of time that an eighth grader spent exercising. Which is greater: the mean or median? How much greater? *Preparation for* **S.ID.1,** (MP) **4**

Exercise Times (min)			
63	58	55	67
75	70	60	60

3 A player's score in a golf tournament is determined by the number of total strokes needed to play a golf course over four days. The table below shows six players' scores at a recent tournament. How much closer is the mode to the median than to the mean? *Preparation for* **S.ID.1,** (MP) **4**

Golf Scores		
267	270	265
273	275	267

_____

4 ✋ **H.O.T. Problem** The table below shows the scores of a student on recent science tests. Construct a box plot of the data. What percent of the data is between 81 and 86? Explain. *Preparation for* **S.ID.1,** (MP) **3**

Science Test Scores						
80	81	84	84	87	86	86

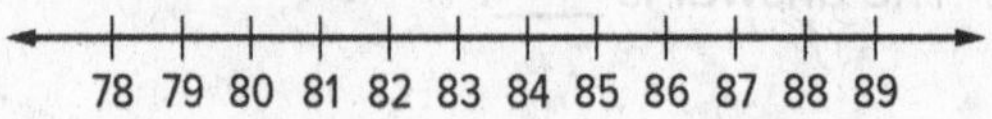

```
  +--+--+--+--+--+--+--+--+--+--+--+-->
 78 79 80 81 82 83 84 85 86 87 88 89
```

_____

_____

_____

_____

Lesson 5 **Multi-Step** Problem Solving

Multi-Step Example

The table shows the total points scored in men's and women's basketball games. The men's scores have a standard deviation of 15.1, and the women's scores have a standard deviation of 7.9. Make a comparison of the variation between the data sets, and use the standard deviations to support your answer. *Preparation for* **S.ID.4, MP 3**

Women	57	69	73	79	62	65	59	54
Men	76	62	103	85	75	97	110	80

Use a problem-solving model to solve this problem.

1 Understand

Read the problem. (Circle) the information you know.
Underline what the problem is asking you to find.

Read to Succeed!
The mean absolute deviation is the average distance of each value from the mean.

2 Plan

What will you need to do to solve the problem? Write your plan in steps.

Step 1   Find the mean absolute deviation _____ scores and mean absolute deviation of the _____ scores.

Step 2   Compare the _____ of the scores and use the _____ to support your comparison.

3 Solve

Use your plan to solve the problem. Show your steps.

The mean absolute deviation of the _____ scores is _____ and of the _____ scores is _____. The _____ scores have a greater variation than the _____ scores.

The _____ support this because the majority of the scores for the men's team are between _____ and the majority of the scores of the women's team are between _____ .

4 Check

How do you know your solution is accurate?

_____

_____

_____

Lesson 5 (continued)

Use a problem-solving model to solve each problem.

1 The table shows the lengths of ribbons used in different craft projects. The standard deviation of the lengths is 2.5 inches. If the mean of the data is rounded to the nearest tenth, which statement describes the data values that are within one standard deviation of the mean? *Preparation for* **S.ID.4,** Ⓜ **3**

Length of Ribbons (in.)			
7	5	6	10
10	7	9	3
9	11	12	7

Ⓐ The mean absolute variation is greater than the standard deviation.

Ⓑ The majority of the lengths will be shorter than 10.5 inches.

Ⓒ The majority of the lengths will be longer than 5.5 inches.

Ⓓ The majority of the lengths will be between 5.5 inches and 10.5 inches.

3 The speeds of cars ticketed in a school zone are listed in the table. What is the difference between the standard deviation of 4.85 and the mean absolute deviation of the data? *Preparation for* **S.ID.4,** Ⓜ **2**

Speeds of Cars (mi/h)			
38	42	39	45
30	37	43	46

_____

2 The standard deviation of test scores is 13.5. What are the test scores within two standard deviations of the mean? Round to the nearest tenth if necessary. *Preparation for* **S.ID.4,** Ⓜ **2**

Test Scores			
79	63	59	86
88	92	100	53
72	76	70	69

_____

_____

_____

4 👆**H.O.T. Problem** Create a data set of 5 numbers with a range of 50. What is the mean absolute deviation? Will every data set with a range of 50 have the same mean absolute deviation? Why or why not? *Preparation for* **S.ID.4,** Ⓜ **3**

_____

_____

_____

_____

Lesson 6   Multi-Step Problem Solving

Multi-Step Example

From Week 1 to Week 2, the number of band members who practiced 3 hours increased by 75% and the number who practiced 4 hours decreased by 50%. Which of the following shows the best measures of center and spread for Week 2 data? *Preparation for S.ID.2,* (MP) 1

Ⓐ median = 3.5, interquartile range = 2

Ⓑ median = 4, interquartile range = 2

Ⓒ mean = 3.85, mean average deviation = 1

Ⓓ mean = 4, mean average deviation = 1

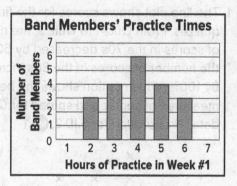

Band Members' Practice Times

Number of Band Members (vertical axis, 0–7)

Hours of Practice in Week #1 (horizontal axis, 1–7)

Use a problem-solving model to solve this problem.

1 Understand

Read the problem. Circle the information you know.
Underline what the problem is asking you to find.

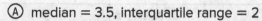

2 Plan

What will you need to do to solve the problem? Write your plan in steps.

Step 1 Use the given _____ to construct the _____ graph.

Step 2 Determine which measure of center and spread to use based

on the _____ of the _____ graph.

3 Solve

Use your plan to solve the problem. Show your steps.

Construct the _____ graph. Since the graph is not symmetric,

the _____ will describe the center and the _____

will describe the spread.

Since the _____ is ____ and the _____ is ____,

the correct answer is ____.

Read to Succeed!

If the data distribution is symmetric, use the mean to describe the center and the mean absolute deviation to describe the spread.

If the data distribution is not symmetric, use the median to describe the center and the interquartile range to describe the spread.

4 Check

How do you know your solution is accurate?

_____

_____

Lesson 6   (continued)

Use a problem-solving model to solve each problem.

1 The line plot shows scores for the first of two quizzes. From Quiz 1 to Quiz 2, the number of scores in the 70s decreased by 50% and the number of scores in the 80s increased by 100%. Which option shows the best measures of center and spread for Quiz 2 data? *Preparation for* **S.ID.2,** **MP** 1

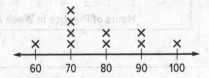

ⓐ median = 75, interquartile range = 20

ⓑ median = 80, interquartile range = 20

ⓒ mean = 78, mean average deviation = 8

ⓓ mean = 80, mean average deviation = 8

2 Lina participated in a flying disc game. The ages of the players are shown below. What measure of spread should Lina use for the data? What is that number? *Preparation for* **S.ID.2,** **MP** 2

Players' Ages									
23	19	30	23	16	27	23	19	23	27

3 Marisol recorded these low temperatures, in degrees Celsius, in her city on 10 consecutive days: 3, 2, 2, 1, −1, 1, 2, 2, 3, 5. What measure of spread should Marisol use for the data? What is the measure of spread? *Preparation for* **S.ID.2,** **MP** 2

4 **H.O.T. Problem** Each test score shown in the histogram below is a multiple of 5. In each interval, $\frac{2}{3}$ of the scores are multiples of 10. What are the measures of center and spread? Defend your answers. *Preparation for* **S.ID.2,** **MP** 3

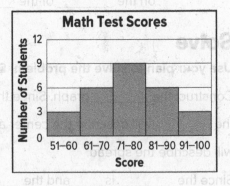

_____

_____

_____

_____

Chapter 2 Lesson 1 Answer Keys

NAME _____ DATE _____ PERIOD _____

Lesson 1 (continued)

Use a problem-solving model to solve each problem.

1. The table below shows the free throws made (FTM) and the free throws attempted (FTA) for three players on the high school basketball team. Based on the table, what is the combined free-throw percentage of all three players? 8.NS.1, MP 1

Free Throws		
Player	FTM	FTA
Jones	38	42
Mason	9	10
Rice	9	10

Ⓐ 0.900
Ⓑ 0.903
Ⓒ 0.904
Ⓓ 0.905

2. Express $0.46\overline{1538}$ as a fraction in simplest form. Show your steps below. 8.NS.1, MP 1

$N = 0.46\overline{1538461538}...$

$1,000,000 (N) = 1,000,000(0.46\overline{1538461538}...)$

$1,000,000 \ N = 461,538.46\overline{1538}...$

$\underline{-N = \qquad 0.46\overline{1538}...}$

$999,999 \ N = 461,538$

$N = \dfrac{461,538}{999,999}$ or $\dfrac{6}{13}$

3. A survey was conducted to determine the favorite sport for members of the eighth grade class. The results are shown in the table. How many students selected either football or baseball? Express your answer as a decimal. 8.NS.1, MP 2

Sport	Part of Class
Football	$\frac{7}{20}$
Baseball	$\frac{1}{5}$
Basketball	$\frac{3}{10}$
Soccer	$\frac{3}{20}$

0.55

4. 🖊 H.O.T. Problem What is the difference of the areas, expressed as a decimal, of the shaded rectangle and the unshaded rectangle? Explain how you determined your answer. 8.NS.1, MP 1

$0.05\overline{83}$ in²; Sample answer: area of shaded rectangle = $\frac{1}{2} \cdot \frac{1}{4}$ or $\frac{1}{8}$ in²; area of unshaded rectangle = $\frac{1}{3} \cdot \frac{1}{5}$ or $\frac{1}{15}$ in²;

difference in areas:
$\frac{1}{8} - \frac{1}{15} = \frac{15}{120} - \frac{8}{120} = \frac{7}{120}$ or $0.05\overline{83}$

NAME _____ DATE _____ PERIOD _____

Lesson 1 Multi-Step Problem Solving

Multi-Step Example

Two teams that have the best win to loss ratio play each other in a one-game playoff. The table shows four teams competing for the playoff spots. Based on the table, which two teams are in the lead to go to the playoffs? 8.NS.1, MP 1

Team	Win	Loss
Blue Sox	97	64
Hawks	96	66
Bombers	95	60
Bears	94	61

Ⓐ Blue Sox and Hawks
Ⓑ Bombers and Bears
Ⓒ Blue Sox and Bombers
Ⓓ Hawks and Bears

Use a problem-solving model to solve this problem.

1 Understand

Read the problem. Circle the information you know. Underline what the problem is asking you to find.

2 Plan

What will you need to do to solve the problem? Write your plan in steps.

Step 1: Write the information for each team as a win to loss ratio.

Step 2: Express each ratio as a __decimal__ and compare __decimals__.

3 Solve

Use your plan to solve the problem. Show your steps.

Blue Sox: $\frac{97}{64} \approx$ __1.516__ Hawks: $\frac{96}{66} \approx$ __1.455__

Bombers: $\frac{95}{60} \approx$ __1.583__ Bears: $\frac{94}{61} \approx$ __1.541__

The two greatest values are __1.541__ and __1.583__.

So, the __Bears__ and __Bombers__ are in the lead to go to the play-offs. The correct answer is __B__. Fill in that answer choice.

4 Check

How do you know your solution is accurate?

Sample answer: I reread the problem to verify that I was asked to find the two teams with the best win-loss records. Then I checked my calculations to make sure my decimal conversions were correct.

Read to Succeed!

When comparing decimals, be sure to round each decimal to the same decimal place.

Answers

NAME _____ DATE _____ PERIOD _____

Chapter 1

Lesson 2 Multi-Step Problem Solving

Multi-Step Example
The table shows the approximate number of Earth hours there are in one day for two planets. Which of the following is the longest amount of time? 8.EE.1, MP 1

Planet	Length of Day (Earth Hours)
Venus	3^5
Neptune	2^4

(A) 8 Venus days
(B) 20 Neptune days
(C) 5 Venus days and 12 Neptune days
(D) 4 Venus days and 15 Neptune days

Use a problem-solving model to solve this problem.

1 Understand
Read the problem. (Circle) the information you know. Underline what the problem is asking you to find.

2 Plan
What will you need to do to solve the problem? Write your plan in steps.
Step 1 Write an expression with exponents for each of the four times.
Step 2 **Evaluate** each expression and **compare** the values.

3 Solve
Use your plan to solve the problem. Show your steps.
8 Venus days = __1,944__ Earth days
20 Neptune days = __320__ Earth days
5 Venus days and 12 Neptune days = __1,407__ Earth days
4 Venus days and 15 Neptune days = __1,212__ Earth days
The greatest value is __1,944__ Earth days. So, the longest amount of time is __8 Venus days__. The answer is __A__. Fill in that answer choice.

Read to Succeed!
When evaluating an expression such as $8 \cdot 3^5$, remember to follow the order of operations. Evaluate 3^5 before multiplying by 8.

4 Check
How do you know your solution is accurate?
Sample answer: I know that powers of 3 increase at a faster rate than powers of 2. So, it makes sense that the choice where 3^5 is multiplied by the greatest factor would be the longest time.

NAME _____ DATE _____ PERIOD _____

Lesson 2 (continued)

Use a problem-solving model to solve each problem.

1 The table shows the approximate number of Earth hours there are in one day for two planets. Which of the following is the same amount of time as 4 Venus days and 6 Neptune days? 8.EE.1, MP 2

Planet	Length of Day (Earth Hours)
Venus	3^5
Neptune	2^4

(A) 1,036 Earth hours
(B) 1,068 Earth hours
(C) 1,522 Earth hours
(D) 1,554 Earth hours

2 What is the volume of the cube, in cubic units, if $x = 3$? 8.EE.1, MP 2

x^2 units

729

3 If $4^2 \cdot 4^x = 8 \cdot 512$, what is the value of x? Show how you solved the problem. 8.EE.1, MP 7
4; Sample answer:
$4^2 \cdot 4^x = 8 \cdot 512$
$16 \cdot 4^x = 4{,}096$
$\dfrac{16 \cdot 4^x}{16} = \dfrac{4{,}096}{16}$
$4^x = 256$
Since $4^4 = 256$, $x = 4$.

4 H.O.T. Problem Consider the following equations.

$$1 = 1 = 1^3$$
$$3 + 5 = 8 = 2^3$$
$$7 + 9 + 11 = 27 = 3^3$$
$$13 + 15 + 17 + 19 = 64 = 4^3$$
$$21 + 23 + 25 + 27 + 29 = 125 = 5^3$$

If the pattern continues, what will be the 10th equation? Explain. 8.EE.1, MP 8
$91 + 93 + 95 + 97 + 99 + 101 + 103 + 105 + 107 + 109 = 1{,}000 = 10^3$; Sample answer: In each equation, the number of values added is equal to the base. The first numbers are 1, 3, 7, 13, and 21. So, the first numbers are increasing by 2, 4, 6, and 8. Continuing the pattern gives first numbers of 1, 3, 7, 13, 21, 31, 43, 57, 73, and 91. So, the tenth equation starts with 91.

NAME _____ DATE _____ PERIOD _____

Lesson 3 (continued)

Use a problem-solving model to solve each problem.

1 The table shows the length of samples of bamboo. Which of the following is true about the two samples? 8.EE.1, MP 1

Sample	Length (cm)
A	100,000
B	100

Ⓐ Sample A is 100 times as long as Sample B.

Ⓑ Sample A is 10^3 times longer than Sample B.

Ⓒ Sample A and B can be combined for a length that is 10 times as long as Sample B.

Ⓓ The difference between the two lengths is 103 cm.

3 Is 5^{98} greater than, less than or equal to 25? Justify your answer using exponents. 8.EE.1, MP 7

$\frac{5^{98}}{5^{95}}$ **is greater than 25; $5^3 > 5^2$**

2 How many times greater is the cube of one million than the square of ten thousand? 8.EE.1, MP 1

10^{10} or 10,000,000,000 times greater

4 ✦ **H.O.T. Problem** What number is triple 3^5? Write using exponents and explain your answer. 8.EE.1, MP 7

3^{45}; $3 \times 3^{45} = 3^{1+45} = 3^{46}$

NAME _____ DATE _____ PERIOD _____

Lesson 3 Multi-Step Problem Solving

Multi-Step Example

The processing speed of a certain computer is 10^{12} instructions per second. A second computer has a processing speed that is 10^5 times as fast. Which statement is true? 8.EE.1, MP 2

Ⓐ The processing speed of the second computer is 10^5 instructions per second.

Ⓑ The processing speed of the second computer is 1,000 times as fast.

Ⓒ The second computer processes 1,000 more instructions per second.

Ⓓ The processing speed of the second computer is 10^{17} instructions per second.

Use a problem-solving model to solve this problem.

1 Understand

Read the problem. Circle the information you know. Underline what the problem is asking you to find.

2 Plan

What will you need to do to solve the problem? Write your plan in steps.

Step 1 Find the processing speed of the second computer.

Step 2 **Multiply** the processing speed of the first computer by the increase of processing speed of the **second computer.**

3 Solve

Use your plan to solve the problem. Show your steps.

Find the processing speed by **multiplying** .

10^{12} × **10^5** = **10^{17}**

The second computer has a processing speed of **10^{17}** instructions per second. Choice **D** is the correct answer. Fill in that answer choice.

Read to Succeed!

Remember when using the product of powers the base stays the same and you add the exponents.

4 Check

How do you know your solution is accurate?

Sample answer: If I divide the second computer's processing speed by the processing speed of the first computer I should get 10^5, because the second computer is 10^5 times as fast.

Chapter 1

Answers

NAME _____ DATE _____ PERIOD _____

Lesson 4 *(continued)*

Use a problem-solving model to solve each problem.

1 How many smaller cubes will fit in the larger cube? **8.EE.1,** MP **7**

$4x^4$
$2x$

Ⓐ $8x^3$ cubes
Ⓑ $8x^9$ cubes
Ⓒ $64x^8$ cubes
Ⓓ $64x^{12}$ cubes

2 The table gives the area of a square and volume of a cube with side lengths as shown. Complete the table. **8.EE.1,** MP **7**

	Side Length x	Side Length $3y^2$	Double the Side Length of $3y^2$
Area of a square	x^2	$9y^4$	$36y^4$
Volume of a cube	x^3	$27y^6$	$216y^6$

3 One cube has side length of $3x^6$ and another has side length $2x^7$. Which cube has the greater volume when $x = 3$? **8.EE.1,** MP **7**

The cube with side length of $2x^7$.

4 ✎ **H.O.T. Problem** A rock is dropped from the top of the bleachers. The expression $4.9x^2$ gives the distance in meters the rock has fallen in x seconds. Mrs. Malone's class wants to know how many meters the rock has fallen in x^2 seconds. One group says the answer is $24.01x^4$ meters. Is their answer correct? Support your answer. **8.EE.1,** MP **3**

Their answer is incorrect. The correct
answer is 4.9x^4. The group incorrectly
applied the order of operations.

_____

_____

_____

_____

_____

_____

NAME _____ DATE _____ PERIOD _____

Lesson 4 **Multi-Step** Problem Solving

Multi-Step Example

The models show a square floor and the square tile that will be used to cover the floor. How many tiles will it take to cover the floor? **8.EE.1,** MP **1**

$8x^3y^2$
xy

Ⓐ $8x^2y$ Ⓒ $64x^4y^2$
Ⓑ $8x^3y^2$ Ⓓ $64x^6y^4$

Use a problem-solving model to solve this problem.

1 Understand

Read the problem. ⟨Circle⟩ the information you know.
Underline what the problem is asking you to find.

2 Plan

What will you need to do to solve the problem? Write your plan in steps.

〔Step 1〕 Find the area of the floor.

〔Step 2〕 Find the area of the tile.

〔Step 3〕 Divide the area of the **floor** by the area of the **tile**.

3 Solve

Use your plan to solve the problem. Show your steps.

Find the area by squaring the length of each side.

floor = $(8x^3y^2)^2 =$ **$64x^6y^4$**   tile = $(xy)^2 =$ **x^2y^2**

Then divide to find how many tiles it will take to cover the floor.

floor $\dfrac{64x^6y^4}{x^2y^2} =$ **$64x^4y^2$**
tile

The correct answer is that it will take **$64x^4y^2$** tiles to cover the floor. The answer is **C** . Fill in that answer choice.

Read to Succeed!
To find the area of a square, just square the length of the side.

4 Check

How do you know your solution is accurate?

Sample answer: I know that to find the area of a square, I square the length of
the sides. To determine how many squares can fit in another square involves
dividing those areas. So, it makes sense that the number of xy tiles that will fit
in an area of $64x^6y^4$ will have a coefficient of 64.

NAME _____ DATE _____ PERIOD _____

Lesson 5 Multi-Step Problem Solving

Multi-Step Example

The table shows the hair lengths of five samples taken for a laboratory study. Which of the following shows the order of these hair lengths from least to greatest? 8.EE.1, MP 2

Sample	Hair Length (in.)
1	2^2
2	2^{-2}
3	2^0
4	2^{-1}
5	2^{-3}

Ⓐ $2^2, 2^{-2}, 2^0, 2^{-1}, 2^{-3}$
Ⓑ $2^0, 2^{-3}, 2^{-2}, 2^{-1}, 2^2$
Ⓒ $2^2, 2^0, 2^{-1}, 2^{-2}, 2^{-3}$
Ⓓ $2^{-3}, 2^{-2}, 2^{-1}, 2^0, 2^2$

Use a problem-solving model to solve this problem.

1 Understand
Read the problem. Circle the information you know. Underline what the problem is asking you to find.

2 Plan
What will you need to do to solve the problem? Write your plan in steps.
Step 1 Evaluate the expressions in the table.
Step 2 Compare and order the values.

3 Solve
Use your plan to solve the problem. Show your steps.
$2^2 = 4$
$2^{-2} = \frac{1}{2^2} = \frac{1}{4}$ or 0.25
$2^{-1} = \frac{1}{2}$ or 0.5
$2^0 = 1$
$2^{-3} = \frac{1}{2^3} = \frac{1}{8}$ or 0.125

Since 0.125 < 0.25 < 0.5 < 1 < 4,
D is the answer. Fill in that answer choice.

4 Check
How do you know your solution is accurate?
Sample answer: Since the bases are the same, it makes sense that the expressions can be ordered based on the value of the exponents.

Read to Succeed!
Be careful when evaluating negative exponents. For example, $2^{-1} = \frac{1}{2^1}$.

Course 3 • Chapter 1 Real Numbers

NAME _____ DATE _____ PERIOD _____

Lesson 5 (continued)

Use a problem-solving model to solve each problem.

1 On the number line shown below, the coordinate of point X is 3^{-3} and the coordinate of point Y is 3^{-2}. Which of the following is the coordinate of a point between X and Y? 8.EE.1, MP 2

Ⓐ 2^{-5}
Ⓑ 4^{-1}
Ⓒ 5^{-2}
Ⓓ 6^{-1}

2 The table shows the dimensions in feet of four rectangles. What is the difference in area of the rectangle with the greatest area and the rectangle with the least area? 8.EE.1, MP 2

Rectangle	Width (ft)	Length (ft)
A	2^{-1}	2^7
B	2^6	2^{-3}
C	2^{-2}	2^5
D	2^5	2^{-5}

63 ft²

3 What is the total surface area of the rectangular prism shown below? 8.EE.1, MP 1 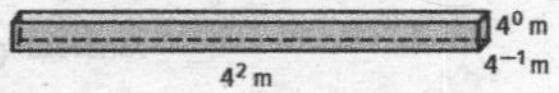
4^0 m, 4^{-1} m, 4^2 m
40.5 m²

4 H.O.T. Problem If a, b, and c are different negative integers less than −1 and $2^a \cdot 2^b \cdot 2^c = \frac{1}{512}$, what is the absolute value of abc? Explain your answer. 8.EE.1, MP 7
Sample answer: I rewrote $\frac{1}{512}$ as 2^{-9}. So, I am looking for three negative exponents that add to −9. The sum of the negative integers −2, −3, and −4 is −9. So, a can equal −2, b can equal −3, and c can equal −4. Since the product of −2, −3, and −4 is −24, $|abc| = |-24| = 24$.

Course 3 • Chapter 1 Real Numbers

Answers

NAME _____ DATE _____ PERIOD _____

Lesson 6 Multi-Step Problem Solving

Multi-Step Example

The attendance records at games for four professional football teams for a recent year are shown in the table. Which of the following lists the teams from greatest attendance to least attendance? 8.EE.4, MP 1

Team	Attendance
W	5.58×10^4
X	5.49×10^5
Y	5.51×10^4
Z	5.53×10^5

Ⓐ W, Z, Y, X
Ⓑ Y, W, X, Z
Ⓒ Z, X, W, Y
Ⓓ X, Y, Z, W

Use a problem-solving model to solve this problem.

1 Understand

Read the problem. Circle the information you know.
Underline what the problem is asking you to find.

2 Plan

What will you need to do to solve the problem? Write your plan in steps.

Step 1   Express each value in standard decimal notation.

Step 2   Order the numbers from greatest to least.

3 Solve

Use your plan to solve the problem. Show your steps.

W: $5.58 \times 10^4 =$ __55,800__   X: $5.49 \times 10^5 =$ __549,000__

Y: $5.51 \times 10^4 =$ __55,100__   Z: $5.53 \times 10^5 =$ __553,000__

Since __553,000__ > __549,000__ > __55,800__ > __55,100__, the teams, in

order of greatest to least attendance, are __Z__ , __X__ , __W__ , and __Y__ .

So, the correct answer is C. Fill in that answer choice.

Read to Succeed!
When comparing numbers with the same number of decimal places, start at the right and compare the digits until you come to the digits that are different.

4 Check

How do you know your solution is accurate?

Sample answer: The expressions where 10 is raised to the 5th power

will be greater than the expressions where 10 is raised to the 4th power.

Since 5.53 > 5.49 and 5.58 > 5.51, my answer is correct.

NAME _____ DATE _____ PERIOD _____

Lesson 6 (continued)

Use a problem-solving model to solve each problem.

1 The table shows the mass of one atom of each of several elements. Which element has the greatest mass per atom? 8.EE.4, MP 1

Element	Mass per Atom
argon	6.64×10^{-23} g
helium	6.65×10^{-24} g
iodine	2.11×10^{-22} g
mercury	3.33×10^{-22} g

Ⓐ argon
Ⓑ helium
Ⓒ iodine
Ⓓ mercury

2 The volume the rectangular prism shown below is 4.8×10^9 cubic meters. What is the height h of the prism expressed in standard decimal notation? 8.EE.4, MP 2

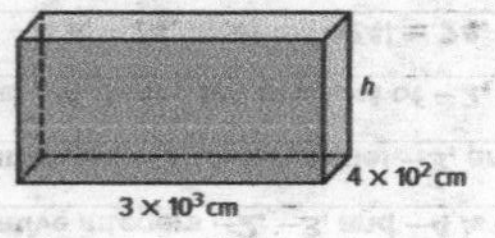

4×10^2 cm

3×10^3 cm

4,000 cm

3 The table shows three numerical expressions. Suppose each expression is evaluated and the result is written in scientific notation. What will be the power of 10 of the expression with the greatest value? 8.EE.4, MP 2

Calculation Number	Expression
1	$\frac{(28,000)(6,000)}{400}$
2	$\frac{(7,000)(600,000)}{3,000}$
3	$\frac{(350,000)(900,000)}{14,000}$

7

4 🤔 H.O.T. Problem Light travels at approximately 186,000 miles per second. A light year is the distance that light can travel in one year. How many miles is a light year? Express your answer in scientific notation and explain your work. 8.EE.4, MP 1

$5.865,696 \times 10^{12}$ miles; Sample answer:

$186,000 \frac{mi}{sec} \times 60 \frac{sec}{min} \times 60 \frac{min}{h} \times 24 \frac{h}{day} \times$

$365 \frac{day}{yr} = 5,865,696,000,000 \frac{mi}{yr}$

Then I converted this product to scientific notation.

12

Chapter 1 Lesson 7 Answer Keys

Lesson 7 Multi-Step Problem Solving

Chapter 1

Multi-Step Example

In 2010, the population of China was 1,370,000,000 and the population of the U.S. was 3×10^8. Which of the following statements is true? 8.EE.4, MP 2

Ⓐ The population of China was approximately 100% greater than the population of the U.S.

Ⓑ The ratio of the population of China to the population of the U.S. was 1:3.

Ⓒ The population of China was about 46 times as great as the population of the U.S.

Ⓓ The total combined population of China and the U.S. was 1.67×10^9 people.

Use a problem-solving model to solve this problem.

1 Understand

Read the problem. (Circle) the information you know. Underline what the problem is asking you to find.

2 Plan

What will you need to do to solve the problem? Write your plan in steps.

Step 1 Write China's population in **scientific notation** and adjust to the __same__ power of 10 as U.S. population.

Step 2 **Compare** the whole numbers to determine the relationship between the two populations.

Read to Succeed!

You can add numbers written in scientific notation if they have the same power of 10.

3 Solve

Use your plan to solve the problem. Show your steps.

China's population in **scientific notation** = __1.37×10^9__

U.S. population = 3×10^8 China's population = __13.7__ $\times 10^8$

Compare the whole numbers.   __13.7__ $\times 10^8 \div$ __3__ $\times 10^8 =$ __4.6__

This means that the population of China was about __4.6__ times as great as the population of the U.S., which is __460__ percent and a ratio of **4.6 :1.**

__13.7__ $\times 10^8 +$ __3__ $\times 10^8 =$ __16.7__ $\times 10^8$ This means that the total combined population in scientific notation is __1.67×10^9__ The answer is __D__.

4 Check

How do you know your solution is reasonable?

Sample answer: $3 \times 10^8 = 300,000,000$ and the sum of this value and **1,370,000,000 is 1,670,000,000. This is the same as 1.67×10^9.**

13

Lesson 7 (continued)

Use a problem-solving model to solve each problem.

1. An internet company averages 7.3×10^7 spam E-mails and 1,300,000,000 regular E-mails per year. How many total E-mails does the internet company average per year? Express the answer in scientific notation. 8.EE.4, MP 2

   Ⓐ 1.373×10^7
   Ⓑ 1.373×10^9
   Ⓒ 13.73×10^7
   Ⓓ 137.3×10^9

2. A music download company averages 3×10^9 music downloads and has 4×10^7 customers. How many songs does the average customer download? 8.EE.4, MP 1

   75 or 7.5×10^1

3. The table shows the amount of mail delivered through three different courier services per year. How many times more per year does Mike's Mail deliver than Send It? 8.EE.3, MP 2

Courier Service	Amount of Mail per Year
Mike's Mail	5×10^9
Fast Package	4,560,000
Send It	5,000,000

   10^3 or 1,000 times more

4. H.O.T. Problem Which expression does not belong? Explain your reasoning. 8.EE.4, MP 1

2.117×10^8
2.117×10^{11}
$(2.9)(7.3) \times 10^{6.7}$
$(2.9 \times 10^3)(7.3 \times 10^5)$

   2.117×10^{11}; The three other expressions are equivalent.

14

Answers

NAME _____ DATE _____ PERIOD _____

Lesson 8 Multi-Step Problem Solving

Multi-Step Example
A bulletin board consists of four equal-sized cork squares arranged in a row to form a rectangle. If the total area of all four cork squares is 100 square feet, what is the length in feet of the bulletin board? 8.EE.2, MP 1

Use a problem-solving model to solve this problem.

1 Understand
Read the problem. Circle the information you know. Underline what the problem is asking you to find.

2 Plan
What will you need to do to solve the problem? Write your plan in steps.

Step 1 Determine the **square root** of the area of one square.

Step 2 Multiply the answer to Step 1 by __4__.

3 Solve
Use your plan to solve the problem. Show your steps.

$100 \div 4 = $ __25__   area of one square in square feet

$\sqrt{25} = $ __5__   length in feet of one side of one square

$(4 \cdot $ __5__ $ = $ __20__   length in feet of entire bulletin board

The answer is __20__ feet.

4 Check
How do you know your solution is accurate?

Sample answer: I can work backward. If the entire length is 20, the length of one square is 5. If the side length is 5 feet, the area of one square is 5^2 or 25 square feet. So, the total area is $4 \cdot 25$ or 100 square feet. So, my answer makes sense.

Read to Succeed!
Since distance cannot be negative, use only the positive square root.

Chapter 1

15

NAME _____ DATE _____ PERIOD _____

Lesson 8 (continued)

Use a problem-solving model to solve each problem.

1 What is the difference in side length of the cubes shown below? 8.EE.2, MP 1

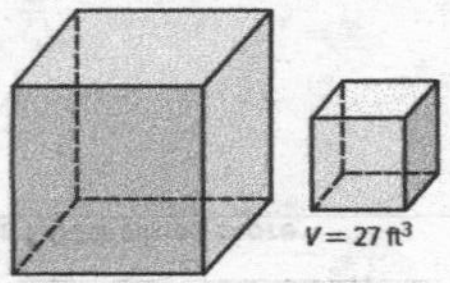

$V = 64 \text{ ft}^3$

$V = 27 \text{ ft}^3$

1 foot

2 The area of the figure below is 300 square centimeters. What is the perimeter of the figure? 8.EE.2, MP 2

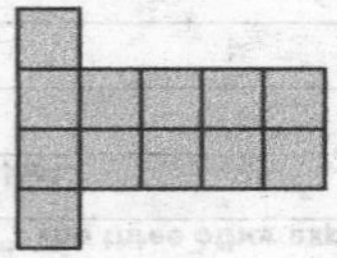

90 cm

3 The volume of the rectangular prism shown is 4,320 cubic centimeters. What is the surface area of the whole prism? Explain. 8.EE.2, MP 3

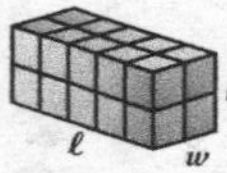

1,728 cm²; The surface area of the whole prism is 360 + 360 + 360 + 144 + 144 + 144 or 1,728 cm².

4 H.O.T. Problem Dario wants to buy paper to wrap a birthday present in the cube-shaped box shown below. If an 8.3-square-foot package of wrapping paper costs $1.25, how much will Dario spend on the wrapping paper? Explain. 8.EE.2, MP 7

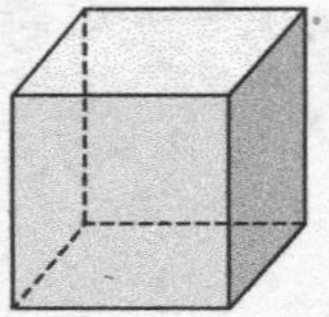

$V = 27 \text{ ft}^3$

$8.75; Sample answer: Since the volume is 27 ft³, each side is 3 feet long and the surface area is $6 \cdot 3^2$ or 54 ft². Since $54 \div 8.3 \approx 6.5$ and Dario cannot buy a partial pack of paper, Dario will spend $1.25 · 7 or $8.75.

Course 3 · Chapter 1 Real Numbers
16

NAME _____ DATE _____ PERIOD _____

Lesson 9 *(continued)*

Use a problem-solving model to solve each problem.

1 The table shows the volume of four cubes. Which is the order of the volumes from least to greatest? **8.NS.2,** MP **1**

Cube	Volume (cm³)
A	$\sqrt[3]{74}$
B	3
C	$\sqrt[3]{110}$
D	5

Ⓐ $\sqrt[3]{74}$, $\sqrt[3]{110}$, 3, 5

Ⓑ 3, 5, $\sqrt[3]{74}$, $\sqrt[3]{110}$

Ⓒ 3, $\sqrt[3]{74}$, $\sqrt[3]{110}$, 5

Ⓓ 5, $\sqrt[3]{110}$, $\sqrt[3]{74}$, 3

2 Roger made a square sign to place in front of the school shown below in the sketch. What is the approximate perimeter, in inches, of his sign? (*Hint:* 1 m ≈ 39.37 in.) **8.NS.2,** MP **2**

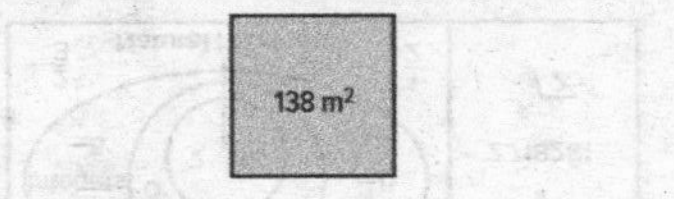

138 m²

about 1,850 in.

3 The diagonal of a box d with length ℓ, width w, and height h is given by the formula $d = \sqrt{\ell^2 + w^2 + h^2}$. What is the length of the diagonal of the box shown below to the nearest whole meter? **8.NS.2,** MP **2**

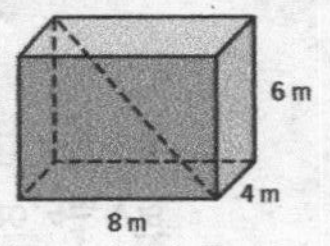

8 m, 6 m, 4 m

11

4 ✎ **H.O.T. Problem** A circle of radius r has an area A of 214 square centimeters. Estimate the radius of the circle to the nearest whole centimeter. Use 3 as an estimate for π. Explain how you found your answer. **8.NS.2,** MP **7**

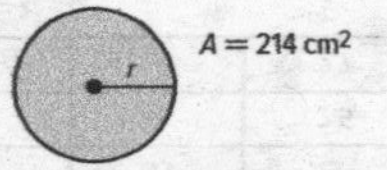

$A = 214$ cm²

8 cm; Sample answer: I solved the formula

$A = \pi r^2$ for r. I know $r = \sqrt{\dfrac{A}{\pi}}$ and $\pi \approx 3$,

so $r \approx \sqrt{\dfrac{214}{3}} = \sqrt{\dfrac{214}{3}} \approx \sqrt{71.3}$ and $\sqrt{64}$

$< \sqrt{71.3} < \sqrt{81}$; $8 < \sqrt{71.3} < 9$; Since

$71.3 - 64 = 7.3$ and $81 - 71.3 = 9.7$,

$\sqrt{71.3}$ is closer to 8.

NAME _____ DATE _____ PERIOD _____

Lesson 9 **Multi-Step** Problem Solving

Multi-Step Example

The table shows the area of four square photos. Which of the following is the order of the photos from greatest area to least area? **8.NS.2,** MP **1**

Photos	Area (cm²)
A	$\sqrt{130}$
B	$\sqrt{172}$
C	13
D	11

Ⓐ B, C, A, D

Ⓑ C, B, A, D

Ⓒ B, A, C, D

Ⓓ D, A, C, B

Use a problem-solving model to solve this problem.

1 Understand

Read the problem. ⟲Circle⟳ the information you know. Underline what the problem is asking you to find.

2 Plan

What will you need to do to solve the problem? Write your plan in steps.

Step 1 Estimate the _area_ of photos A and B.

Step 2 Compare and order the photos from _greatest to least_ according to their _areas_ .

3 Solve

Use your plan to solve the problem. Show your steps.

Since $\sqrt{130}$ is a little less than halfway between $\sqrt{121}$ and $\sqrt{144}$, **11.4** is a good estimate for $\sqrt{130}$.

Since $\sqrt{172}$ is much closer to $\sqrt{169}$ than $\sqrt{196}$, **13.1** is a good estimate for $\sqrt{172}$.

Since $13.1 > 13 > 11.4 > 11$, choice A is correct. Fill in that answer choice.

4 Check

How do you know your solution is accurate?

Rewrite 13 as $\sqrt{169}$ and 11 as $\sqrt{121}$. Since $\sqrt{172} > \sqrt{169} > \sqrt{130}$

$> \sqrt{121}$, I know my answer is correct.

Read to Succeed!
When there is no number, or index, in front of the radical sign, you are finding a square root.

Chapter 1

Answers

NAME _____ DATE _____ PERIOD _____

Lesson 10 *(continued)*

Use a problem-solving model to solve each problem.

1 Which list of numbers are shown on the number line? 8.NS.2, MP 6

4 4.1 4.2 4.3 4.4 4.5 4.6 4.7 4.8 4.9 5

Ⓐ $4\frac{5}{11}$, $\sqrt{23}$, $4.\overline{6}$, $\sqrt{18}$

Ⓑ $4\frac{5}{9}$, $\sqrt{23}$, $4\frac{4}{11}$, $\sqrt{18}$

Ⓒ $4.\overline{6}$, $\sqrt{20}$, $4\frac{4}{11}$, $\sqrt{18}$

Ⓓ $4\frac{5}{9}$, $\sqrt{23}$, $4\frac{4}{9}$, $\sqrt{18}$

2 The table shows the dimensions of four rectangles. What is the difference between the areas of the rectangle with the greatest area and the rectangle with the least area? 8.NS.1, MP 1

Rectangle	Width (cm)	Length (cm)
A	4	4
B	3.1	5
C	7	2.5
D	6	2.7

2 cm²

3 The areas of two squares are shown below. To the nearest whole meter, what is the difference between the side lengths of these squares? 8.EE.2, MP 2

35 m²   8 m²

3 m

4 🖐 **H.O.T. Problem** Label the Venn diagram with the five subsets of real numbers and examples of each subset. Then give a brief description of the set of real numbers. 8.NS.1, MP 3

Sample answer: The rational and irrational numbers combine to form the set of real numbers.

Course 3 • Chapter 1 Real Numbers

NAME _____ DATE _____ PERIOD _____

Lesson 10 Multi-Step Problem Solving

Multi-Step Example

Which number line shows {350%, π, 3.3, √14}? 8.NS.1, MP 6

Ⓐ 3 3.1 3.2 3.3 3.4 3.5 3.6 3.7 3.8 3.9 4

Ⓒ 3 3.1 3.2 3.3 3.4 3.5 3.6 3.7 3.8 3.9 4

Ⓑ 3 3.1 3.2 3.3 3.4 3.5 3.6 3.7 3.8 3.9 4

Ⓓ 3 3.1 3.2 3.3 3.4 3.5 3.6 3.7 3.8 3.9 4

Use a problem-solving model to solve this problem.

1 Understand

Read the problem. Circle the information you know. Underline what the problem is asking you to find.

2 Plan

What will you need to do to solve the problem? Write your plan in steps.

Step 1 Express each number in __standard decimal notation__, rounding to __hundredths__ if necessary.

Step 2 Determine which number line shows {350%, π, 3.3, √14}.

3 Solve

Use your plan to solve the problem. Show your steps.

350% = __3.5__   π ≈ __3.14__

3.3 ≈ __3.33__   √14 ≈ __3.74__

The correct answer is __D__. Fill in that answer choice.

4 Check

How do you know your solution is accurate?

Sample answer: There are only two number lines that show a point at 3.74, choices C and D. Of these two lines, only choice D shows 3.14.

Read to Succeed!

Consider the intervals on the number line and the locations of the points when deciding which decimal place to use in rounding.

Course 3 • Chapter 1 Real Numbers

Chapter 1

Course 3 • Chapter 1 Real Numbers

NAME _____ DATE _____ PERIOD _____

Lesson 1 (continued)

Use a problem-solving model to solve each problem.

1 Yer has read 85% of her new employee manual. She has read 306 pages. How many pages are in the employee manual? 8.EE.7b, MP 1

Ⓐ 26 pages
Ⓑ 36 pages
Ⓒ 260 pages
Ⓓ 360 pages

2 A bakery is keeping track of different baked goods in a table. Complete the table. 8.EE.7b, MP 1

Type of Baked Good	Portion of Total Baked Goods	Number of the Type of Baked Good	Total Baked Goods
Sesame bagels	$\frac{1}{5}$	**35**	175
Raisin cookies	$\frac{9}{20}$	27	**60**

3 Jonah makes deposits in his account based on his paycheck total. Complete the table of deposits Jonah has made this month. 8.EE.7, MP 7

Percent of Deposit	Deposit into Account	Paycheck Total
60%	$405.00	$675.00
75%	$337.50	**$450.00**

4 ✎ **H.O.T. Problem** Write a real-world problem that could be represented by the equation, $\frac{2}{3}b = 24$ and then solve the problem. 8.EE.7a, MP 4

Sample answer: Two thirds of the bees
in a hive have contracted a disease.
Twenty-four bees have contracted the
disease. How many bees are in the hive?
There are 36 bees in the hive.

NAME _____ DATE _____ PERIOD _____

Lesson 1 Multi-Step Problem Solving

Multi-Step Example

The Jackson family drove 175 miles on their road trip. This distance is $2\frac{1}{2}$ times the distance they drove on the first day. How many miles did the Jackson family drive on the first day? 8.EE.7b, MP 1

Ⓐ 70 mi
Ⓑ 175 mi
Ⓒ 350 mi
Ⓓ 437.5 mi

Use a problem-solving model to solve this problem.

1 Understand

Read the problem. Circle the information you know.
Underline what the problem is asking you to find.

2 Plan

What will you need to do to solve the problem? Write your plan in steps.

Step 1 Define the **variables** and write an **equation** that represents the situation.

Step 2 **Solve** the equation.

> **Read to Succeed!**
> Remember the multiplicative inverse of a number is the value that you multiply by to make the number equal 1.

3 Solve

Use your plan to solve the problem. Show your steps.

Define the variables and write an equation.

Let d equal the distance traveled on the first day.

$$\frac{5}{2}d = 175$$

Solve the equation. Multiply each side by the multiplicative inverse.

$$\boxed{\frac{2}{5}} \times \frac{5}{2}d = \frac{\boxed{175}}{1} \times \frac{\boxed{2}}{\boxed{5}}$$

$$d = \boxed{70}$$

The correct answer is __70__ miles. Choice __A__ is correct. Fill in that answer choice.

4 Check

How do you know your solution is accurate?

Sample answer: If I replace d in my equation with 70, I will get 175.
I know my answer is accurate.

NAME _____ DATE _____ PERIOD _____

Lesson 2 (continued)

Use a problem-solving model to solve each problem.

1 The lowest temperature ever recorded in Texas is −31° Celsius. Celsius and Rankine temperatures are related by the formula $C = \frac{5}{9}R - 273$, where C is degrees Celsius and R is degrees Rankine. To the nearest whole number, what is the Rankine equivalent of −31° Celsius? **8.EE.7b,** MP **2**

Ⓐ 547° Rankine

Ⓑ 436° Rankine

Ⓒ 134° Rankine

Ⓓ 48° Rankine

2 The Baker family is driving on a highway. The equation $y = 14 - \frac{1}{32}x$ shows the relationship between y, the number of gallons of fuel in the tank, and x, the number of miles the family has driven since Mrs. Baker filled the tank. How many miles has the Baker family driven when the tank contains $8\frac{1}{2}$ gallons of fuel? **8.EE.7b,** MP **2**

176

3 🔺 **H.O.T. Problem** Riley wants to take a 10-week martial arts course at one of three schools. School B is offering 50% off the regular membership fee. School C is offering 15% off its regular per-class fee.

	Regular Cost ($)		Total Discounted Cost ($)
	Membership Fee	Per Class Fee ($)	
A	40.00	a	152.50
B	20.00	13.50	b
C	20.00	16.00	c

Which school offers the lowest total cost? Justify your answer. **8.EE.7,** MP **1**

School B; Sample answer: The total discounted costs for schools B and C are

$b = 10(13.50) + 0.50(20.00) = 145.00$ and $c = 10(0.85)(16.00) + 20.00 = 156.00$.

So, comparing the costs at all three schools, school B costs the least amount.

24

NAME _____ DATE _____ PERIOD _____

Lesson 2 Multi-Step Problem Solving

Multi-Step Example

Fahrenheit and Kelvin temperatures are related by the formula $F = \frac{9}{5}K - 460$, where F is degrees Fahrenheit and K is degrees Kelvin. The highest temperature ever recorded in Texas is 120° Fahrenheit. To the nearest whole number, what is the Kelvin equivalent of 120° Fahrenheit? **8.EE.7b,** MP **2**

Ⓐ 64° Kelvin

Ⓑ 189° Kelvin

Ⓒ 322° Kelvin

Ⓓ 1,044° Kelvin

Use a problem-solving model to solve this problem.

1 Understand

Read the problem. Ⓒircle the information you know. Underline what the problem is asking you to find.

2 Plan

What will you need to do to solve the problem? Write your plan in steps.

Step 1 Replace __F__ with **120** in $F = \frac{9}{5}K - 460$.

Step 2 Solve for __K__.

Read to Succeed!
When solving for K, remember to multiply each side of the equation by the multiplicative inverse.

3 Solve

Use your plan to solve the problem. Show your steps.

Replacing F with 120 results in the equation $120 = \frac{9}{5}K - 460$.

To solve the equation, I __added__ __460__ to each side and __multiplied__ each side by $\frac{5}{9}$.

So, 120° Fahrenheit is equal to __322° Kelvin__. The correct answer is __C__.

Fill in that answer choice.

4 Check

How do you know your solution is accurate?

Sample answer: I replaced 322 for K in the formula. Since 119.6 rounds to

120, I know my solution is accurate.

Course 3 • **Chapter 2** Equations in One Variable

23

NAME _____ DATE _____ PERIOD _____

Lesson 3 Multi-Step Problem Solving

Multi-Step Example

Brian, Natalie, and Lakita have raised $49.30 for improvements to the science lab. The table shows information about the amount raised. Which equation can be solved to find the amount Brian has raised? 8.EE.7b, MP 4

Science Lab Fundraising	
Student	Amount ($)
Brian	x
Natalie	3.50 more than Brian
Lakita	30% more than Brian

Ⓐ $2.3x + 3.50 = 49.30$ Ⓒ $3.3x + 3.50 = 49.30$

Ⓑ $3x + 3.80 = 49.30$ Ⓓ $5.5x + 0.30 = 49.30$

Use a problem-solving model to solve this problem.

1 Understand

Read the problem. (Circle) the information you know.
Underline what the problem is asking you to find.

2 Plan

What will you need to do to solve the problem? Write your plan in steps.

Step 1 Use the information _in the table_ to write an equation.

Step 2 Collect _like terms_ to write an _equivalent_ equation.

Read to Succeed!
When collecting like terms, remember the x equals 1x.

3 Solve

Use your plan to solve the problem. Show your steps.

X represents the amount of money raised by _Brian_. Write expressions to represent the amounts raised by _Natalie_ and _Lakita_. The equation

x _____ $+ x + 3.5 +$ _____ $1.3x$ $= 49.30$ represents the total amount raised by all three students.

Since the equation can be written as _3.3x_ $+$ _3.5_ $=$ _49.30_, the correct answer is _C_. Fill in that answer choice.

4 Check

How do you know your solution is accurate?
I solved the equation to determine Brian raised $13.88, which means Natalie raised $17.38 and Lakita raised $18.04. Since the three amounts raised add to $49.30, I know my answer is correct.

25

NAME _____ DATE _____ PERIOD _____

Lesson 3 (continued)

Use a problem-solving model to solve each problem.

1 The total land area of the three largest states in the United States is approximately 9.9×10^5 square miles.

Approximate Land Areas	
State	Land Area (sq mi)
Alaska	3.1×10^5 more than Texas
Texas	t
California	40% less than Texas

Which equation can be solved to find the approximate land area of Texas? 8.EE.7b, MP 2

Ⓐ $2.4t + 310,000 = 990,000$

Ⓑ $2.6t + 310,000 = 990,000$

Ⓒ $2.6t + 3,100,000 = 9,900,000$

Ⓓ $3.6t + 3,100,000 = 9,900,000$

2 The diagram shown below represents three streets on a map. The measure of angle 2 is twice the measure of angle 1. The measure of angle 3 is 20° more than the measure of angle 2. What is the measure of angle 4 in degrees? 8.EE.7, MP 1

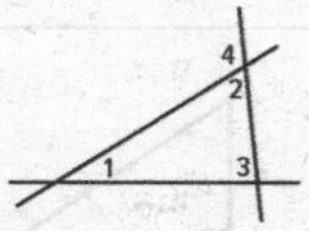

116

3 An engineer drew this cross-section view of a concrete highway support. The cross-section area is 200 square units.

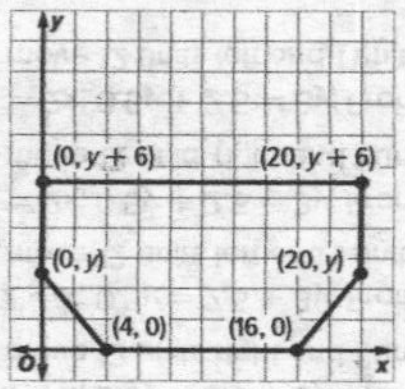

What is the value of y? 8.EE.7b, MP 7

5

4 H.O.T. Problem Tia wants a window like the one shown below. If the outside perimeter of the window is 170 inches, what is its width w? Use $\frac{22}{7}$ for π. Defend your answer. 8.EE.7b, MP 3

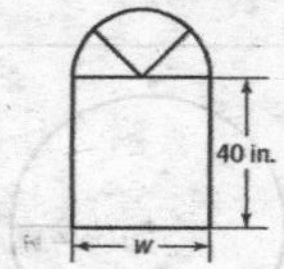

35 inches; Sample answer: Since the circumference of the semicircle is πr, $40 + 40 + w + \frac{1}{2}\pi w = 170$. So, $w = 35$.

26

Answers

NAME _____ DATE _____ PERIOD _____

Lesson 4 (continued)

Use a problem-solving model to solve each problem.

1 Twelve more than (2x) is x. One-half y is two and one-half more than (3y). Which shows the representative equations and the directions to plot a point with the resulting coordinate values? **8.EE.7, MP 4**

Ⓐ $2x + 12 = x$; $0.5y = 2.5 + 3y$; From the origin, move 12 units right and 1 unit up.

Ⓑ $2x + 12 = x$; $0.5y = 2.5 + 3y$; From the origin, move 12 units left and 1 unit down.

Ⓒ $x + 12 = 2x$; $0.5y + 2.5 = 3y$; From the origin, move 12 units right and 1 unit up.

Ⓓ $x + 12 = 2x$; $0.5y + 2.5 = 3y$; From the origin, move 12 units left and 1 unit down.

3 Rectangle A is similar to rectangle B by scale factor r. The length of rectangle A is 1.5r + 2.25 units. The length of rectangle B is 3 units. What is the scale factor? **8.EE.7b, MP 7**

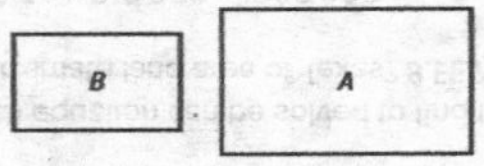

1.5

2 The circumference of a circle with diameter $(6a - 1)$ feet equals the circumference of the circle below. What is the diameter of the circle below in inches? **8.EE.7, MP 1**

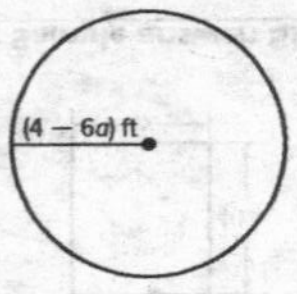

$(4 - 6a)$ ft

24

4 🖊 **H.O.T. Problem** The total area of the composite figure shown below is twice the area of one of its two shapes. What is the value of x? **8.EE.7, MP 7**

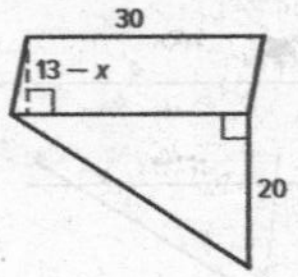

13 − x   30   20

3

NAME _____ DATE _____ PERIOD _____

Chapter 2

Lesson 4 Multi-Step Problem Solving

Multi-Step Example

The sum of the measure of angle A and 15x is 10x less than the sum of the measures of all three of the interior angles of a triangle shown at the right. Which of the following equations could represent this relationship? **8.EE.7, MP 4**

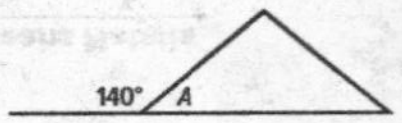

140° A

Ⓐ $40 + 15x = 180 - 10x$

Ⓑ $40 - 15x = 180 + 10x$

Ⓒ $40 - 15x = 180 - 10x$

Ⓓ $40 + 15x = 180 + 10x$

Use a problem-solving model to solve this problem.

1 Understand

Read the problem. Circle the information you know. Underline what the problem is asking you to find.

2 Plan

What will you need to do to solve the problem? Write your plan in steps.

Step 1 Translate the __verbal__ sentence to a mathematical __equation__.

Step 2 Determine which __equation__ listed above represents the situation.

3 Solve

Use your plan to solve the problem. Show your steps.

The measure of angle A is 180 − __140__ or __40__

The mathematical expressions __40 + 15x__ and __180 − 10x__ represent the verbal expressions.

So, the equation __40 + 15x__ = __180 − 10x__ can be used to represent the relationship. The correct answer is __A__. Fill in that answer choice.

Read to Succeed! Remember that the sum of the interior angles of a triangle is 180°.

4 Check

How do you know your solution is accurate?

Sample answer: I solved the equation and determined x = 5.6. Since $40 + 15(5.6) = 124$ and $180 − 10(5.6) = 124$, I know my answer is accurate.

27

NAME _____ DATE _____ PERIOD _____

Lesson 5 (continued)

Use a problem-solving model to solve each problem.

1 The area of Rectangle B is $2x$ square units less than the area of Rectangle A. What is the value of x? 8.EE.7b, MP 4

Rectangle A: 1.6, $10x + 0.4$

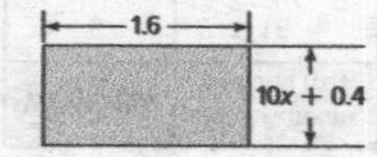

Rectangle B: 0.6, $50x$

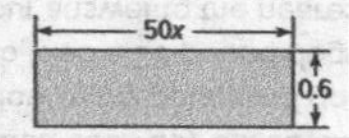

0.04

2 The graph shows the number of coins Pascual has in a jar. How much money, in dollars, does he have if the total number of coins is twice the number of pennies? 8.EE.7a, MP 2

Number of Coins

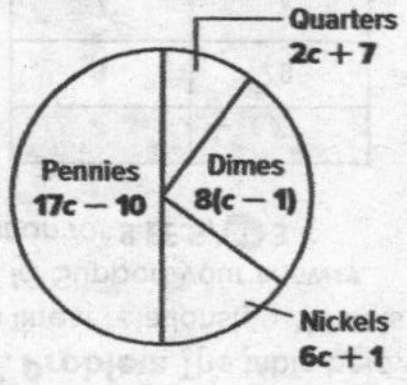

- Quarters $2x + 7$
- Dimes $8(x - 1)$
- Pennies $17x - 10$
- Nickels $6x + 1$

18.60

3 🔺 **H.O.T. Problem** Calvin bought the items described below. Determine the total cost of his purchase. Explain. 8.EE.7a, MP 1

- The price of the shirt is triple the price of the socks.
- The price of the wallet is $6 more than the price of the umbrella.
- The price of the umbrella is 150% of the price of the socks.
- There was no sales tax on the clothing. There was 6% sales tax on the umbrella and wallet.
- The pre-tax price of the wallet and umbrella equals the price of the clothing.

$49.44; Sample answer: Let s, $3s$, $1.5s$, and $1.5s + 6$ represent the cost of the socks, shirt, umbrella, and wallet, respectively. The equation $1.5s + 1.5s + 6 = s + 3s$ represents the pre-tax relationship between the cost of the wallet, umbrella and clothing. So, $s = 6$. Since the socks cost $6, the shirt costs $3(6)$ or $18, the umbrella costs $1.5(6)$ or $9, and the wallet costs $9 + 6$ or $15. The after-tax price of the wallet and umbrella is $1.06(9 + 15)$ or $25.44. So, Calvin's purchase cost $6 + $18 + $25.44 or $49.44.

30

Chapter 2

NAME _____ DATE _____ PERIOD _____

Lesson 5 Multi-Step Problem Solving

Multi-Step Example

The table shows the hours worked by employees at a coffee shop last month. What is the ratio of Jaime's hours worked to Mai's hours worked if the total hours worked for all employees is $7m + 19$? Write your answer as a decimal. 8.EE.7b, MP 1

Employee	Hours Worked
Shantel	48
Lorenzo	$2m + 7$
Jaime	$3.5(m - 6)$
Mai	m

Use a problem-solving model to solve this problem.

1 Understand

Read the problem. Circle the information you know. Underline what the problem is asking you to find.

2 Plan

What will you need to do to solve the problem? Write your plan in steps.

Step 1 Write and solve an __equation__ that represents the total number of __hours worked__.

Step 2 Write the __ratio__ of __Jaime's__ hours worked to __Mai's__ hours worked as a decimal.

Read to Succeed!
Remember that a ratio can be written in a variety of forms, including as a decimal.

3 Solve

Use your plan to solve the problem. Show your steps.

The equation $48 + 2m + 7 + 3.5(m - 6) + m = 7m + 19$ represents the total number of hours worked, so $m = $ __30__.

Since $m = $ __30__, Jaime worked __84__ hours and Mai worked __30__ hours.

So, the ratio of Jaime's hours to Mai's hours is __84__ : __30__ or __2.8__.

4 Check

How do you know your solution is accurate?

Sample answer: I replaced m with 30 in the expression for Lorenzo's number of hours and in the expression $7m + 19$. Then I found the sum of all four employees' hours worked. Since the sum of hours worked equals $7(30) + 19$, I know my answer is accurate.

Course 3 • Chapter 2 Equations in One Variable

29

Answers

NAME _____ DATE _____ PERIOD _____

Lesson 1 (continued)

Use a problem-solving model to solve each problem.

1 The graph shows the amount of pay Jared earned for the number of hours he worked. Which statement best describes the graph? *Preparation for 8.EE.5,* MP 4

Jared's Pay

(graph: Dollars vs Hours, y-axis 20–160, x-axis 5 10 15 20)

Ⓐ It is a proportional linear relationship with a unit rate of 8.

Ⓑ It is a proportional linear relationship with a unit rate of 10.

Ⓒ The graph shows a non-proportional linear relationship.

Ⓓ The graph shows a non-linear relationship.

3 The table below shows the amount of dog food needed each day based on a dog's weight. How many pounds of dog food are needed to feed a 28-pound dog for 1 week? Round your answer to the nearest pound. *Preparation for 8.EE.5,* MP 4

Weight (lb)	Daily Amount of Food (oz)
5	1.6
15	4.8
20	6.4

4

2 The table below shows the print speed for color paper of an office computer. How many pages can the printer print in one hour? *Preparation for 8.EE.5,* MP 4

Minutes	Pages per Minute
2	32
3	48
4	64

960

4 H.O.T. Problem The table below shows a linear relationship. What is the value of *k*? Support your answer. *Preparation for 8.EE.5,* MP 3

x	y
3	9
7	k
9	21

17; The rate of change is $\frac{21-9}{9-3} = \frac{12}{6} = 2$.

Because the relationship is linear, the rate of change is constant; $2 = \frac{21-k}{9-7}$, $2 = \frac{21-k}{2}$,

$4 = 21 - k$; $k = 17$.

32

NAME _____ DATE _____ PERIOD _____

Lesson 1 Multi-Step Problem Solving

Multi-Step Example

The graph shows the relationship between the length of the side of a square and the perimeter of the square. Which statement describes the relationship? *Preparation for 8.EE.5,* MP 7

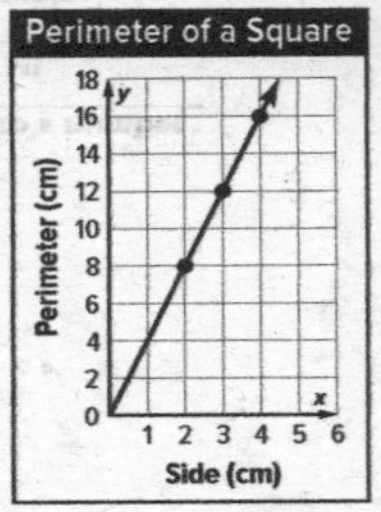

Perimeter of a Square

(graph: Perimeter (cm) vs Side (cm), y-axis 2–18, x-axis 1 2 3 4 5 6)

Ⓐ It is a proportional linear relationship with a unit rate of 8.

Ⓑ It is a proportional linear relationship with a unit rate of 4.

Ⓒ It is a non-proportional linear relationship.

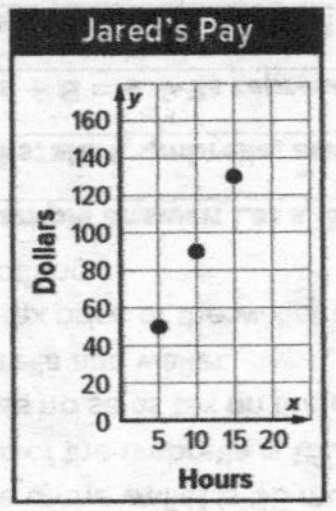

Ⓓ It is a non-linear relationship.

Use a problem-solving model to solve this problem.

1 Understand

Read the problem. **Circle** the information you know. **Underline** what the problem is asking you to find.

2 Plan

What will you need to do to solve the problem? Write your plan in steps.

Step 1 Connect the points to see if they form a __line__ passing through the __origin__ .

Step 2 If the relationship is linear, determine if the __ratios__ of the pairs of points equal __8__ or __4__ .

3 Solve

Use your plan to solve the problem. Show your steps.

The points form a __line__ that passes through the __origin__ .

Since there is a vertical distance of __4__ units and a horizontal distance of __1__ unit between points, the unit rate is $\frac{4}{1} = 4$ or __4__ .

So, the relationship is a __proportional linear relationship__ with a unit rate of __4__ . The correct answer is __B__ .

4 Check

How do you know your solution is accurate?

Since $\frac{8}{2} = 4$, $\frac{12}{3} = 4$ and $\frac{16}{4} = 4$, the graph shows a linear proportional relationship with a unit rate of 4.

Read to Succeed!

When finding a unit rate from a graph, count the units up or down and then the right or left.

31

NAME _____ DATE _____ PERIOD _____

Lesson 2 Multi-Step Problem Solving

Chapter 3

Multi-Step Example

The table shows the coordinates of two points on a line. If the slope of the line is $-\frac{3}{4}$, what is the value of k? *Preparation for 8.EE.5, MP 7*

x	2	6
y	5	k

A −8 C 2
B −2 D 8

Use a problem-solving model to solve this problem.

1 Understand
Read the problem. Circle the information you know. Underline what the problem is asking you to find.

2 Plan
What will you need to do to solve the problem? Write your plan in steps.

Step 1 Replace known values for the variables in the slope formula.

Step 2 Solve the equation for k.

3 Solve
Use your plan to solve the problem. Show your steps.

Replace m with $-\frac{3}{4}$, y_1 with 5, x_2 with 6, and x_1 with 2.
Solve for k.

$$-\frac{3}{4} = \frac{k - 5}{6 - 2}$$

$-3 = k - 5$
$4 = 6 - 2$

Since k = 2, the correct answer is C.

Read to Succeed!
Remember to subtract the y-coordinates and the x-coordinates in the same order.

4 Check
How do you know your solution is accurate?
I replaced k with 2 and found the slope of the line that passes through (2, 5) and (6, k):

$$\frac{2-5}{6-2} = \frac{-3}{-4} = -\frac{3}{4}.$$

Course 3 • Chapter 3 Equations in Two Variables   33

NAME _____ DATE _____ PERIOD _____

Lesson 2 (continued)

Use a problem-solving model to solve each problem.

1 The slope of a line is $-\frac{2}{3}$. One point on the line is (4, 3). Which of the following is another point on the line? *Preparation for 8.EE.5, MP 1*

A (10, 7)
B (10, −1)
C (0, 9)
D (8, 9)

2 The graph shows the times, called split times, for each mile in a 5-mile race. Which rate of change in minutes per mile is greater: the rate of change between miles 1 and 2 or between miles 4 and 5? Explain. *Preparation for 8.EE.5, MP 4*

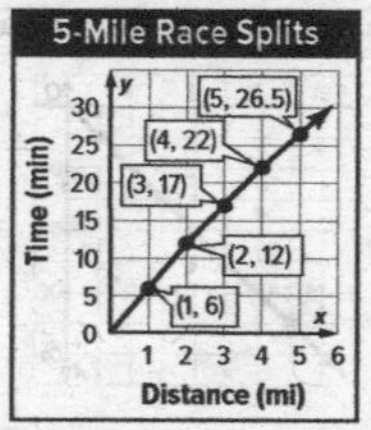

5-Mile Race Splits
points: (5, 26.5), (4, 22), (3, 17), (2, 12), (1, 6)
Time (min) axis: 0, 5, 10, 15, 20, 25, 30; Distance (mi) axis: 1 2 3 4 5 6

between miles 1 and 2 because the rate of change is 6 min per mi, compared to 4.5 min per mi between miles 4 and 5

3 The points in the table below lie on a line. What is the value of y when x is 10? *Preparation for 8.EE.5, MP 7*

x	−1	1	3
y	−87	3	93

408

4 H.O.T. Problem The vertices of parallelogram ABCD are A(11, 5), B(8, 1), C(2, 3), and D(x, 7). What is the value of x? Justify your answer. *Preparation for 8.EE.5, MP 3*

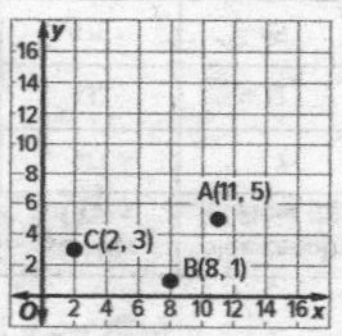

graph points: A(11, 5), B(8, 1), C(2, 3)

5; Sample answer: The opposite sides of a parallelogram are parallel. So, BC ∥ AD.
The slopes of parallel lines are equal.
So, $m_{AD} = \frac{5-7}{11-x} = \frac{1-3}{8-2} = m_{BC}$.
$\frac{-2}{11-x} = -\frac{2}{6}$; $11 - x = 6$; $x = 5$.

Course 3 • Chapter 3 Equations in Two Variables   34

Answers

Chapter 3 Lesson 2 Answer Keys

NAME _____ DATE _____ PERIOD _____

Lesson 3 (continued)

Use a problem-solving model to solve each problem.

1. The table below shows the number of words Luz types over different periods of time. Deepak's typing speed is represented by the equation $w = 34t$. If each student types for 5 minutes at a constant rate, who types more words? how many more? 8.F.2, MP 2

Number of Words (w)	Time in Minutes (t)
84	3
168	6
224	8

Deepak; 30 more words

2. The table below shows the number of rectangular tiles needed to cover square-shaped floors with certain side lengths. If the number of tiles is proportional to the area of the floor, how many tiles would be needed for a square-shaped floor with a side length of 9 feet? 8.F.4, MP 4

Number of Tiles	Side Length of Floor (ft)
147	7
432	12
675	15

243

3. Denzel and Maria played a game and recorded their scores after each turn as ordered pairs. Denzel's ordered pairs included (1, 4), (3, 12), and (4, 16). Maria's ordered pairs included (1, 5), (5, 25), and (6, 30). Each player made a graph using the ordered pairs. Assuming each player's score is proportional, what is the difference between the slope of Denzel's graph and the slope of Maria's graph? 8.F.4, MP 2

1

4. H.O.T. Problem Refer to the graph below. What is the value of x when $y = 125$? Explain 8.EE.5, MP 4

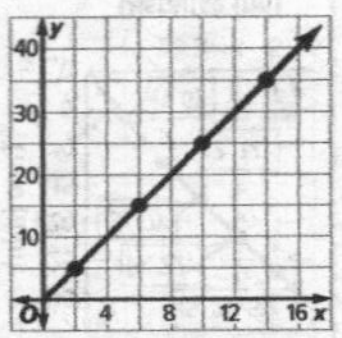

50; Sample answer: Since the slope of the line is 2.5, its equation is $y = 2.5x$. I replaced y with 125 and solved for x.

Course 3 • Chapter 3 Equations in Two Variables

36

NAME _____ DATE _____ PERIOD _____

Lesson 3 Multi-Step Problem Solving

Multi-Step Example

Trevor burns 40 Calories when he cycles for 5 minutes and 80 Calories when he cycles for 10 minutes. The equation $y = 3.25x$ represents the number of Calories he burns when walking. How many more Calories does Trevor burn by cycling for 20 minutes than by walking for 20 minutes? 8.F.2, MP 2

Use a problem-solving model to solve this problem.

1 Understand

Read the problem. Circle the information you know. Underline what the problem is asking you to find.

2 Plan

What will you need to do to solve the problem? Write your plan in steps.

Step 1 Write an equation to represent the Calories burned when **cycling**.

Step 2 Replace **x** in both equations with **20** and determine the number of Calories burned by **20 minutes** each of cycling and walking.

Read to Succeed!
When writing an equation for Calories burned by cycling, find the unit rate of Calories burned per minute.

3 Solve

Use your plan to solve the problem. Show your steps.

The equation **y = 8x** represents the Calories burned when **cycling**.

Trevor burns 8 (20) or **160** Calories when cycling and **3.25**(20) or **65** Calories when walking. Since **160** – **65** = **95**, **95** more Calories are burned by cycling.

4 Check

How do you know your solution is accurate?
I subtracted 3.25 from 8 to get the difference in the unit rates. Then I multiplied 20 by the difference, 4.75. Since 4.75(20) = 95, my answer is correct.

Course 3 • Chapter 3 Equations in Two Variables

35

NAME _____ DATE _____ PERIOD _____

NAME _____ DATE _____ PERIOD _____

Lesson 4 Multi-Step Problem Solving

Multi-Step Example

The table shown at the right represents the online cost of a specific number of tickets, including a $2 handling fee, at a movie theater last week. Next week, the movie theater will increase the online ticket price by $1 each. Which equation represents the new online cost of movie theater tickets, including the $2 handling fee? 8.F.4, MP 2

Number of Tickets	Cost ($)
0	2
1	11
2	20
3	29

Ⓐ $y = 9x$ Ⓒ $y = 10x$

Ⓑ $y = 9x + 2$ Ⓓ $y = 10x + 2$

Use a problem-solving model to solve this problem.

1 Understand

Read the problem. Circle the information you know. Underline what the problem is asking you to find.

2 Plan

What will you need to do to solve the problem? Write your plan in steps.

Step 1 Write an _equation_ that represents _the cost of tickets last week_.

Step 2 Revise the _equation_ to represent _the new cost of tickets_.

3 Solve

Use your plan to solve the problem. Show your steps.

Last week, the cost per ticket was $\boxed{29} - \boxed{20} = \$\boxed{9}$

$\boxed{3} - \boxed{2}$

The equation $y = 9x + 2$ represents the cost of x number of tickets last week. So, the equation $y = 10x + 2$ represents the new cost. The correct answer is __D__.

Read to Succeed! When writing an equation in slope-intercept form, ask yourself what the slope will represent and what the y-intercept will represent.

4 Check

How do you know your solution is accurate?

I checked my equation for last week's cost by replacing x with 0, 1, 2, and 3.

Since m represents the cost per ticket, it makes sense that the equation for

the new cost will be $y = 10x + 2$.

37

Lesson 4 (continued)

Use a problem-solving model to solve each problem.

1 The table shown below shows the number of pizzas ordered from a local pizza shop and the total cost in dollars. The cost includes a $2 delivery fee. Next week, the shop is going to decrease the price of a pizza by $1.50. Which equation represents the new relationship? 8.F.4, MP 2

Number of Pizzas	Total Cost ($)
1	13
2	24
3	35
4	46

Ⓐ $y = 9.50x + 2$

Ⓑ $y = 9.50x$

Ⓒ $y = 12.50x + 2$

Ⓓ $y = 12.50x$

2 Davina is comparing cell phone plans. The first plan has a flat fee of $10 per month plus $0.04 per text message. The second plan has a flat fee of $5 per month plus $0.12 per text message. What is the difference in dollars of the two plans for sending 15 text messages each month for six months? 8.F.4, MP 2

$22.80

3 A puppy grows at a constant rate of 1.25 pounds per week. After 4 weeks, he weighs 8 pounds. How many pounds will he weigh after 6 weeks if he continues to grow at the same rate? 8.F.4, MP 2

10.5

4 ✪ H.O.T. Problem If the given line is slid right 4 and up 2 grid spaces, what will be the equation of the line? 8.F.4, MP 4

$y = x + 1$

38

Answers

NAME _____ DATE _____ PERIOD _____

Lesson 5 (continued)

Use a problem-solving model to solve each problem.

1 Play ticket sales for x number of Friday evening tickets and y number of Saturday evening tickets are represented by the equation $14x + 21y = 12{,}579$. Which statement is *not* true?
Preparation for 8.EE.8c, MP 2

Ⓐ Friday night tickets cost $14 each.

Ⓑ Saturday night tickets cost $21 each.

Ⓒ If nobody attended Saturday night, 599 people attended Friday night.

Ⓓ If nobody attended Friday night, 599 people attended Saturday night.

2 Line ℓ shown in the graph below. What is the x-intercept of the line that has the same y-intercept as, but one-half the slope of, ℓ?
Preparation for 8.EE.8c, MP 2

3 The table shows the cost of paint and paint brushes at a local art store. The art store spent $2,400 on the most recent shipment. What is the sum of the slope and y-intercept of the line that represents this shipment?
Preparation for 8.EE.8c, MP 2

	Paint (gal)	Paint Brushes
Cost ($)	14	8
Amount Ordered	x	y

298.25

4 **H.O.T. Problem** Two rectangles are shown below. The perimeter of the smaller rectangle is 130 units. The perimeter of the larger rectangle is 190 units. Write an equation in standard form for each rectangle. What do you know about the y-intercepts of the graphs of the equations? Support your answer. *Preparation for 8.EE.8c,* MP 4

small rectangle: 2x + 2y = 130; large rectangle: 2x + 2y = 190; Sample answer: The y-intercepts are 65 and 95, respectively.

5

Course 3 • Chapter 3 Equations in Two Variables

NAME _____ DATE _____ PERIOD _____

Lesson 5 Multi-Step Problem Solving

Multi-Step Example

Concession sales for x number of hot dogs and y number of pizza slices at a football game are represented by the equation $2x + 3y = 1{,}728$. Which statement is true?
Preparation for 8.EE.8c, MP 2

Ⓐ Each hot dog cost $3.

Ⓑ Each pizza slice cost $2.

Ⓒ If 0 hot dogs were sold, then 576 pizza sliced were sold.

Ⓓ If 0 hot dogs were sold, then 864 pizza slices were sold.

Use a problem-solving model to solve this problem.

① Understand

Read the problem. Circle the information you know. Underline what the problem is asking you to find.

② Plan

What will you need to do to solve the problem? Write your plan in steps.

Step 1 Write the equation in __slope-intercept__ form.

Step 2 Interpret the meaning of the __y-intercept__.

③ Solve

Use your plan to solve the problem. Show your steps.

The equation can be written as $y = -\dfrac{2}{3}x + 576$, which means that __576__ pizza slices are sold when __0__ hot dogs are sold. Since each hot dog costs __$2__ and each pizza slice costs __$3__ the correct answer is __C__. Fill in that answer choice.

Read to Succeed!

Remember the y-intercept occurs when the x-value is 0.

④ Check

How do you know your solution is accurate?

In the equation $2x + 3y = 1{,}728$, replaced x with 0 and y with 576.

$2(0) + 3(576) = 1728.$

Course 3 • Chapter 3 Equations in Two Variables

39

NAME _____ DATE _____ PERIOD _____

Lesson 6 *(continued)*

Use a problem-solving model to solve each problem.

1 The graph below shows the Calories burned in 30 minutes of hang gliding at various weights. Which equation represents this relationship? *Preparation for 8.EE.8c,* MP 2

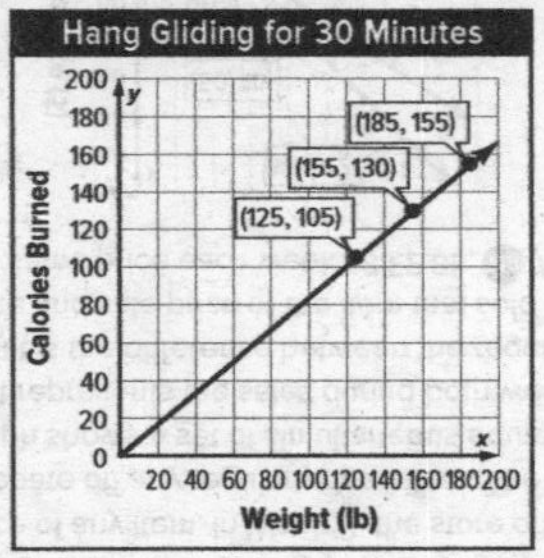

Hang Gliding for 30 Minutes

[185, 155]
[155, 130]
[125, 105]

Ⓐ $y = \frac{6}{5}x - \frac{6}{5}$ Ⓒ $y = \frac{5}{6}x + \frac{5}{6}$

Ⓑ $y = \frac{6}{5}x + \frac{6}{5}$ Ⓓ $y = \frac{5}{6}x$

3 The table below shows the cost C for a taxi ride of m miles. If the equation that represents this relationship is written in slope-intercept form, what is the value of m + b? *Preparation for 8.EE.8c,* MP 2

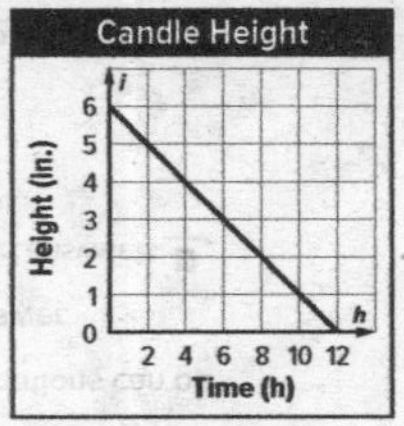

Miles	1	2	3
Cost ($)	6.50	10.00	13.50

6.50

2 A salesperson is paid a daily salary plus commission as shown in the table below. If the equation that represents this relationship is written in slope-intercept form, what is the value of mb? *Preparation for 8.EE.8c,* MP 2

Sales x	Earnings y
$2,000	$200
$2,800	$240
$3,200	$260

5

4 H.O.T. Problem The rate of water flowing from a hose is shown in the table below. A 30,000-gallon swimming pool starts out with 4,000 gallons. About how many days does it take to fill it to capacity? Support your answer. *Preparation for 8.EE.8c,* MP 4

Gallons	18	36	45
Minutes	2	4	5

about 2 days; Sample answer:

$y = 540x + 4,000$; $30,000 = 540x + 4,000$;

$26,000 = 540x$; $x \approx 48.15$ hours or

$\frac{48.15}{24} \approx 2$ days.

42

NAME _____ DATE _____ PERIOD _____

Lesson 6 Multi-Step Problem Solving

Chapter 3

Multi-Step Example

The graph shows the height in inches i of a candle at h number of hours. Which equation represents this relationship? *Preparation for 8.EE.8c,* MP 2

Candle Height

Ⓐ $h - 2i = 12$

Ⓑ $h + 2i = 12$

Ⓒ $-h - 2i = 12$

Ⓓ $-h + 2i = 12$

Use a problem-solving model to solve this problem.

1 Understand

Read the problem. Circle the information you know. Underline what the problem is asking you to find.

2 Plan

What will you need to do to solve the problem? Write your plan in steps.

Step 1 Use the **graph** to write an **equation** in slope-intercept form.

Step 2 Write my **equation** in standard form.

3 Solve

Use your plan to solve the problem. Show your steps.

The equation $i = \frac{1}{2}h + 6$ represents the relationship. An

equivalent equation is $h + 2i = 12$. So, the correct answer is **B**.

Fill in that answer choice.

Read to Succeed!

When determining the slope, be sure to check the scale on each axis.

4 Check

How do you know your solution is accurate?

I substituted the points (0, 6) and (12, 0) in each of the four equations listed

as choices. Only $h + 2i = 12$ is true for both ordered pairs.

41

Answers

NAME _____ DATE _____ PERIOD _____

Lesson 7 Multi-Step Problem Solving

Multi-Step Example

Cody is participating in a walk-a-thon for charity. Cody wants to determine when his uncle's donation will equal the combined total of his sister's and cousin's donations. Which pair of equations and point of intersection represents the situation? 8.EE.8c, MP 4

Family Member	Pledge
Sister	One-time of $30
Uncle	$2.00 per mile
Cousin	50 cents per mile

Ⓐ $y = 2 + x$ and $y = 0.5 + 30x$; (20, 40)

Ⓑ $y = 2 + x$ and $y = 0.5 + 30x$; (0.05, 2.05)

Ⓒ $y = 2x$ and $y = 30 + 0.5x$; (0.05, 2.05)

Ⓓ $y = 2x$ and $y = 30 + 0.5x$; (20, 40)

Use a problem-solving model to solve this problem.

1 Understand

Read the problem. Circle the information you know. Underline what the problem is asking you to find.

2 Plan

What will you need to do to solve the problem? Write your plan in steps.

Step 1 Determine the **pair of linear equations** that represents the situation.

Step 2 Determine the **ordered pair** that satisfies **both** equations.

3 Solve

Use your plan to solve the problem. Show your steps.

Let x represent the **number of miles Cody is walking** . His uncle's donation can be represented by $y = 2x$. The sum of his sister's and cousin's donations can be represented by $y = 30 + 0.5x$. So, either **C** or **D** is the correct answer.

Since $40 = 2(20)$ and $40 = 30 + 0.5(2)$ are true statements, the correct answer is **D** .

Read to Succeed!
The phrase $2 per mile can be represented as two times x or 2x.

4 Check

How do you know your solution is accurate?

Since Cody's uncle is pledging two dollars per mile walked, I know that choice C first two choices cannot be correct. Since $2.05 \neq 2(0.05)$, I know that choice C cannot be correct.

Course 3 • Chapter 3 Equations in Two Variables

NAME _____ DATE _____ PERIOD _____

Lesson 7 (continued)

Use a problem-solving model to solve each problem.

1 The table below shows two price packages for gymnastics classes.

Package	Monthly Price
1	$50 plus $8 per class
2	$15 plus $15 per class

Suppose each session is 2 hours, what is the solution and interpretation of the simultaneous equations that represent the two packages? 8.EE.8c, MP 4

Ⓐ (5, 90); The monthly cost for 10 hours is the same for both packages.

Ⓑ (90, 5); The monthly cost for 5 hours is the same for both packages.

Ⓒ (5, 90); The monthly cost for 10 sessions is the same for both packages.

Ⓓ (90, 5); The monthly cost for 90 sessions is the same for both packages.

2 A pair of linear equations is graphed to show where the perimeters of the two shapes shown below are equal. The lines intersect at (5, 40). What is the value of a? 8.EE.8a, MP 7

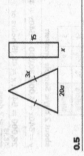

0.5

3 In Week 1, a department store had a store-wide sale of a percentage off the regular price of any item. In Week 2, the store offered a rebate off any regular-priced item. The graph shows a set of simultaneous equations that represents the sales during both weeks. What is the difference between the regular price and sale price of the item that sold for the same price each week? 8.EE.8b, MP 7

Sale Price ($) vs Regular Price ($) graph with Week 1, Week 2, points (0, 0), (50, 40), (100, 70)

$10

4 H.O.I. Problem Miguel orders pizza from two pizza shops. The first shop charges $7 for a cheese pizza and $1.60 per topping. The second shop charges $10 for a cheese pizza and $0.80 per topping. Miguel paid $13.20 for a 4-topping pizza at the second shop. Define a variable, x, and write a pair of linear equations that could help Miguel determine which pizza shop offers the better deal. 8.EE.8c, MP 4

$x =$ **the number of toppings**; $y = 7 + 1.6x$ and $y = 10 + 0.8x$; (3.75, 13); Sample answer: Since x is the number of toppings and the solution is between 3 and 4, the first pizza shop is less expensive for pizzas with 1, 2, and 3 toppings. The second pizza shop is less expensive for pizzas with 4 toppings.

Course 3 • Chapter 3 Equations in Two Variables

43

44

NAME _____ DATE _____ PERIOD _____

Lesson 8 *(continued)*

Use a problem-solving model to solve each problem.

1 Marjorie bought a total of 9 articles of clothing that included shirts and pants. She bought 3 more shirts than pants. How many of each did she buy? 8.EE.8c, MP 4

(A) 6 pants; 3 shirts

(B) 5 pants; 4 shirts

(C) 4 pants; 5 shirts

(D) 3 pants; 6 shirts

2 The table shows the rate at which two motorcycles are racing in an endurance race. Motorcycle A starts 75 miles ahead of motorcycle B. How long will it take for motorcycle B to catch up to motorcycle A, and how far will motorcycle B have traveled? 8.EE.8c, MP 4

Motorcycle	Rate (mph)
A	20
B	80

It will take 1.25 hours for motorcycle B to catch up, and motorcycle B will have traveled 100 miles when it catches up to motorcycle A.

3 The bar diagram represents the sales of popcorn and hot dogs at a baseball game. How many boxes of popcorn and hot dogs were sold at the game? 8.EE.8c, MP 4

x | hot dog |
y | popcorn | popcorn | popcorn | popcorn | } 72

60 boxes of popcorn and 12 hot dogs

4 H.O.T. Problem What is the solution to the system $-2x + y = 6$ and $y = 2x - 3$? Explain your answer. 8.EE.8b, MP 1

Sample answer: There is no solution to this system. If I subtract 2x from both sides in the second equation I would get $-2x + y = -3$. The expressions are the same but equal different numbers. The expression $-2x + y$ cannot equal both 6 and −3. That means there is not a solution to the system.

Course 3 • Chapter 3 Equations in Two Variables

NAME _____ DATE _____ PERIOD _____

Lesson 8 Multi-Step Problem Solving

Multi-Step Example

A total of 85 tickets were sold for the school play. Sixteen times as many adult tickets as children's tickets were sold. How many children's tickets were sold? 8.EE.8c, MP 4

(A) 5   (B) 16   (C) 17   (D) 80

Use a problem-solving model to solve this problem.

1 Understand

Read the problem. Circle the information you know. Underline what the problem is asking you to find.

2 Plan

What will you need to do to solve the problem? Write your plan in steps.

Step 1 Define the **variables** and write a system of **equations** to represent the situation.

Step 2 **Solve** the system algebraically.

Step 3 Interpret the **solution**.

> **Read to Succeed!**
> Remember to define the variables so that you can interpret the answer correctly.

3 Solve

Use your plan to solve the problem. Show your steps.

Let x equal the number of children's tickets sold. Let y equal the number of adult tickets sold. Write an equation to represent the total number of tickets sold.

$x + y =$ __85__

Write an equation to represent the number of children's tickets sold compared to the number of adult tickets sold. $y = 16 \cdot$ __x__

Use substitution to solve the system of equations.

$x + y =$ __85__ $x +$ __16x__ $= 85$ __17x__ $= 85$ $x =$ __5__

Next solve for y. $y =$ __16x__ $y = 16 \cdot$ __5__ $y =$ __80__

Since x is the number of children's tickets sold and y is the number of adult tickets sold we know that there were __80__ adult tickets sold and __5__ children's tickets sold. The correct answer is __A__. Fill in that answer.

4 Check

How do you know your solution is accurate?

Sample answer: I substituted 5 and 80 into the original problem. The values add up to 85, and 16 times 5 equals 80.

Course 3 • Chapter 3 Equations in Two Variables

Answers

NAME _____ DATE _____ PERIOD _____

Lesson 1 (continued)

Use a problem-solving model to solve each problem.

1 The cost of renting a bike using Plan A is given by $y = 5x + 25$, where x represents the number of days and y represents the total cost in dollars. The graph shows the cost for Plan B. What is the difference between the cost of Plan A and Plan B for renting a bike for 8 days? 8.F.4, MP 4

Bike Rental B

(4, 32)
(3, 24)
(2, 16)
(1, 8)

$1

2 Jun recorded the times and distances she rode her bike this weekend. At the rate shown in the table, how long will it take her to ride $7\frac{1}{4}$ miles? 8.F.4, MP 4

Minutes	Miles
90	22.5
150	37.5
210	52.5
330	82.5

285 minutes or 4.75 hours

3 The graph shows the amount, in dollars, in Thiago's savings account each week for several weeks. If the pattern continues, in how many weeks will Thiago have $125 in his savings account? 8.F.4, MP 4

Savings

(4, 45)
(3, 40)
(2, 35)
(1, 30)

20

4 H.O.T. Problem Games R Us offers two plans for renting video games. Plan A charges a one-time membership fee of $24 plus $1 for each game rental. Plan B charges $3 per game rental. For what number of games is the cost of both plans the same? Justify your answer. 8.F.4, MP 1

12; Sample Answer: I let the number of games be x and the cost be y. Plan A can be represented by $y = x + 24$. Plan B can be represented by $y = 3x$. I used guess, check and revise to determine the costs are the same for 12 games.

48

NAME _____ DATE _____ PERIOD _____

Lesson 1 Multi-Step Problem Solving

Multi-Step Example

Bruno and Mia joined yoga classes. The amount Bruno pays is represented by the equation $y = 5x$, where x represents the number of classes and y represents the total cost. The table shows the amount Mia pays for her yoga classes. What is the difference between the costs of each plan for 10 classes? 8.F.4, MP 1

Classes	Cost ($)
1	22
2	24
3	26
4	28

Use a problem-solving model to solve this problem.

1 Understand

Read the problem. Circle the information you know.
Underline what the problem is asking you to find.

2 Plan

What will you need to do to solve the problem? Write your plan in steps.

Step 1 Determine the __cost__ of each plan for 10 classes.

Step 2 Determine the __difference__ in the cost for 10 classes.

3 Solve

Use your plan to solve the problem. Show your steps.

Bruno pays __5__ (__10__) or __$50__ for 10 classes.

Mia's cost increases by __$2__ per class. So, she pays __$40__ for 10 classes.

Since __$50__ − __$40__ is __$10__ , the difference in cost between the two plans is __$10__ .

4 Check

How do you know your solution is accurate?

I found Bruno's cost by replacing x with 5 in the equation $y = 5x$. To check Mia's cost, I wrote the equation $y = 2x + 20$ and replaced x with 10. Since $2(10) + 20 = 40$, I know $40 is correct for Mia's cost. So, my answer is correct.

Read to Succeed!

Notice that the table does not give the y-intercept.

47

Chapter 4

NAME _____ DATE _____ PERIOD _____

Lesson 2 Multi-Step Problem Solving

Multi-Step Example

The relations in the graph at the right show the distances driven by Denzel and Mei on the second day of a two-day road trip. Which statement is true when the time equals 5 hours? *Preparation for 8.F.1,* MP 2

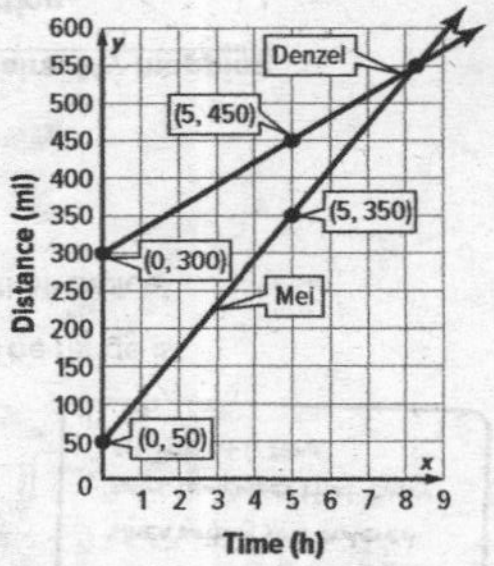

A Mei is driving at a faster speed than Denzel.
B Denzel is driving at a faster speed than Mei.
C Mei and Denzel are driving at the same speed.
D The speeds of Mei and Denzel cannot be determined.

Use a problem-solving model to solve this problem.

1 Understand

Read the problem. Circle the information you know. Underline what the problem is asking you to find.

2 Plan

What will you need to do to solve the problem? Write your plan in steps.

Step 1 Determine the __speed__ of each driver.

Step 2 Compare the __speeds__ of the two drivers.

3 Solve

Use your plan to solve the problem. Show your steps.

Denzel's speed is $\frac{450 - 300}{5 - 0}$ or __30__ miles per hour.

Mei's speed is $\frac{350 - 50}{5 - 0}$ or __60__ miles per hour.

Since __60__ > __30__ , __Mei__ 's speed is faster than __Denzel__ 's speed.

So, the correct answer is __A__ . Fill in that answer choice.

4 Check

How do you know your solution is accurate?

Sample answer: The steeper line represents the faster speed.

Read to Succeed!
When finding slope, remember to subtract the x-coordinates in the same order that you subtracted the y-coordinates.

Course 3 · Chapter 4 Functions

NAME _____ DATE _____ PERIOD _____

Lesson 2 (continued)

Use a problem-solving model to solve each problem.

1 The relations in the graph below show the depth of the water of two swimming pools that are being emptied. Which statement is true when the time equals 3 hours? *Preparation for 8.F.1,* MP 2

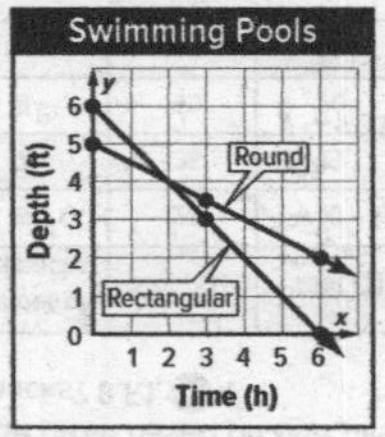

A The rectangular pool is being emptied at a slower rate than the round pool.
B The round pool is being emptied at a slower rate than the rectangular pool.
C The pools are being emptied at the same rate.
D The rates at which the pools are being emptied cannot be determined.

2 The table below shows the pressure in pounds per square foot that an object would be under if it were submerged to various depths. What would be the approximate pressure in pounds per square inch of an object submerged to a depth of 20 feet? *Preparation for 8.F.1,* MP 4

Depth (ft)	Pressure (lb/ft²)
0	2,117
4	2,367
8	2,617
10	2,742

Sample answer: 3,367 lb/ft²

3 The relation shown below shows the cost of downloading songs from an online music Web site. Suppose you spent $36.75 on downloads from this site. How many songs did you download? *Preparation for 8.F.1,* MP 2

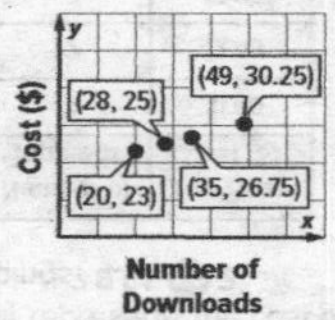

75 songs

4 H.O.T. Problem A concession stand at a high school football game sells a hot dog meal that includes a drink for $3.50. Write a relation consisting of five ordered pairs where the domain represents the number of meals and the range represents the total cost. Then write an equation that represents your relation. Interpret the slope and y-intercept. *8.F.4,* MP 4

Sample answer: (2, 7), (3, 10.5), (5, 17.5), (7, 24.5), and (8, 28); y = $3.50x; The slope represents the cost per meal, and the y-intercept represents the cost for 0 meals.

Course 3 · Chapter 4 Functions

49

50

Answers

Right page — Lesson 3 (continued)

NAME _____ DATE _____ PERIOD _____

Lesson 3 (continued)

Use a problem-solving model to solve each problem.

1 As shown in the table below, Fav Pizza offers half off of each additional topping. Which ordered pair represents the cost of a pizza with 6 toppings? 8.F.1, MP 2

Number of Toppings	Fav Pizza Cost ($)
1	11.60
2	12.40
3	12.80
4	13.00

Ⓐ (6, 13.15)   Ⓒ (13.4, 6)
Ⓑ (6, 13.4)   Ⓓ (13.5, 6)

2 In the mapping below, A maps onto B, and B maps onto C. Assume the function mapping A onto B and B onto C are linear. If the input value for A equals 6, what would the output value for C equal? 8.F.1, MP 2

A: 1, 3, -2
B: 4, 6, 1
C: 7, 11, 1

17

3 The table shows the cost of purchasing and profit from various numbers of backpacks. What is cost of purchasing 20 backpacks? What is the profit based on purchasing 20 backpacks? 8.F.1, MP 4

Number of Backpacks	Cost ($)	Profit ($)
6	120	10
7	135	15
8	150	20
9	165	25

$330; $80

4 ✎ H.O.T. Problem The table shows two relations, A and B. Which relation is not a function? Which single value of x or y could be changed to make the relation a function? Justify your answers. 8.F.1, MP 2

A	
x	y
-4	5
0	-4
-4	-2

B	
x	y
-3	-3
3	3
0	3

Relation A; Sample answer: Relation A is not a function. Changing one —4 to any number other than 0 makes the relation a function.

52 Course 3 · Chapter 4 Functions

Left page — Lesson 3 Multi-Step Problem Solving

NAME _____ DATE _____ PERIOD _____

Chapter 4

Lesson 3 Multi-Step Problem Solving

Multi-Step Example

A store is having a sale on T-shirts. Customers receive one free T-shirt for every three T-shirts purchased. If T-shirts sell for $10 each and a customer selects 6 T-shirts, which of the following statements about the customer's purchase is true? 8.F.1, MP 2

Ⓐ The relation is a function and has a range of {1, 2, 3, 4, 5, 6}.
Ⓑ The relation is a function and has a range of {10, 20, 30, 40, 50}.
Ⓒ The relation is not a function and has a range of {1, 2, 3, 4, 5, 6}.
Ⓓ The relation is not a function and has a range of {10, 20, 30, 40, 50}.

Use a problem-solving model to solve this problem.

1 Understand

Read the problem. Circle the information you know.
Underline what the problem is asking you to find.

2 Plan

What will you need to do to solve the problem? Write your plan in steps.

Step 1 Write a set of <u>ordered pairs</u> that represents the customer's purchase.

Step 2 Determine if the relation is a <u>function</u>, and determine its <u>range</u>.

3 Solve

Use your plan to solve the problem. Show your steps.

The customer's purchase can be represented as the set of ordered pairs (number of T-shirts, total cost).

{(1, 10), (2, 20), (3, **30**), (4, **30**), (5, **40**), (6, **50**)}

Since each member of the domain is mapped to <u>exactly one member of the range</u>, the relation is a function. The range is { **10, 20, 30, 40, 50** }. So, the correct answer is **B** . Fill in that choice.

Read to Succeed!
When writing your ordered pairs, remember that every 4th T-shirt is free.

4 Check

How do you know your solution is accurate?
Sample answer: I made a mapping diagram of the ordered pairs. My mapping diagram was a visual confirmation that the relation is a function.

Course 3 · Chapter 4 Functions   **51**

Chapter 4 Lesson 5 Answer Keys

NAME _____ DATE _____ PERIOD _____

Lesson 4 Multi-Step Problem Solving

Multi-Step Example

Which statement is true about the relationships involving a circle shown at the right? 8.F.4, MP 7

	Relationship
1.	(radius, diameter)
2.	(radius, circumference)
3.	(radius, area)

Ⓐ Only Relationships 1 and 2 are linear functions.

Ⓑ Only Relationship 3 is a linear function.

Ⓒ All three of the relationships are linear functions.

Ⓓ None of the relationships are linear functions.

Use a problem-solving model to solve this problem.

① Understand

Read the problem. (Circle) the information you know.
Underline what the problem is asking you to find.

② Plan

What will you need to do to solve the problem? Write your plan in steps.

Step 1 Determine the __diameter__, __circumference__, and __area__ for various radii.

Step 2 Determine which relations, if any, represent __linear functions__.

③ Solve

Use your plan to solve the problem. Show your steps.

Write ordered pairs using radii of 1, 2, 3, 4, and 5.

(radius, diameter): {(1, __2__), (2, __4__), (3, __6__), (4, __8__), (5, __10__)}

(radius, circumference): {(1, __6.3__), (2, __12.6__), (3, __18.8__),
(4, __25.1__), (5, __31.4__)}

(radius, area): {(1, __3.1__), (2, __12.6__), (3, __28.3__), (4, __50.3__),
(5, __78.5__)}

All three relations are __functions__, but the third relation does not have
a constant __rate of change__. So, the correct answer is __A__ .

④ Check

How do you know your solution is accurate?

__Only the graphs of the first two relations form straight lines. So, only the first__
__two relationships are linear functions.__

Read to Succeed!

Since the circumference and area formulas involve π, round your calculations to the nearest tenth.

Course 3 · Chapter 4 Functions

53

NAME _____ DATE _____ PERIOD _____

Lesson 4 (continued)

Use a problem-solving model to solve each problem.

1 Which statement is true about the relations shown in the tables below? 8.F.4, MP 7

Table 1

x	y
-4	-4
1	2
5	5

Table 2

x	y
-1	1
3	5
5	7

Ⓐ Neither table represents a linear function.

Ⓑ Only Table 1 represents a linear function.

Ⓒ Only Table 2 represents a linear function.

Ⓓ Both tables represent linear functions.

2 The table below shows the number of net Calories Silvia burns swimming for various numbers of minutes. Based on Silvia's metabolism, she must burn 3,500 net Calories to lose 16 ounces of fat. If Silvia swims 30 minutes a day, about how many days will it take her to lose at least 5 pounds? 8.F.4, MP 1

Minutes	Net Calories Burned
2	28
4	56
6	84
8	112

42 days

3 Pablo bought tickets at the state fair to play arcade games. Expressions for the number of tickets he used to play three arcade games are shown in the table below. After playing the third game, he had 6 tickets left. How many total tickets did Pablo buy? 8.F.4, MP 1

Game	Expressions
1	$\frac{1}{2}$ (tickets bought − 2)
2	$\frac{1}{4}$ tickets remaining
3	$\frac{1}{3}$ tickets remaining

22 tickets

4 H.O.T. Problem A faucet is dripping at a constant rate of 400 cubic millimeters per minute. A 6 fluid ounce cup is set under the faucet to collect water. How long will it take for the dripping water to fill the cup? Justify your response. (Hint: 6 fl oz ≈ 177.67 cm³) 8.F.4, MP 7

about 7.4 h; Sample answer: Since
400 mm³ = 0.4 cm³, the water is filling at
0.4 cm³ per minute; 0.4 cm³ per minute
equals 0.4(60) or 24 cm³ per hour. The
equation for the cup filling is y = 24x, where
y is the volume of the cup and x is the time
in hours. Substitute 177.6 for y and solve
for x; 177.67 = 24x, x = $\frac{177.67}{24}$ ≈ 7.4.
So, it will take about 7.4 hours to fill the cup.

54

Course 3 · Chapter 4 Functions

Chapter 4

Answers

NAME _____ DATE _____ PERIOD _____

Lesson 5 *(continued)*

Use a problem-solving model to solve each problem.

1 Sonia's profits from mowing lawns is given by $y = 5.50x$, where y is the profit in dollars and x is the number of hours worked. Victor's profits are shown in the table. Which option describes how the profits compare for 7 hours of work? 8.F.2, MP 2

Victor's Profits

Hours Worked	1	2	3	4
Profit ($)	1.50	8.00	14.50	21.00

Ⓐ The profit of the proportional function is $2.00 more.

Ⓑ The profit of the non-proportional function is $2.00 more.

Ⓒ The profit of the proportional function is $7.00 more.

Ⓓ The profit of the non-proportional function is $7.00 more.

3 Hugo's elevation as he drives his car is represented by $y = 175x$, where y is elevation in feet and x is the number of minutes he has driven. Irene's elevation is shown in the graph.

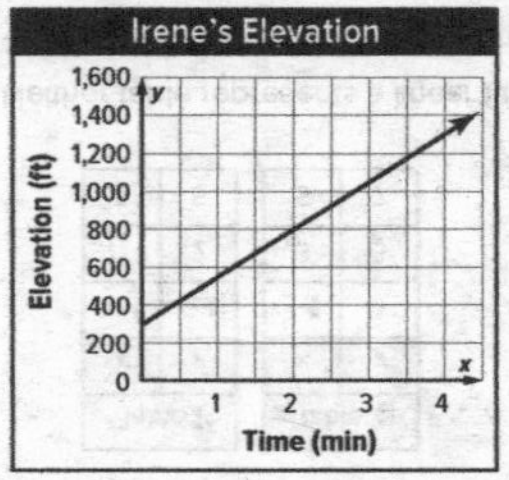

Irene's Elevation

What is the rate of change of the elevation in the non-proportional function? 8.F.2, MP 2

250 ft/min

2 Leto is considering buying books on display at four different tables. Each table has one of the following signs.

Each Book $10

Each Book $8 for Club Members (One-Time Membership Fee: $15)

Each Book 50% off

What will be the total cost if Leto buys 6 books from the table whose sign indicates a non-proportional relationship? 8.F.4, MP 4

$63

4 ✪ H.O.T. Problem Ed and Rayna are cycling in the same direction on the same straight road. Ed's distance from a roadside rest area is given by $d = 6t$. Rayna's distance from the same rest area is given by $d = 4.5t + 12$. In each function, d is distance in miles and t is time in hours. Determine which function(s) is proportional or non-proportional. When are Ed and Rayna the same distance from the rest area? Defend your answers. 8.F.4, MP 3

Sample answer: Ed's relationship is

because it is in the form $y = mx$.

Rayna's relationship is non-proportional

because it is in the form $y = mx + b$. Both

Ed and Rayna are 48 miles from the rest

area at 8 hours; 6(8) = 4.5(8) + 12 = 48.

56   Course 3 • Chapter 4 Functions

NAME _____ DATE _____ PERIOD _____

Chapter 4

Lesson 5 Multi-Step Problem Solving

Multi-Step Example

A librarian is considering two options for calculating overdue late fees. The first option uses $L = 0.30d + 0.50$, where L is the late fee in dollars and d is the number of days late. The second option is shown in the table. Which statement describes how the late fees compare for a book that is 8 days late? 8.F.2, MP 2

		Option 2		
Days Late	1	2	3	4
Late Fee ($)	0.40	0.80	1.20	1.60

Ⓐ The late fee in the proportional option is $0.30 more.

Ⓑ The late fee in the non-proportional plan is $0.30 more.

Ⓒ The late fee in the proportional plan is $0.90 more.

Ⓓ The late fee in the non-proportional plan is $0.90 more.

Use a problem-solving model to solve this problem.

① Understand

Read the problem. Circle the information you know. Underline what the problem is asking you to find.

② Plan

What will you need to do to solve the problem? Write your plan in steps.

Step 1   Determine which option is __proportional__. For each option, determine the late fee for a book that is __8 days late__.

Step 2   Determine which statement is correct.

Read to Succeed!

Recall that the quantities in proportional relationships have equal ratios. Equations of proportional relationships can be written in $y = mx$ form.

③ Solve

Use your plan to solve the problem. Show your steps.

Option 1: $L = \$ \underline{0.30} \, (\underline{8}\,) + \$ \underline{0.50} = \$ \underline{2.90}$

Option 2: $\$ \underline{0.40} \, (\underline{8}\,) = \$ \underline{3.20}$

The fee for a book that is 8 days late is __$0.30 more__ under

Option __2__, which is the __proportional__ option. So, the correct answer is __A__.

④ Check

How do you know your solution is accurate?

I know Option 2 is proportional because all of the ratios simplify to $0.40.

Since the fee for a book that is 8 days late is $0.30 more under Option 2,

I know my answer is correct.

Course 3 • Chapter 4 Functions   55

Chapter 4 Lesson 6 Answer Keys

Chapter 4 Lesson 7 Answer Keys

NAME _____ DATE _____ PERIOD _____

Lesson 6 Multi-Step Problem Solving

Chapter 4

Multi-Step Example

Felicia wants to fence in a rectangular region whose length will be twice its width. She also wants to fence in a rectangular dog pen that will share a length of fence, as shown in the diagram at the right. Which equation represents the amount of fencing Felicia needs? **8.F.4, MP1**

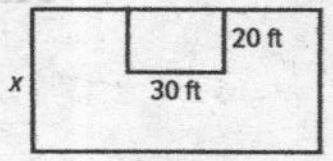

[diagram: 20 ft, 30 ft, x]

Ⓐ $y = 3x + 70$ Ⓒ $y = 3x + 100$
Ⓑ $y = 6x + 70$ Ⓓ $y = 6x + 100$

Use a problem-solving model to solve this problem.

1 Understand
Read the problem. Circle the information you know. Underline what the problem is asking you to find.

2 Plan
What will you need to do to solve the problem? Write your plan in steps.
Step 1 Determine the sum of the perimeters of the **rectangular region** and the **dog pen.**
Step 2 Subtract the **shared** length of fencing.

3 Solve
Use your plan to solve the problem. Show your steps.
The perimeter of the rectangular region is 2(**x**) + 2(**2x**)
or **6x** feet.
The perimeter of the dog pen is 2(**20**) + 2(**30**) or **100** feet.
So, the total amount of fencing, less the shared length, is **6x** + **100** − **30**
or **6x** + **70** feet. The correct answer is **B** . Fill in that answer.

Read to Succeed!
Remember even though coefficients are added or subtracted when combining like terms, the variables remain the same.

4 Check
How do you know your solution is accurate?
Sample answer: I checked my expressions for both perimeters by adding
$x + x + 2x + 2x$, or $6x$, and $20 + 20 + 30 + 30$, or 100. Since the common
side of 30 is subtracted, I know the answer is choice B.

Course 3 • Chapter 4 Functions
57

NAME _____ DATE _____ PERIOD _____

Lesson 6 (continued)

Use a problem-solving model to solve each problem.

1 Izzy wants to place a landscape border around a garden whose length will be 50% more than its width, x. He also wants to place the border on two edges of the patio, as shown in the diagram below.

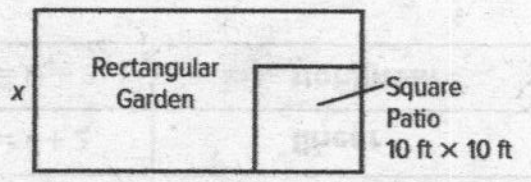

[diagram: Rectangular Garden, Square Patio 10 ft × 10 ft, x]

Which equation represents the amount of border Izzy will need? **8.F.4, MP1**
Ⓐ $y = 2.5x + 20$
Ⓑ $y = 3x + 20$
Ⓒ $y = 5x + 20$
Ⓓ $y = 5x + 40$

2 Rosa wants to buy a motor scooter. The graph shows information about two different scooters.

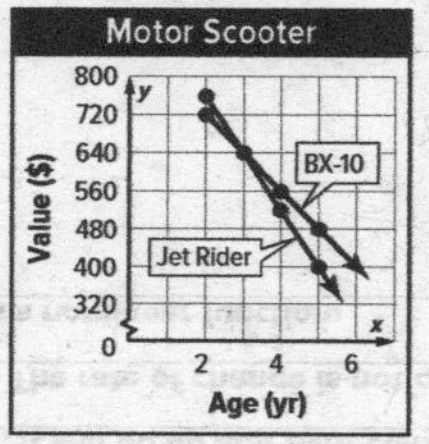

[graph: Motor Scooter, Value ($), Age (yr), BX-10, Jet Rider]

Assuming that the patterns continue, what will be the difference in values of the two scooters when they are 8 years old? **8.F.4, MP4**
$200

3 The population of a city has grown according to the pattern shown in the table, where x represents the number of years since the year 2000. **8.F.4, MP4**

Years, x	City Population, y
3	$3.5 \times 10^5 + 3(5 \times 10^5)$
4	$3.5 \times 10^5 + 4(5 \times 10^5)$
5	$3.5 \times 10^5 + 5(5 \times 10^5)$

Using the pattern in the table, what is the value of rate of increase in population?
0.7

4 H.O.T. Problem Jack and Ryan save at the rates shown in the graph below. In about how many weeks will the boys have a combined savings of $500? **8.F.4, MP4**

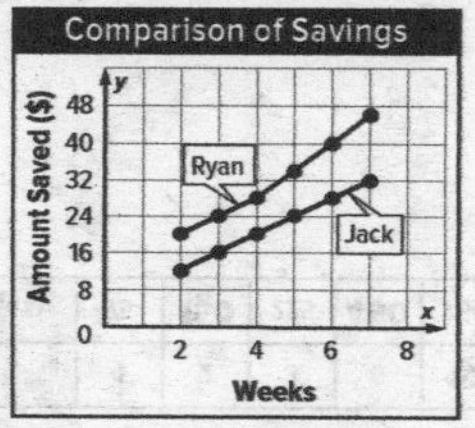

[graph: Comparison of Savings, Amount Saved ($), Weeks, Ryan, Jack]

Sample answer: 50 weeks

Course 3 • Chapter 4 Functions
58

Answers

NAME _____ DATE _____ PERIOD _____

Chapter 4

Lesson 7 Multi-Step Problem Solving

Multi-Step Example

The table shows the rate at which a mountain climber is climbing up a mountain. Does the information in the table represent a linear function? Explain your answer. 8.F.3, MP 2

Time (h)	2	4	6	8	10
Distance (mi)	10	20	30	40	50

(A) No; because the rate of change is constant.
(B) No; because the rate of change is not constant.
(C) Yes; because the rate of change is constant.
(D) Yes; because the rate of change is not constant.

Use a problem-solving model to solve this problem.

1 Understand
Read the problem. Circle the information you know. Underline what the problem is asking you to find.

2 Plan
What will you need to do to solve the problem? Write your plan in steps.

Step 1 Determine the __differences__ in time.

Step 2 Determine the __differences__ in distance.

Step 3 Decide whether the __rate of change__ is __constant__.

3 Solve
Use your plan to solve the problem. Show your steps.

The differences in the times are __2__ hours. The differences in the distances are __10__ miles. The rate of change is __constant__. The correct answer is __yes__; the table represents a linear function because the rate of change is constant.

The correct answer choice is __C__. Fill in that answer choice.

4 Check
How do you know your solution is accurate?

Sample answer: If I were to graph the information in the table, the graph would be a straight line.

Read to Succeed!
Remember, linear functions increase or decrease the same amount between any two points.

Course 3 • Chapter 4 Functions 59

NAME _____ DATE _____ PERIOD _____

Lesson 7 (continued)

Use a problem-solving model to solve each problem.

1 The volume of a cube is a function of its side length. Does this situation represent a linear function? Explain your answer. 8.F.3, MP 2

Side Length (cm)	1	2	3	4	5
Volume (cubic cm)	1	8	27	64	125

(A) Yes; because the rate of change is constant.
(B) Yes; because the rate of change is not constant.
(C) No; because the rate of change is constant.
(D) No; because the rate of change is not constant.

2 Jocelyn drove from Seattle to San Francisco. The table shows the distance driven as a linear function of the hours traveled. Complete the table. 8.F.3, MP 2

Time (h)	1	2	3	6	10	x
Distance (mi)	75	150	225	450	750	75x

3 Determine whether each function represents a linear or nonlinear situation. Complete the table by filling in the word *linear* or *nonlinear*. 8.F.3, MP 2

Function	Linear/Nonlinear
$y = \frac{3}{x}$	nonlinear
$x = 3y$	linear
$y = x + 2$	linear
$y = x^2 - 3$	nonlinear

4 H.O.T. Problem Give an example of a real-world situation that can be represented by a nonlinear function. 8.F.3, MP 4

Sample answer: If someone kicks a ball in the air, it will go up and then come back down. The rate of change is not constant. This is a nonlinear function.

60 Course 3 • Chapter 4 Functions

NAME _____ DATE _____ PERIOD _____

Lesson 8 (continued)

Use a problem-solving model to solve each problem.

1 Graph the parabola $h = 0.66d^2$, which represents the distance d in miles you can see from a height h in feet. Use the graph to estimate how far you can see from the Space Needle in Seattle, which is 605 feet tall. 8.F.5, MP 7

(A) 30 miles
(B) 35 miles
(C) 50 miles
(D) 65 miles

3 Graph the quadratic function $y = x^2 - 5$. Does the graph have a maximum or minimum? What is the coordinate of the maximum or minimum? 8.F.5, MP 7

The graph has a minimum at $(0, -5)$.

2 A tennis ball is dropped from a height of 300 feet. The function $d = -16t^2 + 300$ models the distance d in feet the tennis ball is from the ground at time t seconds. Graph the function and then use the graph to estimate the time it will take for the tennis ball to reach the ground. 8.F.5, MP 7

Sample answer: The tennis ball will hit the ground after about 4.3 seconds.

4 H.O.T. Problem Write an equation of a quadratic function that opens downward and has its maximum at (0, 7.5). 8.F.5, MP 4

Sample answer: $y = -x^2 + 7.5$

62   Course 3 • Chapter 4 Functions

NAME _____ DATE _____ PERIOD _____

Chapter 4

Lesson 8 Multi-Step Problem Solving

Multi-Step Example

Graph the quadratic function $h = -4.9t^2 + 15t$ which gives the height h of a projectile in meters after t seconds. Use the graph to estimate how many seconds it will take for the projectile to reach its maximum height. 8.F.5, MP 7

(A) 1 second
(B) 1.5 seconds
(C) 2 seconds
(D) 2.5 seconds

Use a problem-solving model to solve this problem.

1 Understand

Read the problem. Circle the information you know. Underline what the problem is asking you to find.

2 Plan

What will you need to do to solve the problem? Write your plan in steps.

Step 1 Graph the __quadratic__ function.

Step 2 Look along the __y-axis__ to determine the maximum __height__ then look along the __x-axis__ to determine the __time__ in seconds.

Read to Succeed!

Remember, quadratic functions have a variable with the power of 2.

3 Solve

Use your plan to solve the problem. Show your steps.

The maximum height occurs at about __11.5__ feet. It takes the projectile about __1.5__ seconds to reach its maximum height. The correct answer is __B__. Fill in that answer choice.

4 Check

How do you know your solution is accurate?

Sample answer: On my graph the point (1.5, 11.5) is the highest point on the graph.

61   Course 3 • Chapter 4 Functions

Answers

Chapter 4 Lesson 8 Answer Keys

NAME _____ DATE _____ PERIOD _____

Lesson 9 (continued)

Use a problem-solving model to solve each problem.

1 The graph shows the change in temperature throughout the month. Describe the temperature change over time. 8.F.5, MP 4

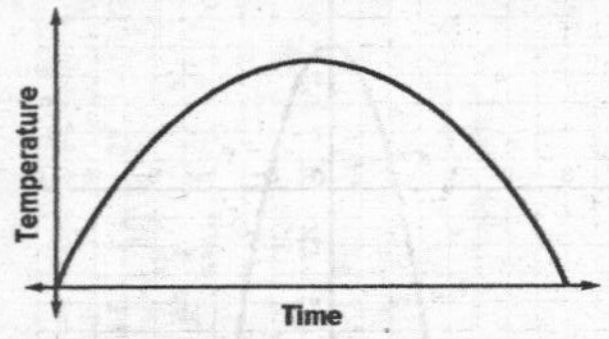

(A) The temperature increases at a varied rate, reaches a maximum, and then decreases at a varied rate.

(B) The temperature decreases at a steady rate, then maintains a constant temperature, and then increases at a steady rate.

(C) The temperature increases at a steady rate, then maintains a constant temperature, and then decreases at a steady rate.

(D) The temperature decreases at a varied rate, reaches a maximum, and then increases at a varied rate.

3 The graph shows a cyclist's speed. Describe a situation that would produce this graph. 8.F.5, MP 4

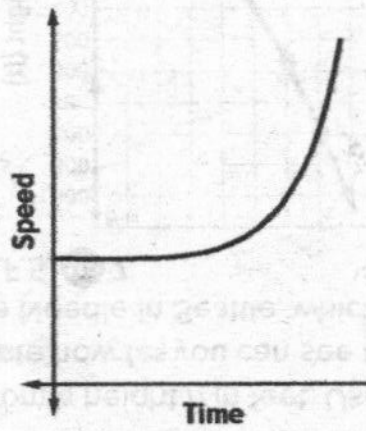

Sample answer: The cyclist rides at a steady rate and then coasts downhill, which increases the speed at increasing rates.

64

2 The graph displays a student's distance from school during the school day. Describe the change in distance from the school over time. 8.F.5, MP 4

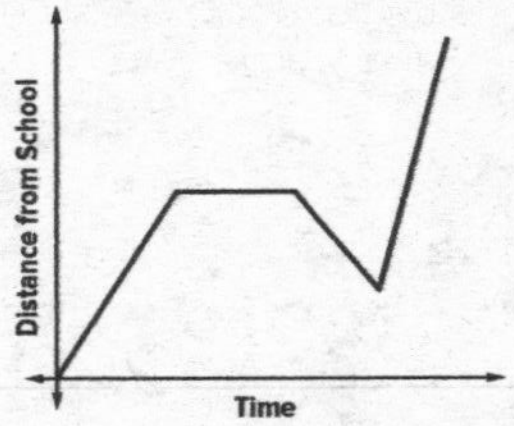

Sample answer: The student starts out at school. The student then walks away from the school and stops to play. The student then walks toward the school and then suddenly turns and runs home.

4 H.O.T. Problem A man enters an elevator in the lobby and pushes the button for the 11th floor. The elevator malfunctions and does not stop at the 11th floor when it gets there, but it immediately returns to the lobby. Draw a graph of the height of the elevator over time. 8.F.5, MP 4

Sample graph:

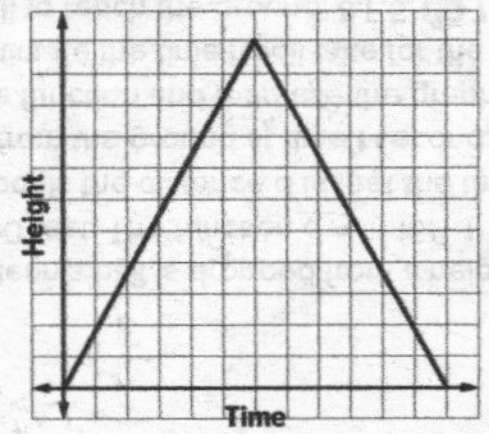

Course 3 • Chapter 4 Functions

NAME _____ DATE _____ PERIOD _____

Lesson 9 Multi-Step Problem Solving

Multi-Step Example

The graph displays the speed of an airplane. Describe the change in speed over time. 8.F.5, MP 4

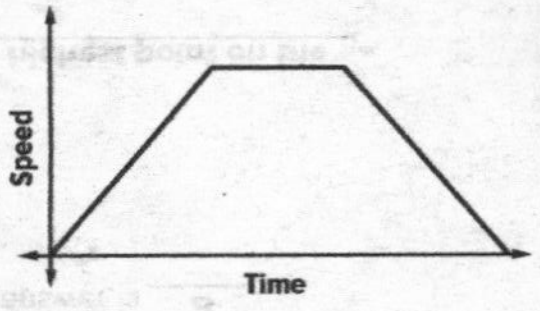

(A) The airplane increases speed at a varied rate, then stops flying, and then decreases speed at a varied rate.

(B) The airplane decreases speed at a varied rate, then stops flying, and then increases speed at a varied rate.

(C) The airplane decreases speed at a constant rate, then maintains a constant speed, and then increases speed at a constant rate.

(D) The airplane increases speed at a constant rate, then maintains a constant rate, and then decreases speed at a constant rate.

Use a problem-solving model to solve this problem.

Read to Succeed!
Remember, linear functions increase or decrease at the same rate. Nonlinear functions increase or decrease at varied rates.

1 Understand

Read the problem. Circle the information you know. Underline what the problem is asking you to find.

2 Plan

What will you need to do to solve the problem? Write your plan in steps.

Step 1 — Look along the **y-axis** to determine the speed.

Step 2 — Look along the **x-axis** to determine the **time** .

3 Solve

Use your plan to solve the problem. Show your steps.

The speed **increases** at a constant rate. The speed then remains the same because the line becomes **horizontal** . Finally, the speed **decreases** at a constant rate. The correct answer is **D** .

4 Check

How do you know your solution is accurate?

Sample answer: An increase at the same rate is linear with a positive slope. Maintaining speed results in a horizontal line. A decrease at the same rate is linear with a negative slope.

Course 3 • Chapter 4 Functions

63

Chapter 4

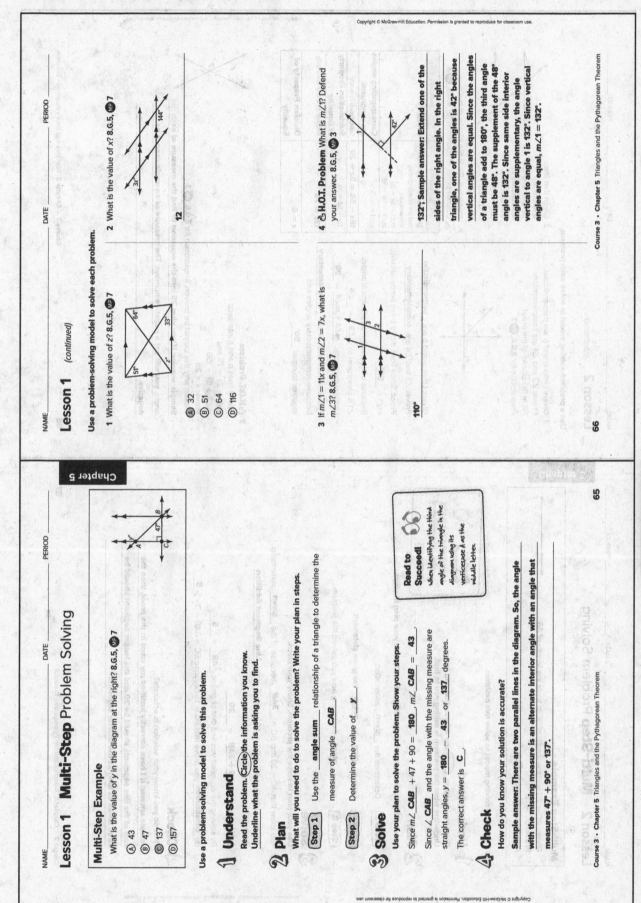

NAME _____ DATE _____ PERIOD _____

Lesson 1 (continued)

Use a problem-solving model to solve each problem.

1 What is the value of z? 8.G.5, MP 7

Ⓐ 32
Ⓑ 51
Ⓒ 64
Ⓓ 116

2 What is the value of x? 8.G.5, MP 7

12

3 If $m\angle 1 = 11x$ and $m\angle 2 = 7x$, what is $m\angle 3$? 8.G.5, MP 7

110°

4 ⚙ **H.O.T. Problem** What is $m\angle 1$? Defend your answer. 8.G.5, MP 3

132°; Sample answer: Extend one of the sides of the right angle. In the right triangle, one of the angles is 42° because vertical angles are equal. Since the angles of a triangle add to 180°, the third angle must be 48°. The supplement of the 48° angle is 132°. Since same side interior angles are supplementary, the angle vertical to angle 1 is 132°. Since vertical angles are equal, $m\angle 1 = 132$°.

NAME _____ DATE _____ PERIOD _____

Lesson 1 Multi-Step Problem Solving

Multi-Step Example

What is the value of y in the diagram at the right? 8.G.5, MP 7

Ⓐ 43
Ⓑ 47
Ⓒ 137
Ⓓ 157

Use a problem-solving model to solve this problem.

1 Understand

Read the problem. Circle the information you know. Underline what the problem is asking you to find.

2 Plan

What will you need to do to solve the problem? Write your plan in steps.

Step 1 Use the __angle sum__ relationship of a triangle to determine the measure of angle __CAB__.

Step 2 Determine the value of __y__.

3 Solve

Use your plan to solve the problem. Show your steps.

Since $m\angle$ __CAB__ + 47 + 90 = __180__, $m\angle$ __CAB__ = __43__.

Since $\angle$ __CAB__ and the angle with the missing measure are straight angles, y = __180__ − __43__ or __137__ degrees.

The correct answer is __C__.

4 Check

How do you know your solution is accurate?

Sample answer: There are two parallel lines in the diagram. So, the angle with the missing measure is an alternate interior angle with an angle that measures 47°. 90° or 137°.

Read to Succeed!

When identifying the third angle of the triangle in the diagram using its vertices, use A as the middle letter.

Answers

Chapter 5 Lesson 1 Answer Keys

NAME _____ DATE _____ PERIOD _____

Lesson 2 Multi-Step Problem Solving

Multi-Step Example

Given: $AC = 20$ and the length of BC is triple the length of AB.
Prove: $BC = 15$.
Preparation for 8.G.6, MP 3

$A \bullet \quad B \bullet \quad \bullet C$

Use a problem-solving model to solve this problem.

1 Understand

Read the problem. (Circle) the information you know.
Underline what the problem is asking you to find.

2 Plan

What will you need to do to solve the problem? Write your plan in steps.

Step 1 Determine the __given__ information.

Step 2 Form a __plan__ to __prove__ the given statement.

Step 3 Write a __proof__ explaining how you solved the problem.

3 Solve

Use your plan to solve the problem. Show your steps.

You know that $AC = 20$ and $BC =$ __3AB__ because of the __given__ statements.

You can state that $AB + BC = AC$ because of the __Line Segment Addition__ Property.

By substitution, __AB + 3AB__ = __20__

By solving the equation you find that segment __AB__ = __5__

By substitution you prove that $BC = 15$ because $BC = 3AB = 3 \cdot$ __5__

4 Check

How do you know your solution is accurate?
Sample answer: If I have correctly justified my steps in the proof, then the sum of the line segments should be 20 and the longer segment should be three times as long as the shorter segment.

Read to Succeed!
A proof is just a plan to solve a problem with justifications for each step.

NAME _____ DATE _____ PERIOD _____

Lesson 2 (continued)

Use a problem-solving model to solve each problem.

1 Given: Lines a and b are perpendicular.
Prove: $\angle 3$ and $\angle 4$ are complementary.
Fill in the blanks of the proof.
Preparation for 8.G.6, MP 3

Given: Lines a and b are __perpendicular__.

Prove: $\angle 3$ and $\angle 4$ are __complementary__.

Proof: Since lines a and b are perpendicular,
$m\angle 1 =$ __90°__.

Because of the definition of vertical angles,
$\angle 1$ is congruent to __$\angle 3$__ + __$\angle 4$__.

Using substitution, __$m\angle 3 + m\angle 4$__ = __90°__

Therefore, $\angle 3$ and $\angle 4$ are __complementary__ because complementary angles add together to equal __90°__

2 Given that lines a and b are parallel and are intersected by transversal c,
$m\angle 1 = 5x + 20$, and $m\angle 5 = 18x - 58$, prove that $x = 6$. Fill in the blanks of the two-column proof. Preparation for 8.G.6, MP 3

Statements	Reasons
Lines a and b are parallel and are intersected by transversal c.	Given
$m\angle 1 = 5x + 20$ $m\angle 5 = 18x - 58$	
$m\angle 1 = m\angle 5$	Corresponding angles are congruent.
$18x - 58 = 5x + 20$	Substitution Property
$13x - 58 = 20$	Subtraction Property of Equality
$13x = 78$	Addition Property of Equality
$x = 6$	Division Property of Equality

3 H.O.T. Problem

Given: lines a and b intersect;
$m\angle 1 = 2x - 75$ and
$m\angle 3 = 5x - 150$
Prove: $x = 25$
Explain why this cannot be proven. Preparation for 8.G.6, MP 3
Sample answer: If you plug 25 into the equation to find the measure of each angle, you will get a negative number. The measure of an angle cannot be negative.

NAME _____ DATE _____ PERIOD _____

Lesson 3 Multi-Step Problem Solving

Multi-Step Example

What are the values of x and y? 8.G.5, MP 7

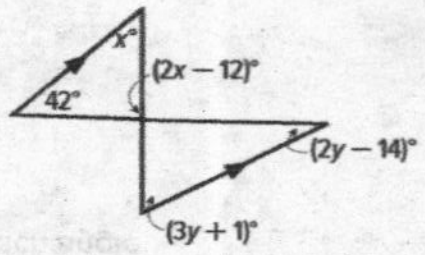

Ⓐ $x = 42$, $y = 24.2$
Ⓑ $x = 50$, $y = 21$
Ⓒ $x = 50$, $y = 28.6$
Ⓓ $x = 70$, $y = 13$

Use a problem-solving model to solve this problem.

1 Understand
Read the problem. Circle the information you know. Underline what the problem is asking you to find.

2 Plan
What will you need to do to solve the problem? Write your plan in steps.

Step 1 Write an equation to determine the value of x.

Step 2 Write an equation to determine the value of y.

3 Solve
Use your plan to solve the problem. Show your steps.

Since the sum of the interior angles of a triangle is __180°__.

$x + (2x - 12) + $ __42__ $ = $ __180__ and $x = $ __50__. So, the value of $2x - 12$ is $2($__50__$) - 12$ or __88__. Since the two triangles form a pair of vertical angles, solve the equation

__88__ $ + (2y - 14) + (3y + 1) = $ __180__ to determine the value of y.

Since the value of y is __21__ the correct answer is __B__. Fill in that answer choice.

4 Check
How do you know your solution is accurate?

If $x = 50$, then the angle measures of one triangle are 42°, 50°, and 88°, which add to 180°. If $y = 21$, then the angle measures of the other triangle are 88°, 28°, and 64°, which add to 180°.

Course 3 • Chapter 5 Triangles and the Pythagorean Theorem

69

Read to Succeed!
Remember to simplify the expressions on the left side of the equation by combining like terms.

NAME _____ DATE _____ PERIOD _____

Lesson 3 (continued)

Use a problem-solving model to solve each problem.

1 The triangles have measures shown in the sketch. What are the values of x and y? 8.G.5, MP 7

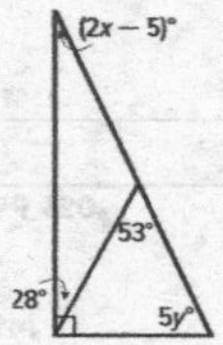

Ⓐ $x = 25$, $y = 65$
Ⓑ $x = 65$, $y = 25$
Ⓒ $x = 15$, $y = 13$
Ⓓ $x = 13$, $y = 15$

2 In the diagram below, the two vertical lines are parallel. What is the value of y? 8.G.5, MP 7

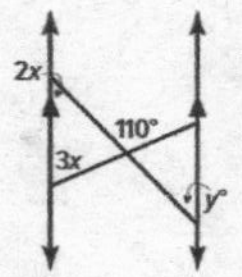

44

3 The measures of the angles of a triangle have ratio 3:4:5. What is the measure of the exterior angle formed at the vertex of the angle with the greatest measure? 8.G.5, MP 1

105°

4 H.O.T. Problem The parallelogram has angle measures as shown. If $a = 100°$ and $e = 50°$, what is the value of $a + b + e + f$? Justify your answer. 8.G.5, MP 3

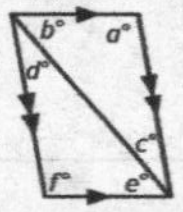

300°, Sample answer. Since the lines are parallel, b and e are alternate interior angles, $m\angle b = m\angle e = 50°$. Since the sum of the interior angles of a triangle add to 180°, $m\angle c = 180° - 100° - 50° = 30°$. Since d and c are alternate interior angles, $m\angle d = m\angle c = 30°$. So, $m\angle f = 180° - 50° - 30° = 100°$. $a + b + e + f = 100° + 50° + 50° + 100° = 300°$

Course 3 • Chapter 5 Triangles and the Pythagorean Theorem

70

Answers

NAME _____ DATE _____ PERIOD _____

Lesson 4 Multi-Step Problem Solving

Multi-Step Example

Hiro wants to build a birdhouse with a floor, two walls, and a peaked roof. If the shape is a regular pentagon, what angle will Hiro need to make each interior angle of his birdhouse? *Extension of 8.G.5,* MP 4

Ⓐ 90° Ⓑ 108° Ⓒ 360° Ⓓ 540°

Use a problem-solving model to solve this problem.

1 Understand

Read the problem. Circle the information you know.
Underline what the problem is asking you to find.

2 Plan

What will you need to do to solve the problem? Write your plan in steps.

Step 1 Find the number of __triangles__ in the pentagon if all the diagonals are drawn from one vertex.

Step 2 Multiply the number of triangles by __180__ to determine the sum of the interior angles in the birdhouse.

Step 3 __Divide__ the __sum of the angles__ by the number of __angles__ in a pentagon. The angles will all be equal because the pentagon is __regular__.

3 Solve

Use your plan to solve the problem. Show your steps.

The pentagon can be divided into __3__ triangles. Multiply 3 by __180__.

The sum of the interior angles is __540°__ in a pentagon.

By dividing the total number of degrees by __5__, you find that each angle should be __108°__. Fill in answer choice __B__.

4 Check

How do you know your solution is accurate?

<u>Sample answer: The formula to find the total number of degrees of the interior angles in a polygon is (n − 2)180. The pentagon has 5 sides. Since this is a regular pentagon, all the interior angles are equal. (3)180 = 540.</u>

540 ÷ 5 = 108°. Each angle is 108°.

Course 3 • Chapter 5 Triangles and the Pythagorean Theorem

Read to Succeed!

To find the total sum of the interior angles of a polygon, subtract 2 from the number of sides and multiply by 180. The sum of the exterior angles of a polygon is always 360°.

NAME _____ DATE _____ PERIOD _____

Lesson 4 *(continued)*

Use a problem-solving model to solve each problem.

1 Kyra wants to build an octagon-shaped pen for her dogs. If she wants the pen to be a regular octagon, what will be the measure of each interior angle? *Extension of 8.G.5,* MP 4

Ⓐ 1080°
Ⓑ 540°
Ⓒ 135°
Ⓓ 90°

2 Find the missing measures of the angles of this irregular hexagon. *Extension of 8.G.5,* MP 4

85°, 85°

3 Find the measures of the exterior angles of the polygon. *Extension of 8.G.5,* MP 4

90°, 120°, and 150°

4 ✎ **H.O.T. Problem** How many sides does a regular polygon have if each interior angle measures 162°? *Extension of 8.G.5,* MP 4

20 sides

Course 3 • Chapter 5 Triangles and the Pythagorean Theorem 71

72

NAME _____ DATE _____ PERIOD _____

Lesson 5 Multi-Step Problem Solving

Multi-Step Example

Alma has a motor boat that averages 3 miles per gallon of gasoline, and the tank holds 15 gallons of gasoline. At 9 A.M., Alma left the dock in her boat. At 10 A.M., she was 3 miles west and 4 miles north of the dock. If she continues at this rate, in how many more hours will the tank be out of gasoline? 8.G.7, MP 4

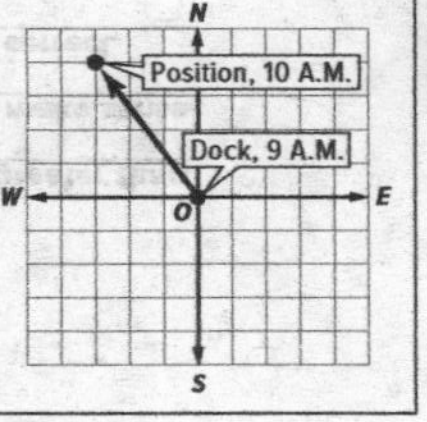

Ⓐ 45 Ⓒ 8
Ⓑ 25 Ⓓ 5

Use a problem-solving model to solve this problem.

1 Understand

Read the problem. Circle the information you know. Underline what the problem is asking you to find.

2 Plan

What will you need to do to solve the problem? Write your plan in steps.

Step 1 Determine the number of **miles** possible on one tank of gasoline.

Step 2 Determine the number of **miles** Alma traveled in one **hour**.

Then determine the number of **hours** before the motor boat's tank is out of gasoline.

3 Solve

Use your plan to solve the problem. Show your steps.

The tank holds **15 gallons** of gasoline, and the boat averages **3 miles per gallon**. So, the boat can travel **15** (**3**) or **45** miles on 1 tank of gasoline.

In 1 hour, Alma traveled $\sqrt{3^2 + 4^2}$ or **5** miles. At this rate, there will be enough gasoline for **45** ÷ **5** or **9** hours. Since Alma has already traveled for 1 hour, the correct answer is **C**. Fill in that answer choice.

Read to Succeed!

Remember distance has to be positive, so only the positive square root will be used.

4 Check

How do you know your solution is accurate?

Sample answer: By my calculations, traveled 5 miles in 1 hour. It makes sense that she will be able to travel 45 miles in 9 hours.

Course 3 • Chapter 5 Triangles and the Pythagorean Theorem 73

NAME _____ DATE _____ PERIOD _____

Lesson 5 (continued)

Use a problem-solving model to solve each problem.

1 Reggie and Yoki are riding their bikes to meet at the library. Yoki rode 4 miles south and 4 miles west, and Reggie rode 8 miles east and 5 miles north as shown below. To the nearest mile, what is the straight-line distance that Reggie lives from Yoki? 8.G.7, MP 4

Ⓐ 6 Ⓒ 15
Ⓑ 9 Ⓓ 225

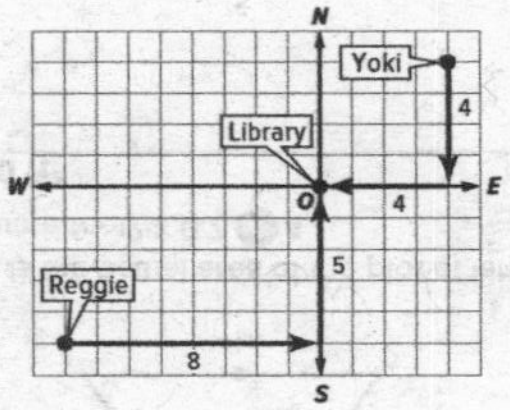

2 Triangle A has side lengths of 10 units, 24 units, and 26 units. Ryan cut out two copies of triangle A and joined them together to form a rectangle. What is the perimeter of the rectangle formed when the two triangles are joined? 8.G.7, MP 1

68 units

3 Felix hits three croquet balls from the same spot as shown in the diagram below. Starting at point F, he picks up each ball. What is the shortest distance Felix can travel to pick up all three croquet balls, ending at the point where he picks up the third ball? 8.G.7, MP 4

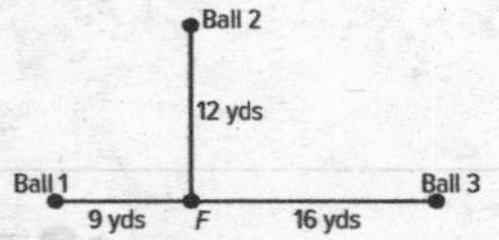

44 yd

4 H.O.T. Problem What is the perimeter of parallelogram PTRU shown in the diagram below? Explain. 8.G.7, MP 4

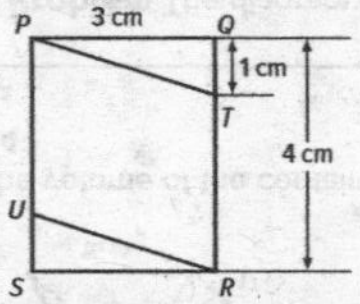

12.3; Sample answer: $PT = \sqrt{1^2 + 3^2} = \sqrt{10}$. **Since the opposite sides of a parallelogram are congruent, $PT = UR$ and $RT = UP$. So, the perimeter is $3 + 3 + \sqrt{10} + \sqrt{10}$ or about 12.3 centimeters.**

Course 3 • Chapter 5 Triangles and the Pythagorean Theorem 74

Answers

NAME _____ DATE _____ PERIOD _____

Lesson 6 (continued)

Use a problem-solving model to solve each problem.

1 Pablo walks west for 16 minutes, north for 4 minutes, west for 8 minutes, and north for 6 minutes. If Pablo walks at a steady rate of 3 miles per hour, what is the straight-line distance in miles that Pablo walks? 8.EE.2, MP 4

1.3

2 A shipping container with bases that are isosceles triangles is shown below.

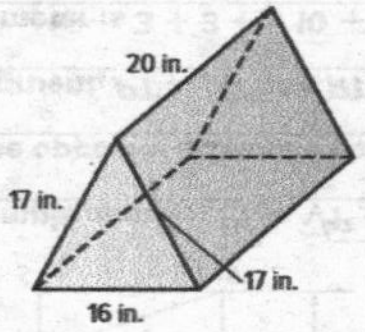

What is the volume of the container? 8.G.7, MP 4

2,400 in³

3 In the scale drawing shown below, polygon *ABCD* represents a plot of land. The scale is 1 inch: 10 feet.

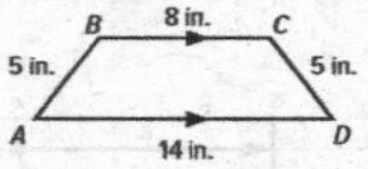

What is the actual area of the plot of land, in square feet? 8.G.7, MP 4

4,400 ft²

4 H.O.T. Problem The diagram of a kite is shown below.

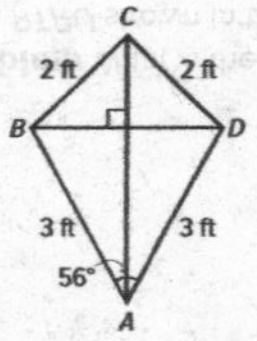

If $BD = \sqrt{8}$ ft, what are the measures of $\angle BCD$, $\angle ABC$, and $\angle ADC$? Justify your answers. 8.G.7, MP 7

$m\angle BCD = 90°$, $m\angle ABC = m\angle ADC = 107°$.

Sample answer: $2^2 + 2^2 = (\sqrt{8})^2$, so

$m\angle BCD = 90°$ by the converse of the

Pythagorean Theorem. $\triangle BCD$ is isosceles

and the sum of the angle measures of any

triangle is 180°, so $m\angle CBD = m\angle CDB =$

45°. $\triangle ABD$ is isosceles and the sum of the

angle measures of any triangle is 180°,

so $m\angle ABD = m\angle ADB = 62°$. Adding

the angle measures at points *B* and *D*,

$m\angle ABC = m\angle ADC = 45° + 62° = 107°$.

Course 3 • Chapter 5 Triangles and the Pythagorean Theorem

76

NAME _____ DATE _____ PERIOD _____

Lesson 6 Multi-Step Problem Solving

Multi-Step Example

Olivia walks at a steady rate of 4 miles per hour. She walks east for 24 minutes, north for 15 minutes, east for 24 minutes, and north for 20 minutes. What is the approximate straight-line distance in miles between Olivia's starting point and ending point? 8.EE.2, MP 4

Use a problem-solving model to solve this problem.

1 Understand

Read the problem. Circle the information you know. Underline what the problem is asking you to find.

2 Plan

What will you need to do to solve the problem? Write your plan in steps.

Step 1 Determine the __straight-line__ distance between Olivia's starting point and ending point in minutes.

Step 2 Express Olivia's distance in __miles__.

Read to Succeed!

You may wish to draw a diagram that shows the route Olivia walks.

3 Solve

Use your plan to solve the problem. Show your steps.

Use the Pythagorean Theorem to determine Olivia's distance in minutes;

$\text{distance}_{min} = \sqrt{24^2 + 15^2} + \sqrt{24^2 + 20^2} \approx 28.3 + 31.2 \approx 59.5$.

So, Olivia walks for about __60__ minutes.

Since there are 60 minutes in __1 hour__ and Olivia walks at a rate of __4 miles__ per hour, the __straight-line__ distance is about __4 miles__.

4 Check

How do you know your solution is accurate?

Sample answer: Since 28.3 is greater than 24 and 15 and 31.2 is greater than

24 and 20, I know my values for the straight-line minutes walked make sense.

Since Olivia walks at a rate of 4 miles per hour, I know my answer is correct.

Course 3 • Chapter 5 Triangles and the Pythagorean Theorem

75

NAME _____ DATE _____ PERIOD _____

Lesson 7 Multi-Step Problem Solving

Multi-Step Example

The map at the right shows two walking trails in a park. Both paths end at the picnic area, located at $C(6, 1)$. Trail A starts at $A(-6, 6)$, and Trail B starts at $B(-10, -11)$. If each unit on the map represents 0.5 mile, how many miles longer is Trail B than Trail A? 8.EE.2, MP 4

Ⓐ 3.5   Ⓒ 16.5
Ⓑ 13   Ⓓ 20

Use a problem-solving model to solve this problem.

1 Understand

Read the problem. Circle the information you know. Underline what the problem is asking you to find.

Read to Succeed!
Since the diagram does not include the scale, refer back to the problem to find the scale of the map.

2 Plan

What will you need to do to solve the problem? Write your plan in steps.

Step 1 Use the **Distance Formula** to determine the length in **units** of both trails.

Step 2 Determine how much longer **Trail B** is than **Trail A** in **miles**.

3 Solve

Use your plan to solve the problem. Show your steps.

Trail B is $\sqrt{(-10 - 6)^2 + (-11 - 1)^2}$ or **20** units long. Trail A is
$\sqrt{(-6 - 6)^2 + (6 - 1)^2}$ or **13** units long. Trail B is **20** − **13** or **7** units longer than Trail A.

Since one unit represents **0.5** mile, Trail B is **0.5** (**7**) or **3.5** miles longer than Trail A. Fill in answer choice **A**.

4 Check

How do you know your solution is accurate?

I checked the lengths of Trails A and B by switching my (x_1, y_1) and (x_2, y_2) values and recalculating. Then I checked that I used the correct map scale when expressing the difference in miles.

Course 3 • Chapter 5 Triangles and the Pythagorean Theorem   77

NAME _____ DATE _____ PERIOD _____

Lesson 7 (continued)

Use a problem-solving model to solve each problem.

1 The locations of Ivan's house, Avery's house, and their school as shown on the map below. Each unit on the map represents 0.25 mile. How many more miles does Ivan travel to school than Avery? 8.EE.2, MP 4

Ⓐ 5
Ⓑ 25
Ⓒ 20
Ⓓ 125

2 The map shows a bike trail in a park. Emilio rides from point A to point B and then rides back to point A. He rides at an average rate of 15 miles per hour. If each unit on the map represents 0.5 mile, how many minutes does Emilio's ride take? 8.G.8, MP 4

100

3 A rectangle is drawn on a coordinate grid and has vertices at $(-10, 4)$, $(5, 4)$, $(5, -4)$, and $(-10, -4)$. If each unit on the grid represents 6 inches, what is the approximate length of the diagonal of the rectangle in feet? Round your answer to the nearest tenth. 8.G.8, MP 4

8.5

4 H.O.T. Problem A circle with center $C(2, -2)$ passes through $A(5, 2)$. Determine the area of the circle. Use 3.14 for π. Justify your response. 8.EE.2, MP 4

78.5 units²; Sample answer: The radius is a segment from the center of a circle to any point on the circle. So connecting point A and point C forms a radius.

Since $AC = \sqrt{(5 - 2)^2 + (2 - (-2))^2} =$ $\sqrt{9 + 16} = 5$, the radius is 5 units.

So, the area is $A = \pi r^2 \approx 3.14(5^2)$ or 78.5 square units.

Course 3 • Chapter 5 Triangles and the Pythagorean Theorem   78

NAME _____ DATE _____ PERIOD _____

Lesson 1 *(continued)*

Use a problem-solving model to solve each problem.

1 Parallelogram *PQRS* is translated to parallelogram *P'Q'R'S'*. Which of the following algebraic representations describes the translation? 8.G.3, MP 2

Vertices of *PQRS*	Vertices of *P'Q'R'S'*
$P(-4, -4)$	$P'(-1, -5)$
$Q(-3, -1)$	$Q'(0, -2)$
$R(-1, -1)$	$R'(2, -2)$
$S(-2, -4)$	$S'(1, -5)$

Ⓐ $(x, y) \rightarrow (x + 3, y - 1)$

Ⓑ $(x, y) \rightarrow (x - 3, y + 1)$

Ⓒ $(x, y) \rightarrow (x - 1, y + 3)$

Ⓓ $(x, y) \rightarrow (x + 1, y - 3)$

3 $\triangle XYZ$ is translated 4 units right and 2 units down to $\triangle X'Y'Z'$. What is the sum of all of the x-coordinates and y-coordinates of the vertices of $\triangle X'Y'Z'$? 8.G.3, MP 2

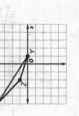

5

2 The vertices of a rectangle are $A(-3, 2)$, $B(1, 2)$, $C(1, -1)$, and $D(-3, -1)$. Rectangle *ABCD* is translated 2 units right and 4 units down to rectangle *A'B'C'D'*. What is the quotient of diagonal *AC* and diagonal *A'C'*? 8.G.3, MP 2

1

4 🖐 **H.O.T. Problem** $\triangle ABC$ is translated to $\triangle A'B'C'$, and $\triangle A'B'C'$ is then translated to $\triangle A''B''C''$. Use algebraic notation to explain the effect of both translations. Then use algebraic notation to explain the effect of translating $\triangle ABC$ to $\triangle A''B''C''$. 8.G.3, MP 6

$\triangle ABC$ to $\triangle A'B'C'$: $(x, y) \rightarrow (x + 5, y - 4)$,

$\triangle A'B'C'$ to $\triangle A''B''C''$: $(x, y) \rightarrow (x - 2, y + 3)$;

$\triangle ABC$ to $\triangle A''B''C''$: $(x, y) \rightarrow (x + 3, y - 1)$

Course 3 • **Chapter 6** Transformations

80

NAME _____ DATE _____ PERIOD _____

Lesson 1 **Multi-Step** Problem Solving

Multi-Step Example

$\triangle ABC$ is translated to $\triangle A'B'C'$. Then $\triangle A'B'C'$ is translated 2 units to the right and 1 unit up to form $\triangle A''B''C''$. Which of the following describes the translation of $\triangle ABC$ to $\triangle A''B''C''$? 8.G.3, MP 2

Ⓐ $(x, y) \rightarrow (x + 2, y + 1)$

Ⓑ $(x, y) \rightarrow (x - 2, y - 4)$

Ⓒ $(x, y) \rightarrow (x - 4, y - 5)$

Ⓓ $(x, y) \rightarrow (x + 2, y + 4)$

Use a problem-solving model to solve this problem.

1 Understand

Read the problem. Circle the information you know. Underline what the problem is asking you to find.

2 Plan

What will you need to do to solve the problem? Write your plan in steps.

Step 1 Graph __$\triangle A''B''C''$__ to determine its coordinates.

Step 2 Count the number of units from __$\triangle ABC$__ to __$\triangle A''B''C''$__.

3 Solve

Use your plan to solve the problem. Show your steps.

Vertex A'' is (__-1__ , __0__), vertex B'' is (__1__ , __1__), and

vertex C'' is (__2__ , __-3__).

So, $\triangle ABC$ is translated **2 units left** and **4 units down**.

The correct answer is __B__. Fill in that answer choice.

4 Check

How do you know your solution is accurate?
Sample answer: I used an algebraic representation to explain the effect of the translation from $\triangle ABC$ to $\triangle A'B'C'$. Then I revised the algebraic representation to explain the effect of a translation 2 units right and 1 unit up.

Course 3 • **Chapter 6** Transformations

79

Read to Succeed!

Be sure to use the correct triangles for the original figure and the final image.

NAME _____ DATE _____ PERIOD _____

Lesson 2 (continued)

Use a problem-solving model to solve each problem.

1. Quadrilateral *LMNP* is reflected over the *y*-axis to form quadrilateral *L'M'N'P'*. Quadrilateral *L'M'N'P'* is then translated 1 unit right and 1 unit down to form quadrilateral *L"M"N"P"*. If point *L* is (−4, −4), what are the coordinates of point *L"*? 8.G.3, MP 4

   (A) *L"*(4, −4)
   (B) *L"*(5, −5)
   (C) *L"*(−3, −5)
   (D) *L"*(−3, 3)

2. Quin is playing an online puzzle game, moving puzzle pieces from Quadrant III to Quadrant I. The puzzle pieces can be moved with three different transformations: a reflection over the *x*-axis, a reflection over the *y*-axis, or a translation. Each transformation counts as one move. Quin has one more piece to move to complete the puzzle. What are the fewest number of moves he can use to move the puzzle piece shown below into its appropriate place? 8.G.1, MP 7

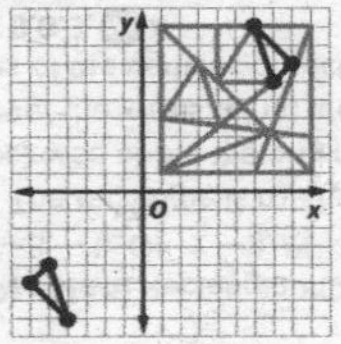

3. △*ABC* is reflected over the *x*-axis, reflected over the *y*-axis, and then translated. Point *A"* is the image of point *A* after the three transformations. What are the coordinates of *B"*? 8.G.3, MP 4

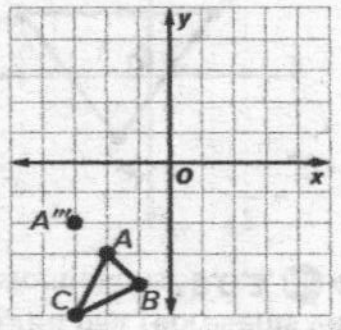

(−4, −1)

4. H.O.T. Problem A triangle is reflected and then translated. Will the image of this triangle be the same if the translation is applied first followed by the reflection? Defend your answer. 8.G.3, MP 7

no; Suppose one of the vertices is A(2, 3). Reflecting A over the y-axis gives A'(−2, 3). A translation 4 units right and 4 units down gives A"(2, −1). If the same vertex A(2,3) is first translated 4 units right and 4 units down, A' is (6, −1). Then a reflection over the y-axis gives A"(−6, −1), which is not the same.

82   Course 3 • Chapter 6 Transformations

NAME _____ DATE _____ PERIOD _____

Lesson 2 Multi-Step Problem Solving

Multi-Step Example

△*ABC* is reflected over the *x*-axis and then translated 4 units left and 5 units down to △*DEF*. Which algebraic representation explains the effect of the transformation of △*ABC* to △*DEF*? 8.G.3, MP 4

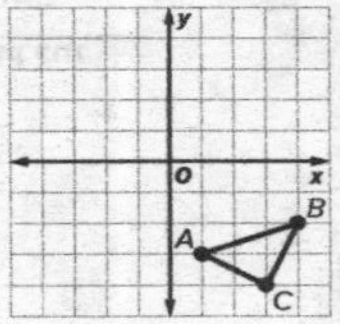

   (A) (x, y) → (−x − 4, y − 5)
   (B) (x, y) → (−x + 4, y + 5)
   (C) (x, y) → (x + 4, −y + 5)
   (D) (x, y) → (x − 4, −y − 5)

Use a problem-solving model to solve this problem.

1 Understand

Read the problem. Circle the information you know. Underline what the problem is asking you to find.

2 Plan

What will you need to do to solve the problem? Write your plan in steps.

Step 1 Reflect △*ABC* over **the *x*-axis**. Then translate the image **4 units left** and **5 units down** to form △*DEF*.

Step 2 Use the **coordinates** of a pair of corresponding **vertices** to evaluate the statements above.

3 Solve

Use your plan to solve the problem. Show your steps.

Vertex A is (1 , −3) and vertex D is (−3 , −2).

Since 1 − 4 = −3 and −(−3) − 5 = −2, (x, y) → (x − 4, −y − 5) explains the effect of the transformation. So, __D__ is the correct answer. Fill in that answer choice.

Read to Succeed!
Since the algebraic representation explains the effect of a reflection followed by a translation, it will be necessary to multiply one of the coordinates by −1.

4 Check

How do you know your solution is accurate?

Sample answer: I used a second pair of corresponding vertices, B and E, to verify my answer.

Course 3 • Chapter 6 Transformations   81

Answers

NAME ______ DATE ______ PERIOD ______

Lesson 3 **Multi-Step** Problem Solving

Chapter 6

Multi-Step Example

Before moving furniture in her bedroom, Jasmine made a diagram of the current arrangement. She drew rectangle *ABCD* to represent her desk with vertices at (2, 4), (6, 4), (6, 1), and (2, 1), respectively. She moved the desk twice, first translating it 3 units left and 2 units down, and then rotating it 90° counterclockwise about the image of vertex *D*. What is the *y*-coordinate of vertex *C* after these transformations are applied? 8.G.3, MP 4

Use a problem-solving model to solve this problem.

1 Understand

Read the problem. Circle the information you know.
Underline what the problem is asking you to find.

2 Plan

What will you need to do to solve the problem? Write your plan in steps.

Step 1 Determine the coordinates of rectangle *A'B'C'D'* following a translation **3 units left** and **2 units down**.

Step 2 Determine the *y*-coordinate of **C'** following a **90° counterclockwise** rotation about **D'**.

Read to Succeed!
Be sure to use the correct angle of rotation and center of rotation.

3 Solve

Use your plan to solve the problem. Show your steps.

A' is (**−1**, **2**), *B'* is (**3**, **2**), *C'* is (**3**, **−1**), and *D'* is (**−1**, **−1**). Since there are 4 horizontal units between *C'* and *D'*, there will be 4 vertical units between *C''* and *D''* following a **90° counterclockwise** rotation.

Since −1 + 4 = **3**, the *y*-coordinate of *D''* is **3**.

4 Check

How do you know your solution is accurate?

I graphed rectangle *ABCD* and translated the figure. Then I traced and cut out the rectangle and rotated it 90° counterclockwise about *D'* to verify my answer.

NAME ______ DATE ______ PERIOD ______

Lesson 3 *(continued)*

Use a problem-solving model to solve each problem.

1 A planter in Vincent's office is represented by △*JKL* on the coordinate plane below. He moves the planter by a translation of 4 units left and 3 units up, followed by a rotation of 180° clockwise about the image of vertex *K*. Which ordered pair represents vertex *J* after these transformations? 8.G.3, MP 4

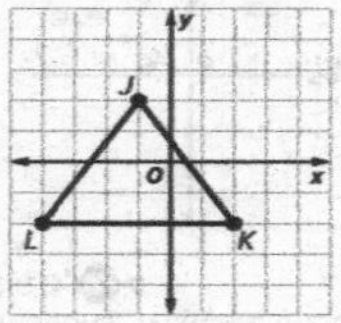

Ⓐ (−5, 5)
Ⓑ (4, 1)
Ⓒ (1, −3)
Ⓓ (3, 5)

2 Kendra made a sun with rotational symmetry out of mosaic tiles as shown below. She then placed the sun on a coordinate plane so that the center of the sun was the origin. What is the smallest angle of clockwise rotation in degrees that the sun can be rotated about the origin and match the original orientation of Kendra's sun? 8.G.1, MP 4

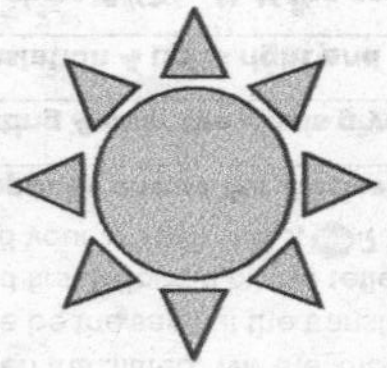

45

3 Belinda drew triangle *TUV* on graph paper. Then, she rotated the triangle 90° clockwise about vertex *U*. Finally, she translated the triangle 2 units down and 1 unit to the left. How many vertical units away from the preimage *V* is the image of vertex *V*? 8.G.3, MP 4

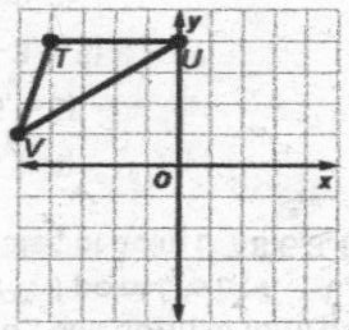

6

4 **H.O.T. Problem** Rectangle *PQRS* has vertices *P*(−3, −1), *Q*(−1, −1), *R*(−1, −4), and *S*(−3, −4). The rectangle is rotated 90° counterclockwise about the origin. It is then reflected over the *x*-axis. What are the coordinates of the vertices of rectangle *P''Q''R''S''*? 8.G.3, MP 4

***P''*(1, 3), *Q''*(1, 1), *R''*(4, 1), *S''*(4, 3)**

NAME _____ DATE _____ PERIOD _____

Lesson 4 (continued)

Use a problem-solving model to solve each problem.

1 Fina is an architect. She drew quadrilateral *ABCD* to represent a window. Then, using the origin as the center, she dilated it to obtain the larger quadrilateral *A'B'C'D'*. Which statement is true? 8.G.3, MP 4

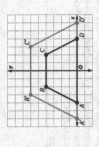

Ⓐ $m\angle A' = 1.5 \times m\angle A$

Ⓑ $m\angle A' = 2.25 \times m\angle A$

Ⓒ area of *A'B'C'D'* = 1.5 × area of *ABCD*

Ⓓ area of *A'B'C'D'* = 2.25 × area of *ABCD*

2 Aponi is a structural engineer. She drew △*PQR* to represent a roof truss. Using point *P* as the center, she dilated △*PQR* by a scale factor of 2 and then dilated the resulting image by a scale factor of 1.1 to obtain a final image. The area of the final image, *A''*, is related to the original area *A* by the equation $A'' = x \cdot A$. What is the value of *x*? 8.G.3, MP 4

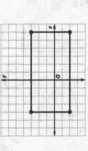

4.84

3 The rectangle below is dilated, increasing both dimensions by 20%. Then the image is dilated, decreasing both dimensions by 20%. The origin is the center of both dilations. The perimeter of the final image, *P''*, is related to the original perimeter *P* by the equation $P'' = x \cdot P$. What is the value of *x*? 8.G.3, MP 4

0.96

4 ⬆ **H.O.T. Problem** Polygon *PQRS* has vertices *P*(−4, −2), *Q*(3, −2), *R*(3, 6), and *S*(−4, 6). Polygon *PQRS* is dilated, using the origin as the center of the dilation. The image is polygon *P'Q'R'S'*, and *P'* has coordinates (−10, −5). What is the perimeter of polygon *P'Q'R'S'*? Support your answer. 8.G.3, MP 6

75; Sample answer: I drew *PQRS* and found it has a perimeter of 30 units. I wrote *P*(−4, −2) → *P'*(−10, −5) = (−4*k*, −2*k*) to represent the dilation with a scale factor *k* and solved −2*k* = −5 to find that *k* = 2.5. Since every side of polygon *P'Q'R'S'* is 2.5 times the corresponding side of polygon *PQRS*, its perimeter is 2.5 times the perimeter of polygon *PQRS*. So, the perimeter of polygon *P'Q'R'S'* is 2.5 × 30, or 75 units.

Course 3 • Chapter 6 Transformations

86

NAME _____ DATE _____ PERIOD _____

Chapter 6

Lesson 4 Multi-Step Problem Solving

Multi-Step Example

Malik uses a dilation in a perspective drawing. Using the origin as the center of the dilation, he dilates Rectangle I to obtain Rectangle II. Which option describes the change in perimeter, using the following variables? 8.G.3, MP 4

P_I = perimeter of Rectangle I

P_{II} = perimeter of Rectangle II

SF = scale factor of the dilation

Ⓐ $P_I = SF \times P_{II}$ Ⓒ $P_{II} = SF \times P_I$

Ⓑ $P_I = (SF)^2 \times P_{II}$ Ⓓ $P_{II} = (SF)^2 \times P_I$

Use a problem-solving model to solve this problem.

1 Understand

Read the problem. Circle the information you know. Underline what the problem is asking you to find.

2 Plan

What will you need to do to solve the problem? Write your plan in steps.

Step 1 Determine which equations model the relationship between scale factor and **perimeter** when dilating a figure.

Step 2 Determine which equation models the dilation of **Rectangle I** to obtain **Rectangle II**.

3 Solve

Use your plan to solve the problem. Show your steps.

Answer choices **A** and **C** show the relationship between scale factor and perimeter.

Of these two choices, **C** shows the dilation of **Rectangle I** to obtain **Rectangle II**. So, the correct answer is **C**. Fill in that answer choice.

4 Check

How do you know your solution is accurate?

Sample answer: I used the diagram to determine the perimeters of the figures and scale factor of the dilation. I then used these values to verify my answer.

Read to Succeed!

Remember that perimeter uses linear units of measure, while area uses square units of measure.

Course 3 • Chapter 6 Transformations

85

Answers

NAME _____ DATE _____ PERIOD _____

Lesson 1 (continued)

Use a problem-solving model to solve each problem.

1 James made these designs with pieces of string. Which statement best describes the relationship between the figures? 8.G.2, MP 3

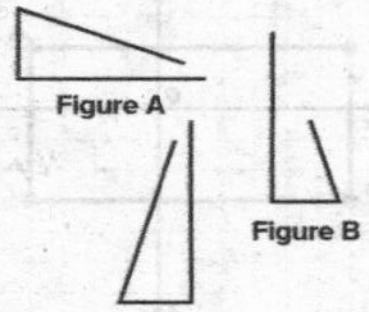

Figure A

Figure B

Figure C

Ⓐ A is rotated and translated to make B, and is not congruent to C.

Ⓑ A is rotated and translated to make C, and is not congruent to B.

Ⓒ A is rotated and reflected to make B, and rotated and translated to make C.

Ⓓ A is rotated and reflected to make C, and rotated and translated to make B.

3 A line segment has endpoints A(−2, 2) and B(7, 2). Segment AB is first reflected across the y-axis, then reflected across the x-axis, and finally rotated counterclockwise about the origin to create segment A'B'. If B' has coordinates (2, −7), how many degrees counterclockwise was segment AB rotated? 8.G.1a, MP 4

90

2 Beth used △JKL as a preimage for a series of transformations such that △J'K'L' and △JKL are congruent. If her resulting image has coordinates L'(4, −1) and K'(1, −3), what whole number is a possible x-coordinate of J? 8.G.2, MP 4

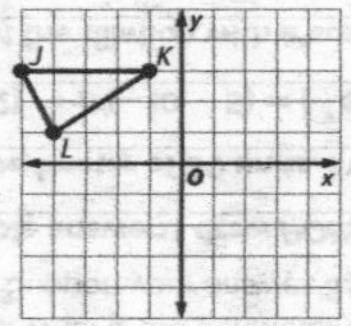

5

4 H.O.T. Problem Miranda drew the design shown below. She translated the design 6 units right and 6 units down. Then she dilated the image using a scale factor of 2. Which transformation(s) produced congruent figures? Support your answer. 8.G1, MP 3

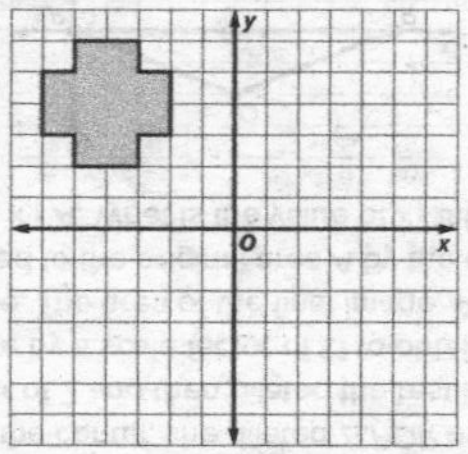

the translation; Sample answer: A translation produces congruent figures. A dilation changes the dimensions of the figure, which means the figures are not congruent.

88

87

NAME _____ DATE _____ PERIOD _____

Lesson 1 Multi-Step Problem Solving

Multi-Step Example

Serena arranged sixteen floor tiles into patterns A and B as shown. Are Serena's two designs congruent? If so, describe the transformation or series of transformations that map pattern A to pattern B. 8.G.2, MP 3

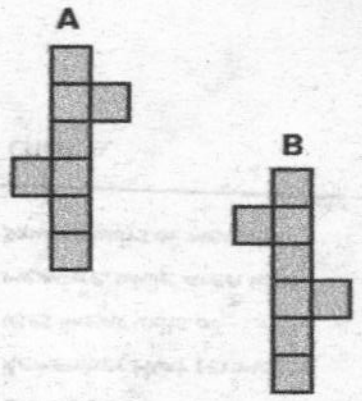

A

B

Ⓐ Design A is translated to make design B.

Ⓑ Design A is translated and rotated to make design B.

Ⓒ Design A is reflected and translated to make design B.

Ⓓ The designs are not congruent.

Use a problem-solving model to solve this problem.

1 Understand

Read the problem. Circle the information you know. Underline what the problem is asking you to find.

2 Plan

What will you need to do to solve the problem? Write your plan in steps.

Step 1 Trace design A on a separate sheet of paper.

Step 2 Translate and reflect design A as described above to determine if the designs are congruent.

3 Solve

Use your plan to solve the problem. Show your steps.

No matter how design A is transformed, it is congruent to design B.

So, the correct answer is C. Fill in that answer choice.

4 Check

How do you know your solution is accurate?

When I translated and reflected design A, I used the placement of the side squares to determine whether the designs are congruent.

Read to Succeed!

When checking for congruency, pay close attention to the position of the squares located to the left and right of the center squares.

NAME _____ DATE _____ PERIOD _____

Lesson 2 Multi-Step Problem Solving

Multi-Step Example

Which composition of transformations will map △DEF to △LMN so that the two triangles coincide? 8.G.2, MP 2

(A) reflection over the x-axis followed by a translation 6 units down
(B) reflection over the y-axis followed by a translation 6 units down
(C) a 90° clockwise rotation about the origin followed by a reflection over the y-axis
(D) a 90° clockwise rotation about the origin followed by a reflection over the x-axis

Use a problem-solving model to solve this problem.

1 Understand

Read the problem. Circle the information you know. Underline what the problem is asking you to find.

2 Plan

What will you need to do to solve the problem? Write your plan in steps.

Step 1 Trace △DEF on a separate sheet of paper.

Step 2 **Translate**, **rotate**, and **reflect** △DEF to determine which **composition of transformations** maps △DEF onto **△LMN**.

3 Solve

Use your plan to solve the problem. Show your steps.

A **90° clockwise rotation** about the origin followed by a **reflection over the x-axis** maps △DEF onto △LMN. So, the correct answer is **D**. Fill in that answer choice.

4 Check

How do you know your solution is accurate?

I labeled the vertices on my traced triangle to be sure that corresponding sides and vertices were matching up when I performed each composition of transformation.

Read to Succeed!
Be sure that corresponding sides and angles match up when you are determining the correct series of transformations.

89

Course 3 • Chapter 7 Congruence and Similarity

NAME _____ DATE _____ PERIOD _____

Lesson 2 (continued)

Use a problem-solving model to solve each problem.

1 How can △DEF be transformed to show it is congruent to △ABC? 8.G.2, MP 2

(A) reflection over the y-axis followed by a translation 5 left and 6 down
(B) reflection over the x-axis followed by a translation 5 left and 6 up
(C) rotation 270° counterclockwise about the origin
(D) rotation 270° clockwise about the origin

2 △ABC is translated 2 units right and 3 units up. △A'B'C' is then reflected over the y-axis. What are the lengths of A"B", B"C", and A"C"? 8.G.1a, MP 4

A"B" = **4**, B"C" = **3**, A"C" = **5**

3 △ABC ≅ △RST. What is the measure in degrees of ∠T? 8.G.1b, MP 2

4 H.O.T. Problem △PQR is reflected over the x-axis and then rotated 90° counterclockwise about the origin to form △P'Q'R'. List all of the corresponding parts of the two triangles. What are the coordinates of △P'Q'R'? What is the length P'R'? 8.G.2, MP 7

PQ ≅ P'Q', PR ≅ P'R', RQ ≅ R'Q',
∠P ≅ ∠P', ∠Q ≅ ∠Q', ∠R ≅ ∠R', P'(5, 6),
Q'(0, 6), R'(5, −6); P"R" = 12 units

90

Course 3 • Chapter 7 Congruence and Similarity

Answers

NAME _____ DATE _____ PERIOD _____

Lesson 3 Multi-Step Problem Solving

Multi-Step Example

A website developer enlarges an image with a length of 6 centimeters and width of 9 centimeters by a scale factor of 3. The developer decides that the enlarged image is too large and reduces it by a scale factor of 0.5. Will the final image fit into a space that has an area of 121 square centimeters? Explain your answer. 8.G.4, MP 4

Ⓐ Yes, the area of the image is 54 square centimeters.

Ⓑ Yes, because the area of the image is 121 square centimeters.

Ⓒ No, because the area of the image is 486 square centimeters.

Ⓓ No, because the area of the image is 121.5 square centimeters.

Use a problem-solving model to solve this problem.

1 Understand

Read the problem. Circle the information you know. Underline what the problem is asking you to find.

2 Plan

What will you need to do to solve the problem? Write your plan in steps.

Step 1 Determine the dimensions of the **enlargement** and then determine the dimensions of the **reduction** .

Step 2 Determine the **area** of the final image.

3 Solve

Use your plan to solve the problem. Show your steps.

To find the dimensions of the **enlargement** , multiply the dimensions by **3** .

So, **6** × 3 = **18** and **9** × 3 = **27** . Multiply these dimensions by **0.5** to find the dimensions of the **reduction** . The final dimensions of the image are **9** centimeters and **13.5** centimeters. The area of the image would be **9** × 13.5 = **121.5** square centimeters. This makes the correct answer **D** .

4 Check

How do you know your solution is accurate?

Sample answer: To find dimensions of a similar figure, I multiply the original dimensions by the scale factor used. To find the area, I multiply $\ell \times w$.

Read to Succeed!
Similar figures are the same shape but not the same size.

NAME _____ DATE _____ PERIOD _____

Lesson 3 *(continued)*

Use a problem-solving model to solve each problem.

1 A fashion designer needs to reduce the pattern she has made for a rectangular decal she plans to use on her garment. The original dimensions of the decal are 5 inches by 10 inches. She reduces the decal by a scale factor of $\frac{2}{5}$. After placing it on the garment, she decides the decal is now too small. She enlarges the decal by a scale factor of $\frac{3}{2}$. Will the decal fit in a space that has an area of 12 square inches? Explain your answer. 8.G.4, MP 4

Ⓐ Yes, because the area of the image is 8 square inches.

Ⓑ Yes, because the area of the image is 5 square inches.

Ⓒ No, because the area of the image is 18 square inches.

Ⓓ No, because the area of the image is 12.5 square inches.

2 A gardener drew plans for a rectangular garden. The original drawing was 1.5 inches by 4 inches. Before he showed the drawing to the client, he enlarged it to show more detail. His enlarged drawing was 2 feet 6 inches by 7 feet 5 inches. The client points out to him that something does not look right. Explain the error. 8.G.4, MP 2

The same scale factor was not used on both dimensions.

3 Are the two figures similar? Explain your reasoning. 8.G.4, MP 7

The figures are not similar. The scale factor of each side is not the same:

$$\frac{AD}{FI} = \frac{6}{4} = \frac{3}{2} \text{ and } \frac{AB}{FG} = \frac{4}{3}. \text{ If the figures}$$

were similar, the scale factors would be the same.

4 H.O.T. Problem Describe the differences between congruent figures and similar figures. Make sure to compare the side lengths, the angle measures, and the transformations that can be used in your description. 8.G.4, MP 3

Sample answer: Congruent figures have the same side lengths and angle measures. Congruent figures can be translated, rotated, or reflected. Congruent figures cannot be dilated because dilation changes the size of the figure. Similar figures have different side lengths but the same angle measures. Similar figures can be translated, rotated, reflected, and dilated.

NAME _____ DATE _____ PERIOD _____

Lesson 4 *(continued)*

Use a problem-solving model to solve each problem.

1 Triangle *ABC* is shrunk to obtain triangle *DEC*. Using the same scale factor, triangle *DEC* is shrunk to obtain triangle *FGC*. *AB* = 50 centimeters, *BC* = 40 centimeters, *CA* = 40 centimeters, and *DE* = 45 centimeters. What is the perimeter of triangle *FGC*? 8.G.4, MP 4

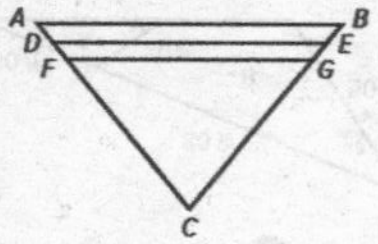

Ⓐ 87.2 cm
Ⓑ 100 cm
Ⓒ 105.3 cm
Ⓓ 117 cm

3 Abril drew the scale drawing shown below to represent the front of a garage she plans to build. The scale is 1 inch:2.5 feet. The equation $A_2 = A_1x$, where A_2 is the actual area in square feet and A_1 is the area of the drawing, represents the relationship between the areas. What is the value of *x*? 8.G.4, MP 2

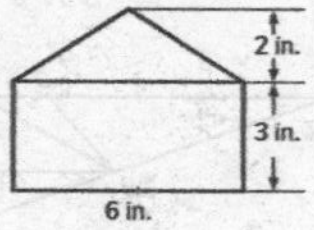

6.25

2 The rectangle shown below was used in a magazine advertisement for a digital camera. It represents the image sensor region of the camera. The actual image sensor region in the camera is a dilation of the rectangle by a scale factor of 4×10^{-2}. What is the area of the actual image sensor region, in square centimeters, rounded to the nearest hundredth? 8.G.4, MP 2

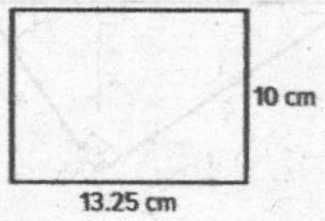

0.21 cm²

4 🖐 **H.O.T. Problem** Triangle *ABC* is shown on the graph. Triangle *XYZ* is similar to triangle *ABC* and has the same orientation. The *x*-coordinate of *Y* in triangle *XYZ* is 12.

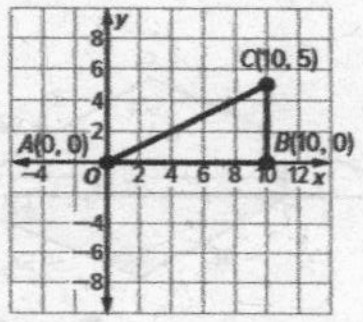

What are the coordinates of *Z*? Justify your answer. 8.G.4, MP 3

(12, 6); Sample answer: I found the scale factor using 10x = 12, x = 1.2. So, Z has coordinates (10 × 1.2, 5 × 1.2) = (12, 6).

Course 3 • Chapter 7 Congruence and Similarity

94

NAME _____ DATE _____ PERIOD _____

Chapter 7

Lesson 4 Multi-Step Problem Solving

Multi-Step Example

Alex used reflective tape to make the design shown on a jacket. First, he made the small polygon. Then he enlarged the small polygon to make the large polygon, using a scale factor that extended the 8-centimeter side by 2 centimeters. What total length of reflective tape did Alex use to create the entire design? 8.G.4, MP 4

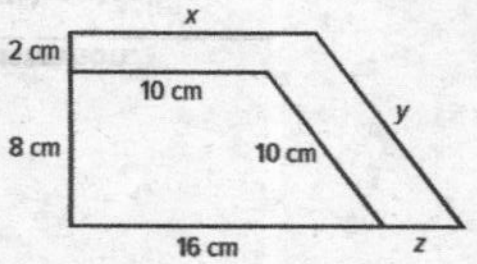

Ⓐ 44 cm
Ⓑ 55 cm
Ⓒ 75 cm
Ⓓ 99 cm

Use a problem-solving model to solve this problem.

1 Understand

Read the problem. Circle the information you know. Underline what the problem is asking you to find.

2 Plan

What will you need to do to solve the problem? Write your plan in steps.

Step 1 Determine the scale factor from the small polygon to the large polygon.

Step 2 Use the scale factor to determine the measures needed to find the total length of tape used.

3 Solve

Use your plan to solve the problem. Show your steps.

Multiply **16** and **10** by the scale factor $\frac{5}{4}$ to determine the missing measures *x*, *y*, and *z*. Remember that the length of the large polygon is 16 + *z*.

Add 8 + 10 + 10 + 16 + 2 + **12.5** + **12.5** + **4**.

Alex used **75** centimeters of tape. So, the correct answer is **C**. Fill in that answer choice.

4 Check

How do you know your solution is accurate?
Sample answer: Since the ratios of the corresponding sides $\frac{10}{8}$, $\frac{20}{16}$, and $\frac{12.5}{10}$ simplify to $\frac{5}{4}$, the scale factor is correct. After checking the sum of the lengths, I know my answer is correct.

Read to Succeed!

When determining the total amount of tape used, remember to add all the 10-centimeter lengths.

Course 3 • Chapter 7 Congruence and Similarity

93

Course 3 • **Chapter 7** Congruence and Similarity

171

Answers

Chapter 7 Lesson 4 Answer Keys

NAME _____ DATE _____ PERIOD _____

Lesson 5 (continued)

Use a problem-solving model to solve each problem.

1 Neema is creating a tile mosaic. The diagram shows part of her mosaic. Points *B*, *D*, and *F* lie on various sides of triangle *ACE*. Which option shows all the similar triangles in the design, and only similar triangles? 8.G.5, MP 2

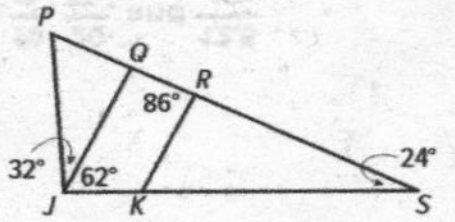

Ⓐ △AFB, △AEC
Ⓑ △AFB, △BDC
Ⓒ △AFB, △AEC, △BDC
Ⓓ △AFB, △BDC, △ABE

2 The diagram shows a municipal park formed by two triangular lots. A sidewalk is planned from point *P* to point *R* and from point *R* to point *S*. The shaded section from points *P* and *Q* has been paved. What is the remaining length in meters that needs to be paved? 8.G.5, MP 4

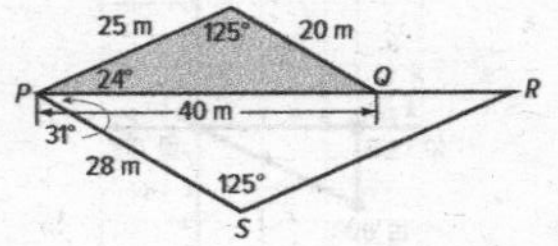

51

3 A triangular plot in a zoo is separated into regions A and B as shown in the diagram. A 10-foot-high fence, *x*, will be placed along an edge of region A, and a 12-foot-high fence, *y*, will be placed along an edge of region B. How many feet of 12-foot-high fence are needed? 8.G.5, MP 4

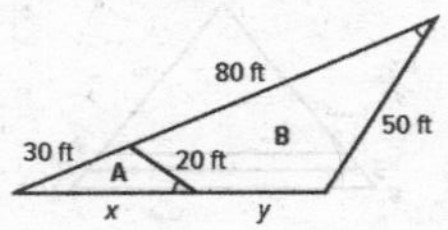

31

4 🏆 **H.O.T. Problem** The length of segment *JP* is indicated by *x*. What is the value of *x* to the nearest whole number? Justify your answer. 8.G.5, MP 3

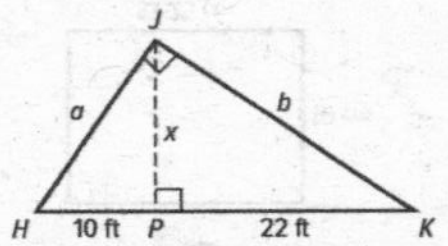

15 feet; Sample answer: Since ∠H ≅ ∠H and ∠HPI ≅ ∠HJK, △HPI ~ △HJK. Since ∠K ≅ ∠K and ∠JPK ≅ ∠HJK, △JPK ~ △HJK.

$$\frac{10}{x} = \frac{a}{b}, \frac{x}{22} = \frac{a}{b}.$$ Therefore, $\frac{10}{x} = \frac{x}{22}.$

I solved this proportion to find that

$x = \sqrt{220}$, which is between 14 and 15,

closer to 15.

Course 3 • Chapter 7 Congruence and Similarity

96

Chapter 7

NAME _____ DATE _____ PERIOD _____

Lesson 5 Multi-Step Problem Solving

Multi-Step Example

Emilio is creating designs for a stained glass window. In his design, points *Q* and *R* lie on line segment *PS* and point *K* lies on line segment *JS*. Which option shows all of the similar triangles in the design, and only similar triangles? 8.G.5, MP 2

Ⓐ △SKR, △SJQ
Ⓑ △JPQ, △SKR
Ⓒ △SKR, △SJQ, △SPJ
Ⓓ △JPQ, △SJQ, △SPJ

Use a problem-solving model to solve this problem.

1 Understand

Read the problem. Circle the information you know. Underline what the problem is asking you to find.

2 Plan

What will you need to do to solve the problem? Write your plan in steps.

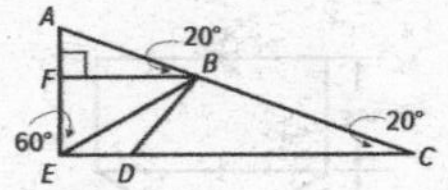

Step 1 Determine the measures of the interior angles of △SKR, △SJQ, △JPQ, and △SPJ.

Step 2 Identify all of the triangles that have equal angle measures.

3 Solve

Use your plan to solve the problem. Show your steps.

Since the sum of the interior angles of a triangle is **180°** and the sum of two supplementary angles is **180°**, ∠SKR = **62°**.

∠SRK = **94°**, and ∠JPQ = **62°**.

Since the measures of the interior angles of triangles *SKR*, *SJQ*, and *SPJ* are 24°, 94°, and 62°, the triangles are similar. So, the correct answer is **C**. Fill in that answer choice.

4 Check

How do you know your solution is accurate?

Sample answer: I traced and cut out several copies of the illustration. Then I verified my answer by placing the two smaller similar triangles inside the largest similar triangle.

> **Read to Succeed!**
> When identifying similar triangles, remember that similar triangles can have different sizes and orientations.

Course 3 • Chapter 7 Congruence and Similarity

95

NAME _____ DATE _____ PERIOD _____

Lesson 6 Multi-Step Problem Solving

Multi-Step Example

The graph shows a line and a slope triangle RST for the line. Which of the following are the coordinates of another slope triangle for the line? 8.EE.6, MP 7

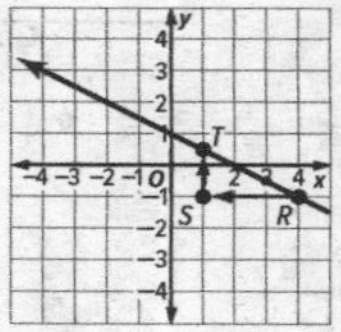

(A) $X(2, 0)$, $Y(−5, 0)$, and $Z(−5, 3)$

(B) $X(2, 1)$, $Y(−4, 1)$, and $Z(−4, 3)$

(C) $X(2, −1)$, $Y(−5, −1)$, and $Z(−5, 3)$

(D) $X(2, 0)$, $Y(−4, 0)$, and $Z(−4, 3)$

Use a problem-solving model to solve this problem.

1 Understand

Read the problem. Circle the information you know. Underline what the problem is asking you to find.

2 Plan

What will you need to do to solve the problem? Write your plan in steps.

Step 1 Graph each set of vertices. Determine which triangles have two **vertices** that lie on $\overline{RT}$.

Step 2 Determine the slopes of the triangles with two **vertices** on line $\overline{RT}$.

3 Solve

Use your plan to solve the problem. Show your steps.

The vertices of choices __A__ and __D__ form triangles with two **vertices** that lie on line $\overline{RT}$.

The slope of RT is $\frac{1}{2}$. Count units to determine that only the line XZ formed by the triangle with vertices at (__2__, __0__), (__−4__, __0__), and (__−4__, __3__) has the same slope. Fill in that answer choice __D__.

4 Check

How do you know your solution is accurate?

I used the slope formula to confirm the slopes of the lines formed by answer choices A and D.

NAME _____ DATE _____ PERIOD _____

Lesson 6 (continued)

Use a problem-solving model to solve each problem.

1 Triangle ABC is a slope triangle for the line shown in the graph. What are the coordinates of another slope triangle for the line, given that the triangle shares a vertex with triangle ABC? 8.EE.6, MP 7

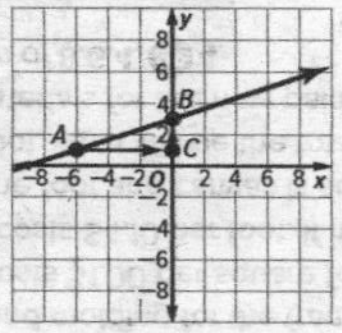

(A) $D(6, 5)$, $E(6,3)$, and A

(B) $D(6, 5)$, $E(6, 1)$, and C

(C) $D(6, 5)$, $E(6, 3)$, and B

(D) $D(6, 5)$, $E(6, 1)$, and B

2 The tables show the coordinates of two slope triangles for a line. What is the slope of the line? 8.EE.6, MP 4

Point	R	S	T
x	−3	−1	−1
y	−10	−10	−4

Point	U	V	W
x	1	2	2
y	2	2	5

3

3 H.O.T. Problem Xavier is making a wooden box frame formed by an 8-inch square and two connecting triangles. What is the total amount of wood, in inches, needed to make the frame? Explain. 8.EE.6, MP 3

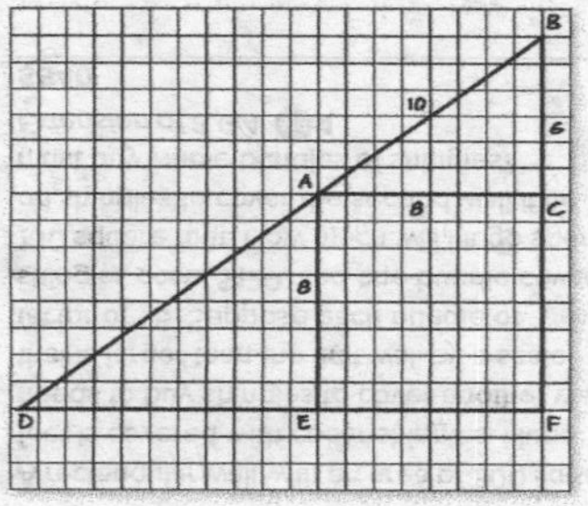

72; Sample answer: Since quadrilateral $ACFE$ is a square, $FC = EF = 8$. Triangles ABC and DAE are similar slope triangles. So, $\frac{6}{10} = \frac{8}{AD}$, $AD = 13\frac{1}{3}$. To determine DE, $\frac{BC}{AE} = \frac{AC}{DE}$. I set up and solved the proportion $\frac{6}{8} = \frac{DE}{10}$, $DE = 10\frac{2}{3}$. Then I added $6 + 10 + 4(8) + 13\frac{1}{3} + 10\frac{2}{3}$.

Answers

NAME _____ DATE _____ PERIOD _____

Lesson 7 (continued)

Use a problem-solving model to solve each problem.

1 A rectangular wall with an area of 300 square feet is covered with cedar shingles. Hugo needs to buy shingles to cover another wall that is larger than the first wall by a scale factor of 1.5. Suppose each bundle of shingles costs $120, and one bundle covers 100 square feet. How much will Hugo spend on shingles to cover the second wall if he must buy whole bundles of shingles? *Extension of 8.G.4, MP 4*

$840

2 The "T" shape is a target on a square board at a carnival game. It is formed by two rectangles that are each 40 centimeters long and 10 centimeters wide. The game operator wants to make the target smaller. He dilates the target by a scale factor of $\frac{1}{2}$ and replaces the target on the square board. What is the area of the new target? *Extension of 8.G.4, MP 4*

200 cm²

3 The diagram shown below represents a rectangular painting. The artist wants to create another painting of the same shape by dilating the rectangle by a scale factor of 1.4. She needs to buy canvas for the painting surface and molding for the frame. Suppose canvas costs $1.00 per square foot and molding costs $4.10 per foot. If molding is sold by the foot and canvas is sold by the square foot, what will be the total cost of the materials for the new painting? *Extension of 8.G.4, MP 4*

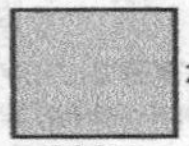

2 ft
2 ft 6 in.

$63.30

4 **H.O.T. Problem** The table provides information about three shapes and their dilated images. Which shape was dilated by the greatest scale factor? Support your answer. *Extension of 8.G.4, MP 1*

Shapes and Dilated Images
A rectangle has a width of 10 cm and an area of 200 cm². The perimeter of the dilated figure is 90 cm.
A circle has a radius of 10 cm. The area of the dilated figure is 628 cm².
A trapezoid has an area of 150 cm² and parallel side lengths of 10 cm and 20 cm. The height of the dilated figure is 20 cm.

trapezoid; Sample answer: The scale factors are $\sqrt{2}$ for the circle, 1.5 for the rectangle, 2 for the trapezoid.

NAME _____ DATE _____ PERIOD _____

Lesson 7 Multi-Step Problem Solving

Multi-Step Example

Ella is painting two walls that have the shape of the figure at the right. The first wall has an area of 720 square feet. The second wall is a dilation of the first wall with a scale factor of 1.2. One gallon of paint will cover 300 square feet. If paint costs $25.00 per gallon, how much will Ella spend to paint both walls? *Extension of 8.G.4, MP 4*

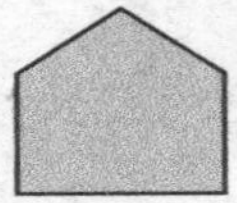

Use a problem-solving model to solve this problem.

1 Understand

Read the problem. Circle the information you know.
Underline what the problem is asking you to find.

2 Plan

What will you need to do to solve the problem? Write your plan in steps.

Step 1 Determine the total area of both walls.

Step 2 Determine the cost of the total number of gallons needed to paint both walls.

Read to Succeed!
Remember that perimeter uses linear units of measure, while area uses square units of measure.

3 Solve

Use your plan to solve the problem. Show your steps.

The area of the larger wall is __1,036.8__ square feet. So, the total
area is 720 + __1,036.8__ or __1,756.8__ square feet.

To find the number of gallons needed, divide __1,756.8__ by
__300__ and round to the nearest whole number. To find the
total cost, multiply __6__ gallons by __$25.00__ .

Ella will spend __$150__ to paint both walls.

4 Check

How do you know your solution is accurate?
Sample answer: I used estimation to check my calculations and verify
my answer.

NAME _____ DATE _____ PERIOD _____

Lesson 1 (continued)

Use a problem-solving model to solve each problem.

1 A cylindrical container of oats is shown below. Each serving of oats is 8 cubic inches. If a container of oats this size costs $2.20, what is the cost for each serving of oats? 8.G.9, MP 4

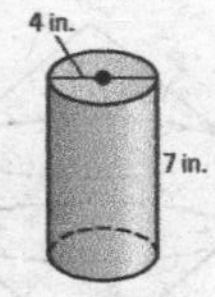

7 in.

4 in.

$0.20

2 A triangular prism has a cylindrical hole cut through it as shown below. What is the volume of the resulting solid to the nearest tenth of a cubic foot? 8.G.9, MP 4

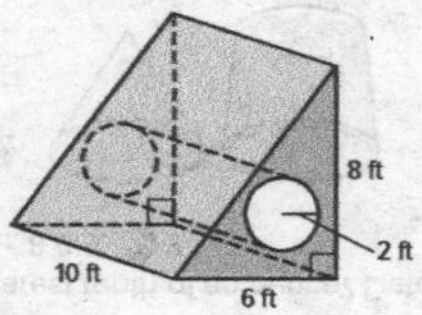

8 ft

2 ft

6 ft

10 ft

114.3 ft³

3 A cylinder-shaped glass with a base area of 7.07 square inches and a height of 6 inches weighs 1.06 ounces when empty. The glass is then filled with water to one inch from the top. If 1 cubic inch of water weighs 0.6 ounce, how many ounces does the glass of water weigh, including the weight of the glass? Round to the nearest hundredth. 8.G.9, MP 1

22.27 oz

4 H.O.T. Problem Refer to the cylinder shown below. By what factor is the volume increased if both the radius and height are doubled? Explain your answer. 8.G.9, MP 3

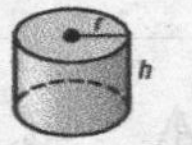

h

8; Sample answer: I substituted values for r and h in the formula $V_1 = \pi r^2 h$. Then I doubled my values for r and h and recalculated the volume. I found the new volume was eight times greater than the original volume.

NAME _____ DATE _____ PERIOD _____

Lesson 1 Multi-Step Problem Solving

Multi-Step Example

A pool with dimensions as shown is filling with water at a rate of 20 gallons per minute. About how many hours will it take to fill the pool? (Hint: 1 cubic foot ≈ 7.5 gallons) 8.G.9, MP 4

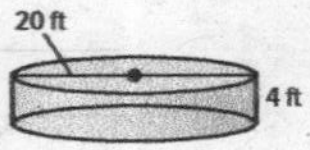

20 ft

4 ft

   Ⓐ 471   Ⓒ 31

   Ⓑ 56   Ⓓ 8

Use a problem-solving model to solve this problem.

1 Understand

Read the problem. (Circle) the information you know. Underline what the problem is asking you to find.

2 Plan

What will you need to do to solve the problem? Write your plan in steps.

Step 1   Determine the number of **gallons** of water needed to fill the pool.

Step 2   Determine the number of **hours** it will take to fill the pool.

3 Solve

Use your plan to solve the problem. Show your steps.

Replace r with **10** and h with **4** in the formula $V = \pi r^2 h$, and multiply the product by **7.5** to determine the number of gallons needed.

Divide the number of gallons by **20** to determine the number of minutes and then by **60** to determine the number of hours.

About **7.85** hours are needed to fill the pool. So, the correct answer is **D**. Fill in that answer.

4 Check

How do you know your solution is accurate?

Sample answer: Since all of the answer choices were rounded to the nearest whole number, I used 3 for pi and 8 for the number of gallons per cubic foot. Then I checked my calculations.

Read to Succeed!

Notice that the pool is filling at a rate of 20 gallons per minute, but the question asks for the number of hours needed to fill the pool.

Chapter 8

Answers

NAME _____ DATE _____ PERIOD _____

Lesson 2 (continued)

Use a problem-solving model to solve each problem.

1 What is the ratio of the volume of the smaller cone to the larger cone? 8.G.9, MP 7

A 1:3
B 1:9
C 3:1
D 9:1

3 What is the volume of the solid figure made up of two congruent cones and a cylinder as shown below? Round to the nearest whole number. 8.G.9, MP 4

1,357 cm²

2 Cone A and Cone B are shown in the figure. The volume of Cone A is 942 cm³. The volume of Cone B is $\frac{1}{4}$ the volume of Cone A. How many *times* longer is the diameter of Cone A than the diameter of Cone B? 8.G.9, MP 2

2

4 **H.O.T. Problem** A conical paper cup has a diameter of 3 inches and a height of 3 inches. A cylindrical paper cup has a radius of 1.5 inches and a height of 3 inches. Suppose both cups are filled with water. If 1 cubic inch of water weighs 0.6 ounce, how much more does the water in the cylindrical cup weigh, to the nearest tenth of an ounce? Defend your answer. 8.G.9, MP 3

8.5 oz, Sample answer:

conical cup: $V = \frac{(1.5^2)(3)\pi}{3} \approx 7.07$;

cylindrical cup: $V = (1.5^2)(3)\pi \approx 21.21$,

$21.21 - 7.07 = 14.14,\ 14.14 \times 0.6 \approx 8.5$

NAME _____ DATE _____ PERIOD _____

Lesson 2 Multi-Step Problem Solving

Chapter 8

Multi-Step Example

A movie theater offers popcorn in two sizes as shown. The cost of the smaller container is $1.00. The cost per cubic inch of the larger container is the same as the cost per cubic inch of the smaller container. What is the ratio of the cost of the smaller container to the cost of the larger container? 8.G.9, MP 4

A 1:3
B 2:3
C 3:2
D 3:1

Use a problem-solving model to solve this problem.

1 Understand

Read the problem. Circle the information you know. Underline what the problem is asking you to find.

2 Plan

What will you need to do to solve the problem? Write your plan in steps.

Step 1 Determine the **volume** of each solid.

Step 2 Determine the ratio of the cost of the **smaller** container to the **larger** container.

3 Solve

Use your plan to solve the problem. Show your steps.

Replace r with 2 and h with 6 in the formulas for the volume of a cylinder and the volume of a cone. Then determine the ratio of the volume of the cone to the volume of the cylinder. **25** cubic inches **75** cubic inches

4 Check

How do you know your solution is accurate?

Sample answer: Since the radii and heights of the solids are the same,

I know the volume of the cone is one third the volume of the cylinder.

Since each container of popcorn has the same cost per cubic unit,

I know the cost ratio is also 1:3.

> **Read to Succeed!**
> When finding the ratio, round the values for each volume to the same place value.

NAME _____ DATE _____ PERIOD _____

Lesson 3 *(continued)*

Use a problem-solving model to solve each problem.

1 The radius of a tennis table ball is 2 centimeters. Olivia is packing 30 tennis table balls in a box with a length of 24 centimeters, a width of 20 centimeters, and a height of 4 centimeters. What is the approximate volume of empty space? 8.G.9, MP 4

  Ⓐ 1,920 cm³   Ⓒ 915 cm³

  Ⓑ 1,005 cm³   Ⓓ 335 cm³

2 Trevor is creating a concrete sculpture of an ice cream cone. His sculpture consists of a hemisphere on top of a cone as shown below. Trevor needs to order a whole number of cubic yards of concrete. How many cubic yards of concrete should Trevor order so that the amount left over is minimized? 8.G.9, MP 4

4 _____

3 A spherical water tank has a 20-foot diameter and is completely filled. How many hours will it take to empty the tank at the rate of 100 gallons per minute? Round your answer to the nearest hour. (*Hint:* 1 cubic foot ≈ 7½ gallons) 8.G.9, MP 4

5 _____

4 ✎ **H.O.T. Problem** A cylinder and a sphere have the same radius, and the height of the cylinder equals that radius. The equation $V_{sphere} = k \times V_{cylinder}$ shows the relationship between the volumes of the two solids. What is the value of *k*? Justify your answer. 8.G.9, MP 3

$k = \frac{4}{3}$; Sample answer: $V_{sphere} = \frac{4}{3}\pi r^3$ and

$V_{cylinder} = \pi r^2 h = \pi r^2 r = \pi r^3$, where *r*

represents the common radius and also

the height of the cylinder. So,

$V_{sphere} = \frac{4}{3} \times V_{cylinder}$.

NAME _____ DATE _____ PERIOD _____

Lesson 3 Multi-Step Problem Solving

Multi-Step Example

Brad is packing 3 bouncy balls in a cylindrical container. The radius of each bouncy ball is 10 centimeters. The cylinder has a base area of 314 square centimeters and a height of 65 centimeters. What is the volume of empty space in the container rounded to the nearest whole number? 8.G.9, MP 4

  Ⓐ 4,189 cm³   Ⓒ 12,566 cm³

  Ⓑ 7,844 cm³   Ⓓ 20,410 cm³

Use a problem-solving model to solve this problem.

1 Understand

Read the problem. Circle the information you know. Underline what the problem is asking you to find.

2 Plan

What will you need to do to solve the problem? Write your plan in steps.

Step 1   Determine the volumes of the __container__ and the three __bouncy balls__ .

Step 2   __Subtract__ to find the volume of __empty space__ .

3 Solve

Use your plan to solve the problem. Show your steps.

The volume of the container is __20,410__ cubic centimeters, and the volume of the three bouncy balls is about __12,566__ cubic centimeters.

The volume of the empty space is __20,410__ – __12,566__ , or __7,844__ cubic centimeters. The correct answer is __B__ .

4 Check

How do you know your solution is accurate?

Sample answer: Answer choice A is the volume of one sphere, C is the volume of 3 spheres, and D is the volume of the cylindrical container.

Read to Succeed!

Remember to multiply the value you find for the volume of one bouncy ball by 3 since Brad is packing 3 bouncy balls.

Answers

NAME _____ DATE _____ PERIOD _____

Lesson 4 Multi-Step Problem Solving

Multi-Step Example

To the nearest whole square centimeter, what is the total surface area of all three cylinders described in the table?
Extension of 8.G.9, MP 4

Cylinder	Diameter (cm)	Height (cm)
A	6	5
B	4	2
C	12	3

Use a problem-solving model to solve this problem.

1 Understand
Read the problem. Circle the information you know. Underline what the problem is asking you to find.

2 Plan
What will you need to do to solve the problem? Write your plan in steps.

Step 1 Determine the surface area of each cylinder.

Step 2 Determine the total surface area of all three cylinders.

Read to Succeed!
Remember to use the radius when determining the surface area of each cylinder.

3 Solve
Use your plan to solve the problem. Show your steps.

Use the formula $S = 2\pi rh + 2\pi r^2$ determine the surface area for each cylinder: $S_{\text{Cylinder A}} \approx 150.8$ cm², $S_{\text{Cylinder B}} \approx 50.3$ cm², $S_{\text{Cylinder C}} \approx 339.3$ cm².

So, the total surface area of all three cylinders is about 540 square centimeters.

4 Check
How do you know your solution is accurate?

I used 3 for pi to recalculate my surface area values and check my answer.

NAME _____ DATE _____ PERIOD _____

Lesson 4 (continued)

Use a problem-solving model to solve each problem.

1 To the nearest whole square foot, what is the total surface area of all three cylinders described in the table below?
Extension of 8.G.9, MP 4

Cylinder	Height (ft)	Radius (ft)
R	2.5	1
S	10	4
T	3	9

1,052

2 A painter paints the two circular bases of figure A, and paints just the lateral area of figure B. How many square yards are painted in all? Round your answer to the nearest whole square yard.
Extension of 8.G.9, MP 4

6.5 yd, A, 4 yd, B, 2.5 yd, 6.5 yd

203

3 Miguel is wrapping cylindrical cans with colored paper for an art project. Two cylinders have a height of 20 inches and diameter of 16 inches. One cylinder has a height of 10 inches and diameter of 6 inches. How much colored paper will Miguel need to wrap all three cans? Round your answer to the nearest whole square inch.
Extension of 8.G.9, MP 4

3,060 in²

4 H.O.T. Problem If all the exposed surfaces of the figure are painted, including the bottom of the figure, how many square inches will be painted? Justify your response. Round your answer to the nearest whole square inch.
Extension of 8.G.9, MP 4

3 in., 8 in., 5 in., 4 in.

729 in²; Sample answer: The surface areas of the larger and smaller cylinders are about 653 in² and 132 in², respectively. Since they share a surface of about 28 in², 653 + 132 − 28 − 28 or approximately 729 in² will be painted.

NAME _____ DATE _____ PERIOD _____

Lesson 5 Multi-Step Problem Solving

Multi-Step Example

Campers would like to make a cone-shaped tent with a covered floor with the dimensions shown. How much fabric would be used to cover the tent and the floor? (Use 3.14 for π.) Extension of 8.G.9, MP 4

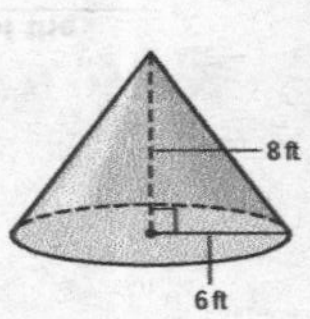

[figure: cone, 8 ft, 6 ft]

Use a problem-solving model to solve this problem.

1 Understand

Read the problem. Circle the information you know. Underline what the problem is asking you to find.

2 Plan

What will you need to do to solve the problem? Write your plan in steps.

Step 1 Use the _Pythagorean theorem_ to find the _slant height_ of the cone.

Step 2 Use the _slant height_ to find the _surface area_ of the tent.

3 Solve

Use your plan to solve the problem. Show your steps.

Using the _Pythagorean theorem_, you find the _slant height_ is 10 feet. By using the formula for the surface area of a cone $S.A. = \pi r \ell + \pi r^2$, you find that the campers need _301.44 ft²_ of fabric to cover the tent.

4 Check

How do you know your solution is accurate?

Sample answer: I know I need the slant height to find the surface area. I have to find the slant height by using the Pythagorean theorem. I must apply the formula for the surface area because the fabric needs to cover the floor of the tent. If I substitute all the values correctly into the formulas, my answer should be correct.

Course 3 • Chapter 8 Volume and Surface Area   109

NAME _____ DATE _____ PERIOD _____

Lesson 5 (continued)

Use a problem-solving model to solve each problem.

1 A party planner wants to make her own party hats. How much paper will it take to make 6 party hats? (Use 3.14 for π.) Extension of 8.G.9, MP 4

[figure: cone, 12 cm, 5 cm]

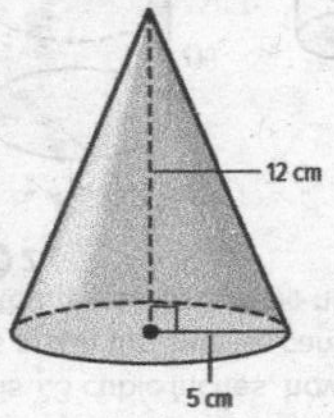

Ⓐ 1,130.4 cm²
Ⓑ 1,224.6 cm²
Ⓒ 1,601.4 cm²
Ⓓ 1,695.6 cm²

2 A cone has a surface area of 75.36 square centimeters and a radius of 3 centimeters. What is the height of the cone? (Use 3.14 for π.) Extension of 8.G.9, MP 4

The height of the cone is 4 cm.

3 A cone has a surface area of 113.04 square centimeters and a diameter that is two thirds the length of the slant height. What is the slant height of the cone? (Use 3.14 for π.) Extension of 8.G.9, MP 1

9 cm

4 H.O.T. Problem Jamal is finding the lateral area of a waffle cone with a height of 24 centimeters and radius of 10 centimeters. Are the steps he used to solve the problem correct? (He used 3.14 for π.) Explain your answer.

$L.A. = (24)(10)\pi$
$L.A. \approx 753.6 \text{ cm}^2$

Extension of 8.G.9, MP 3

Sample answer: No. He used the height of the cone. You have to find the slant height to find the lateral area. He should use the Pythagorean theorem first to find the slant height.

Course 3 • Chapter 8 Volume and Surface Area   110

Answers

NAME _____ DATE _____ PERIOD _____

Lesson 6 Multi-Step Problem Solving

Multi-Step Example

Mika is making dollhouse furniture out of cardboard to match the actual furniture in his house. His television has a total surface area of 14 square feet. It sits on a cube-shaped chest with sides measuring 3 feet. Using a scale factor of $\frac{1}{10}$, how many square inches of cardboard will Mika use for the dollhouse's television and chest? 8.G.9, MP 4

Ⓐ 8.3   Ⓒ 9.792

Ⓑ 47.2   Ⓓ 979.2

Use a problem-solving model to solve this problem.

① Understand

Read the problem. (Circle) the information you know. Underline what the problem is asking you to find.

② Plan

What will you need to do to solve the problem? Write your plan in steps.

Step 1 Determine the __total surface area__ of the __actual__ television and chest in square inches.

Step 2 Use the __scale factor__ to determine the __total surface area__ of the __dollhouse__ television and chest.

③ Solve

Use your plan to solve the problem. Show your steps.
The total surface area of the actual television and chest is

$14 + 6 \left(3\right)^2$ or __68__ square feet, or __9,792__ square inches.

The total surface area of the dollhouse television and chest is

$9,792 \left(\frac{1}{10}\right)^2$ or __97.92__ square inches. So, the correct

answer is __C__. Fill in that answer choice.

Read to Succeed!
Remember to convert the total surface area of the actual items to square inches.

④ Check

How do you know your solution is accurate?
Sample answer: When a figure is dilated by a scale factor, the area of the dilated figure is determined by multiplying the original area by the square of the scale factor.

NAME _____ DATE _____ PERIOD _____

Lesson 6 (continued)

Use a problem-solving model to solve each problem.

1 Carlos makes geometrical artworks out of sheet metal for public parks. The dimensions of a full-size sculpture will be 6 times the dimensions of the model shown below. He will not use any metal for the bottom base of the cylinder. How many square feet of sheet metal will Carlos use for the full-size sculpture? 8.G.9, MP 4

Ⓐ 172.8   Ⓒ 772.8

Ⓑ 193.2   Ⓓ 27,820.8

2 Bethany is filling two conical containers with water. The larger container has dimensions twice those of the smaller container. If there is 0.6 fluid ounce per cubic inch of water, how many ounces of water are in the larger container? Round your answer to the nearest whole number. 8.G.9, MP 4

__34__

3 Kurt made burrito filling for a scout troop and now he is making the same recipe at home. At home, he is using a can of beans that has dimensions one-half the dimensions of the can of beans he used for the troop. If a serving is 7.3 cubic inches, how many servings are in the smaller can? Round your answer to the nearest whole number. 8.G.9, MP 2

__3__

4 ✎ **H.O.T. Problem** Trisha made a giant cereal box for the scenery of a play about nutrition. The original box is 30 centimeters long, 5 centimeters wide, and 20 centimeters tall. She enlarged the box by a scale factor of 8. Trisha says that the surface area of the giant box is 870,400 cm². Explain her mistake and show the correct calculations. 8.G.9, MP 3

Sample answer: Trisha cubed the scale factor instead of squaring it. The surface area of the original box = 1,700 cm²;

$8^2 = 64$, $1,700(64) = 108,800$ cm²

NAME _____ DATE _____ PERIOD _____

Lesson 1 Multi-Step Problem Solving

Chapter 9

Multi-Step Example

The table shows the 40-yard dash times in seconds for athletes at varying weights in pounds. Which describes the association between speed and weight as shown by a scatter plot of the data? 8.SP1, MP 7

Speed (s)	Weight (lb)
4.24	178
4.28	176
4.29	155
4.29	186
4.24	197
4.29	188
4.29	193
4.28	181
4.29	184
4.29	200

(A) negative linear association
(B) positive linear association
(C) non-linear association
(D) no association

Use a problem-solving model to solve this problem.

1 Understand
Read the problem. Circle the information you know. Underline what the problem is asking you to find.

2 Plan
What will you need to do to solve the problem? Write your plan in steps.
Step 1 Construct a **scatterplot** of the data on a separate sheet of grid paper.
Step 2 Determine the **association**, if any, among the observed data.

3 Solve
Use your plan to solve the problem. Show your steps.
The graph shows that weights for specific speeds vary greatly. For example, the weights for a speed of 4.29 seconds range from 155 to 200. Since there is no obvious **pattern**, the correct answer is D.

Sample answer:

Read to Succeed!
A graph's scales can change its appearance. Choose scales for the x- and y-axes that will accurately show relationships among sets of data.

4 Check
How do you know your solution is accurate?
Sample answer: I also checked the weights for a speed of 4.24 seconds, 178 and 197 pounds. There does not appear to be an association among these data either.

Course 3 • Chapter 9 Scatter Plots and Data Analysis
113

NAME _____ DATE _____ PERIOD _____

Lesson 1 (continued)

Use a problem-solving model to solve each problem.

1 The tables below show the average monthly temperatures in degrees Fahrenheit for a certain city for one year, with January representing month 1 and December representing month 12. Which describes the association among the data? 8.SP1, MP 7

Month	1	2	3	4	5	6
°F	31	37	39	49	60	74

Month	7	8	9	10	11	12
°F	78	80	73	58	50	35

(A) negative linear association
(B) positive linear association
(C) non-linear association
(D) no association

2 The table shows the number of gallons in thousands of water in a swimming pool after each hour. What conjecture can be made from the data about the number of gallons of water in the pool after 9 hours? 8.F.5, MP 2

Time (h)	Water (1,000 gal)
1	27
2	24
3	22
4	18
5	15
6	13

Sample answer: between 3,000 and 5,000 gallons.

3 H.O.T. Problem The table shows Dario's savings for seven months. Construct a scatterplot of the data. Analyze the scatterplot for patterns of association, outliers, and clusters. If a relationship exists, make a conjecture about how much money Dario will have saved after 10 months. 8.SP1, MP 7

Dario's Savings

Month	1	2	3	4	5	6	7
Total Savings (dollars)	20	45	75	78	80	121	145

See students' work for graphs. Sample answer: The data have a positive association and a cluster between Weeks 3–5 at around 80. There are no outliers. Dario will have saved $195 after 10 months.

Course 3 • Chapter 9 Scatter Plots and Data Analysis
114

Answers

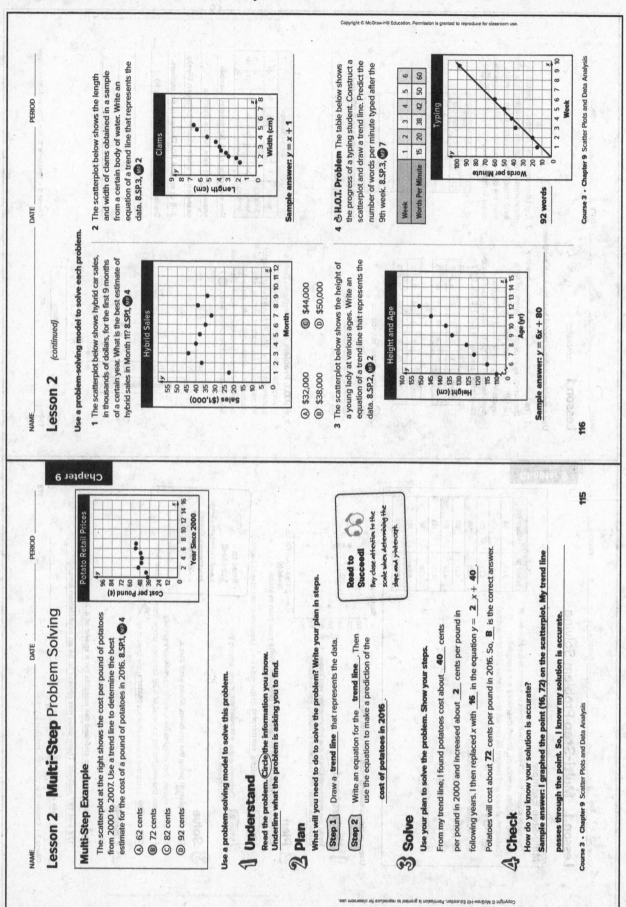

NAME _____ DATE _____ PERIOD _____

Lesson 2 Multi-Step Problem Solving

Multi-Step Example

The scatterplot at the right shows the cost per pound of potatoes from 2000 to 2007. Use a trend line to determine the best estimate for the cost of a pound of potatoes in 2016. 8.SP.1, MP 4

Ⓐ 62 cents
Ⓑ 72 cents
Ⓒ 82 cents
Ⓓ 92 cents

Potato Retail Prices

Use a problem-solving model to solve this problem.

1 Understand

Read the problem. Circle the information you know.
Underline what the problem is asking you to find.

2 Plan

What will you need to do to solve the problem? Write your plan in steps.

Step 1 Draw a __trend line__. Then

Step 2 Write an equation for the __trend line__. Then use the equation to make a prediction of the __cost of potatoes in 2016__.

3 Solve

Use your plan to solve the problem. Show your steps.

From my trend line, I found potatoes cost about __40__ cents per pound in 2000 and increased about __2__ cents per pound in following years. I then replaced x with __16__ in the equation y = __2__ x + __40__.

Potatoes will cost about __72__ cents per pound in 2016. So, __B__ is the correct answer.

4 Check

How do you know your solution is accurate?
Sample answer: I graphed the point (16, 72) on the scatterplot. My trend line passes through the point. So, I know my solution is accurate.

Read to Succeed!
Pay close attention to the scale when determining the slope and y-intercept.

Chapter 9

115

NAME _____ DATE _____ PERIOD _____

Lesson 2 *(continued)*

Use a problem-solving model to solve each problem.

1 The scatterplot below shows hybrid car sales, in thousands of dollars, for the first 9 months of a certain year. What is the best estimate of hybrid sales in Month 11? 8.SP.1, MP 4

Hybrid Sales

Ⓐ $32,000   Ⓒ $44,000
Ⓑ $38,000   Ⓓ $50,000

2 The scatterplot below shows the length and width of clams obtained in a sample from a certain body of water. Write an equation of a trend line that represents the data. 8.SP.3, MP 2

Clams

Sample answer: y = x + 1

3 The scatterplot below shows the height of a young lady at various ages. Write an equation of a trend line that represents the data. 8.SP.2, MP 2

Height and Age

Sample answer: y = 6x + 80

4 🖐 **H.O.T. Problem** The table below shows the progress of a typing student. Construct a scatterplot and draw a trend line. Predict the number of words per minute typed after the 9th week. 8.SP.3, MP 7

Week	1	2	3	4	5	6
Words Per Minute	15	20	38	42	50	60

Typing

92 words

116

NAME _____ DATE _____ PERIOD _____

Lesson 3 Multi-Step Problem Solving

Multi-Step Example

A group of males and females were surveyed about what color of car they owned. The data are shown in the two-way table. Which statement is true about males and females who own a black car? 8.SP.4, MP 7

Car Color	Males	Females
Red	14	15
Black	12	12
White	15	12

Ⓐ The same percentage of males and females own black cars.

Ⓑ A larger percentage of males than females own black cars.

Ⓒ A larger percentage of females than males own black cars.

Ⓓ There is not enough information in this table to make a comparison.

Use a problem-solving model to solve this problem.

1 Understand

Read the problem. Circle the information you know.
Underline what the problem is asking you to find.

Read to Succeed!

A two-way table shows data of one sample group as it relates to two different categories.

2 Plan

What will you need to do to solve the problem? Write your plan in steps.

Step 1 Find the total number of __males__ and the total number of __females__.

Step 2 Use the totals to find the relative frequencies of __males and females__ who own black cars.

Step 3 Compare the percentages and choose the correct statement.

3 Solve

Use your plan to solve the problem. Show your steps.

Total males: __41__   Total females: __39__

The __relative frequency__ of a male who owns a black car is __0.29__, and the __relative frequency__ of a female who owns a black car is __0.31__.

The percentage of females who own black cars is __greater__ than the percentage of males who own black cars.

The correct answer is __C__. Fill in that answer choice.

4 Check

How do you know your solution is accurate?

Sample answer: Since there are the same number of males and females who own a black car and there are more total males, I know that the percentage of females should be greater.

NAME _____ DATE _____ PERIOD _____

Lesson 3 (continued)

Use a problem-solving model to solve each problem.

1 A group of 21-year-olds were surveyed about whether they live with their parents and if they are in college. The results are shown in the two-way table. Which statement is true about the 21-year-olds? 8.SP.4, MP 7

	Attends College	Does Not Attend College
Lives with Parents	30	30
Does Not Live with Parents	55	60

Ⓐ The percentage of students who attend college is the same for those who do and do not live at home.

Ⓑ A larger percentage of those who attend college live with their parents than those who do not attend college.

Ⓒ A larger percentage of those who do not attend college live with their parents than those who do attend college.

Ⓓ There is not enough information in this table to make a comparison.

2 There are 203 male and 175 female students at Nathan Middle School. A survey showed that 117 males and 97 females ride the bus. What is the difference between the relative frequency of males who ride the bus and the relative frequency of females who do not ride the bus, rounded to the nearest hundredth? 8.SP.4, MP 1

	Rides Bus	Does Not Ride Bus	Total
Males	117	86	203
Females	97	78	175
Total	214	164	378

__0.13__

3 Martin surveyed 150 tenth-grade students to find out if they have a part-time job. There are 94 students who have a part-time job, including 57 honor roll students. Half of the students who do not have a job are on the honor roll. Complete the two-way table. What is the relative frequency of an honor roll student with no job rounded to the nearest hundredth? 8.SP.4, MP 2

	Honor Roll	No Honor Roll	Total
Job	57	37	94
No Job	28	28	56
Total	85	65	150

__0.33__

4 ⚙ H.O.T. Problem Grace is interpreting survey data about people who own a truck. Out of 100 females surveyed, 37 own a truck. Grace makes the statement that of the people who own a truck, 37% are female. Is her statement accurate? Why or why not? 8.SP.4, MP 3

Sample answer: No; Grace should have said 37% of the females surveyed own a truck.

NAME _____ DATE _____ PERIOD _____

Lesson 4 Multi-Step Problem Solving

Multi-Step Example

The box plot shows the number of books read by students during the summer. How much greater is the range than the interquartile range? *Preparation for S.ID.1,* MP 4

Summer Reading

```
   4  6  8  10  12  14  16  18  20  22
```

Use a problem-solving model to solve this problem.

1 Understand

Read the problem. (Circle) the information you know.
Underline what the problem is asking you to find.

2 Plan

What will you need to do to solve the problem? Write your plan in steps.

Step 1 Use the box plot to determine the **difference** between the range and interquartile range.

Step 2 **Subtract** the lesser value from the greater value.

3 Solve

Use your plan to solve the problem. Show your steps.

The range is __20__ – __5__, or __15__. The interquartile range is __14__ – __8__, or __6__. The range is __15__ – __6__ or __9__ units greater.

The answer is __9__.

4 Check

How do you know your solution is accurate?

Sample answer: I used the box plot to count units to verify my range and interquartile range values. Then I added 6 and 9 to check my subtraction.

> **Read to Succeed!**
> Remember the range is the difference between the maximum and minimum values and the interquartile range is the difference between the third and first quartiles.

NAME _____ DATE _____ PERIOD _____

Lesson 4 *(continued)*

Use a problem-solving model to solve each problem.

1 The heights of the girls on a basketball team are shown in the table below. How many inches greater is the range than the interquartile range? *Preparation for S.ID.1,* MP 4

Heights (in.)

65	70	66	73	67
71	65	68	70	69

4

2 The table below shows the amount of time that an eighth grader spent exercising. Which is greater: the mean or median? How much greater? *Preparation for S.ID.1,* MP 4

Exercise Times (min)

63	58	55	67
75	70	70	60

mean; 2 min

3 A player's score in a golf tournament is determined by the number of total strokes needed to play a golf course over four days. The table below shows six players' scores at a recent tournament. How much closer is the mode to the median than to the mean? *Preparation for S.ID.1,* MP 4

Golf Scores

267	270	265
273	275	267

1 stroke

4 🖐 **H.O.T. Problem** The table below shows the scores of a student on recent science tests. Construct a box plot of the data. What percent of the data is between 81 and 86? Explain. *Preparation for S.ID.1,* MP 3

Science Test Scores

80	81	84	87	86	86

```
78 79 80 81 82 83 84 85 86 87 88 89
```

50%; Sample answer: The interquartile range represents 50% of the data. Since 81 is the lower quartile and 86 is the upper quartile, the data between 81 and 86 is 50% of the data.

NAME _____ DATE _____ PERIOD _____

Lesson 5 Multi-Step Problem Solving

Multi-Step Example

The table shows the total points scored in men's and women's basketball games. The men's scores have a standard deviation of 15.1, and the women's scores have a standard deviation of 7.9. Make a comparison of the variation between the data sets, and use the standard deviations to support your answer. *Preparation for S.ID.4, MP 3*

Women	57	69	73	79	62	65	59	54
Men	76	62	103	85	75	97	110	80

Read to Succeed!
The mean absolute deviation is the average distance of each value from the mean.

Use a problem-solving model to solve this problem.

1 Understand

Read the problem. (Circle) the information you know. Underline what the problem is asking you to find.

2 Plan

What will you need to do to solve the problem? Write your plan in steps.

Step 1 Find the mean absolute deviation __men's__ scores and mean absolute deviation of the __women's__ scores.

Step 2 Compare the __variations__ of the scores and use the __standard deviations__ to support your comparison.

3 Solve

Use your plan to solve the problem. Show your steps.

The mean absolute deviation of the __men's__ scores is __13__ and of the __women's__ scores is __6.75__. The __men's__ scores have a greater variation than the __women's__ scores.

The __standard deviations__ support this because the majority of the scores for the men's team are between __70.9 and 101.1__ and the majority of the scores of the women's team are between __56.85 and 72.65__.

4 Check

How do you know your solution is accurate?

Sample answer: The men's mean absolute deviation is greater, so their scores have a greater variation. After applying the standard deviation, I know that the men's score have a greater range of variability and my answer is supported.

NAME _____ DATE _____ PERIOD _____

Lesson 5 *(continued)*

Use a problem-solving model to solve each problem.

1 The table shows the lengths of ribbons used in different craft projects. The standard deviation of the lengths is 2.5 inches. If the mean of the data is rounded to the nearest tenth, which statement describes the data values that are within one standard deviation of the mean? *Preparation for S.ID.4, MP 3*

Length of Ribbons (in.)			
7	5	6	10
10	7	9	3
9	11	12	7

Ⓐ The mean absolute variation is greater than the standard deviation.

Ⓑ The majority of the lengths will be shorter than 10.5 inches.

Ⓒ The majority of the lengths will be longer than 5.5 inches.

Ⓓ The majority of the lengths will be between 5.5 inches and 10.5 inches.

2 The standard deviation of test scores is 13.5. What are the test scores within two standard deviations of the mean? Round to the nearest tenth if necessary. *Preparation for S.ID.4, MP 2*

Test Scores			
79	63	59	86
88	92	100	53
72	76	70	69

Sample answer: Test scores within two standard deviations are between 48.6 and 102.6.

3 The speeds of cars ticketed in a school zone are listed in the table. What is the difference between the standard deviation of 4.85 and the mean absolute deviation of the data? *Preparation for S.ID.4, MP 2*

Speeds of Cars (mi/h)			
38	42	39	45
30	37	43	46

0.85

4 **H.O.T. Problem** Create a data set of 5 numbers with a range of 50. What is the mean absolute deviation? Will every data set with a range of 50 have the same mean absolute deviation? Why or why not? *Preparation for S.ID.4, MP 3*

Sample answer: 10, 25, 40, 55, 60; 16.4;

No, because there are many different numbers with a range of 50.

Answers

NAME _____ DATE _____ PERIOD _____

Lesson 6 *(continued)*

Use a problem-solving model to solve each problem.

1 The line plot shows scores for the first of two quizzes. From Quiz 1 to Quiz 2, the number of scores in the 70s decreased by 50% and the number of scores in the 80s increased by 100%. Which option shows the best measures of center and spread for Quiz 2 data? *Preparation for S.ID.2,* **MP 1**

```
     ×
     ×         ×
×    ×    ×    ×
×    ×    ×    ×    ×
├────┼────┼────┼────┼
60   70   80   90   100
```

Ⓐ median = 75, interquartile range = 20
Ⓑ median = 80, interquartile range = 20
Ⓒ mean = 78, mean average deviation = 8
Ⓓ mean = 80, mean average deviation = 8

3 Marisol recorded these low temperatures, in degrees Celsius, in her city on 10 consecutive days: 3, 2, 2, 1, −1, 1, 2, 2, 3, 5. What measure of spread should Marisol use for the data? What is the measure of spread? *Preparation for S.ID.2,* **MP 2**

mean absolute deviation; 1

2 Lina participated in a flying disc game. The ages of the players are shown below. What measure of spread should Lina use for the data? What is that number? *Preparation for S.ID.2,* **MP 2**

Players' Ages				
23	19	30	23	16
27	23	19	23	27

mean absolute deviation; 3

4 🔷 **H.O.T. Problem** Each test score shown in the histogram below is a multiple of 5. In each interval, $\frac{2}{3}$ of the scores are multiples of 10. What are the measures of center and spread? Defend your answers. *Preparation for S.ID.2,* **MP 3**

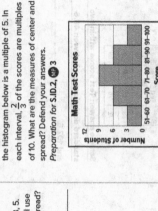

Math Test Scores

median = 80, IQR = 20; Sample answer:
I used the median and IQR; I determined
$Q_1 = 70$, the median = $Q_2 = 80$, $Q_3 = 90$,
and IQR = $Q_3 − Q_1 = 90 − 70 = 20$.

124

NAME _____ DATE _____ PERIOD _____

Lesson 6 Multi-Step Problem Solving

Multi-Step Example

From Week 1 to Week 2, the number of band members who practiced 3 hours increased by 75% and the number who practiced 4 hours decreased by 50%. Which of the following shows the best measures of center and spread for Week 2 data? *Preparation for S.ID.2,* **MP 1**

Band Members' Practice Times

Ⓐ median = 3.5, interquartile range = 2
Ⓑ median = 4, interquartile range = 2
Ⓒ mean = 3.85, mean average deviation = 1
Ⓓ mean = 4, mean average deviation = 1

Use a problem-solving model to solve this problem.

1 Understand

Read the problem. Circle the information you know. Underline what the problem is asking you to find.

2 Plan

What will you need to do to solve the problem? Write your plan in steps.

Step 1 Use the given **percentages** to construct the **Week 2** graph.

Step 2 Determine which measure of center and spread to use based on the **shape** of the **Week 2** graph.

3 Solve

Use your plan to solve the problem. Show your steps.

Construct the **Week 2** graph. Since the graph is not symmetric, the **median** will describe the center and the **interquartile range** will describe the spread.

Since the **median** is **3.5** and the **interquartile range** is **2**, the correct answer is **A**.

4 Check

How do you know your solution is accurate?

Sample answer: I confirmed which measure of center and spread to use.

Then I checked my median and interquartile range values.

Read to Succeed!

If the data distribution is symmetric, use the mean to describe the center and the mean absolute deviation to describe the spread.

If the data distribution is not symmetric, use the median to describe the center and the interquartile range to describe the spread.

123

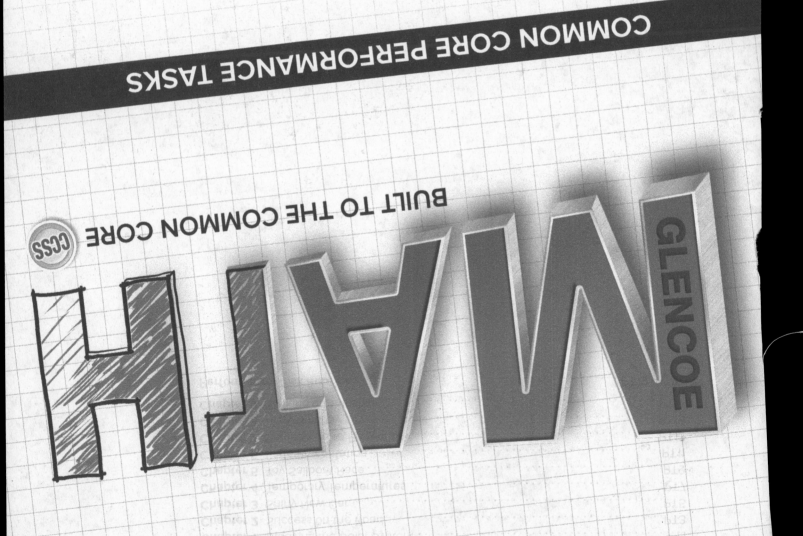

GLENCOE

MATH

CCSS

BUILT TO THE COMMON CORE

COMMON CORE PERFORMANCE TASKS

AUTHORS
Carter • Cuevas • Day • Malloy
Kersaint • Reynosa • Silbey • Vielhaber

Mc
Graw
Hill
Education

Bothell, WA • Chicago, IL • Columbus, OH • New York, NY

Contents

Performance Tasks

Performance Task

Studying the Solar System

Adie is analyzing data on a cluster of asteroids. The asteroids align to form a single line with respect to the largest asteroid in the cluster. The table shows the data for the distance of each asteroid from asteroid A. (*Note:* A negative distance refers to positions left of asteroid A.)

Asteroid	A	B	C	D	E	F
Distance from A (10^8 km)	0	2,354	-7.5×10^5	3×10^{17}	120×10^{16}	34×10^{16}
Radius (km)	8^3	3^5	2^{-3}	11^2	1	4^4
Mass (10^{15} kg)	870,000	20,000	0.0003	1,500	0.004	300,000

Write your answers on another piece of paper. Show all your work to receive full credit.

Part A
Using asteroid A as the reference point, write the order of the asteroids from left to right. Explain your reasoning.

Part B
How many times farther away is asteroid E from asteroid A compared to asteroid D?

Performance Task (continued)

Next Adie wants to study the volumes of the asteroids. She estimates that the asteroids are relatively spherical in shape. The volume of a sphere is equal to $\frac{4}{3}\pi r^3$.

Part C

Write an expression in terms of π for the volumes of the asteroids with the largest and smallest radii by assuming they are both spherical. Use this information to determine approximately how many times greater the volume of the largest asteroid is than the smallest asteroid.

Part D

Adie notices some misplaced data for an additional asteroid. The volume of this asteroid is 114 cubic kilometers. Adie claims that the asteroid has a greater volume than all of the other asteroids. Use the radii of the asteroids to support or deny her claim.

Performance Task (continued)

Chapter 2

Success on the Road

Part D

A city is looking at toll roads as a way to increase its revenue, and the mayor is holding a meeting to present an overview of the forthcoming changes.

Write your answers on another piece of paper. Show all your work to receive full credit.

Part A

The mayor announces that there will be a toll to cover the cost of a new road project. It will cost a driver $0.35 plus $0.01 per mile traveled on the new road. How much would it cost a driver to travel 10 miles on the new road? Write an equation to solve.

Part B

On average, there are $(1 + 3x)$ tickets given to cars on roads going north and $(4(0.5 + 0.75x) - 1)$ tickets given to cars on roads going south, where x is the average number of cars that pass through a certain toll booth every minute. How many different solutions are possible if there are an equal number of tickets given to cars on roads going north and south?

There are $(2 + 3x)$ tickets given to cars on roads going west and $(1 + 3x)$ tickets given to cars on roads going east. How many different solutions are possible if there are an equal number of tickets given to cars on roads going east and west?

Part C

The mayor also announces an initiative to try different rates at the toll booth and comes up with the following rates, where x is the number of cars that pass through the toll booth per minute:

Rate 1: $4 - 3x + 2 - 6 + 2x - 4 = -3x$

Rate 2: $\frac{2}{3} = \frac{4x}{16}$

Rate 3: $2(x - 4) + 2x + \frac{1}{2}(2x + 3) - \frac{5}{2} = 2 - (3x + 2) - x$

Which rate allows the fewest number of cars per minute?

Performance Task (continued)

Part D

The mayor wants to bring in $10,000 of extra revenue from the toll booths. Booth A has brought in $2,000; Booths B and C have brought in $1,250 each. Unfortunately, Booth D was robbed and lost $895. Write a linear equation explaining this scenario, where x is the remaining amount required to reach the goal of $10,000. Solve your linear equation.

Part E

The mayor is comparing multiple methods of creating income that include the following, where x is the amount of days that the method has been in effect:

Toll booth: $5x + 25$

Speeding tickets: $7x - 3(0.25x - 15.5)$

Car registration tax: $\sqrt{3}\left(\dfrac{x}{\sqrt{3}} - \sqrt{3}\right) + \dfrac{3}{2}$

If the unit of these methods is in dollars, what is the total combined amount of income generated by the three methods after two weeks?

Which of the three methods generates income the fastest? Explain.

Chapter 3

Performance Task (continued)

Shiny New Car

Diangelo is a test car driver. He is testing a new car. He is curious about its acceleration and braking capabilities, so he decides to do a few trial tests. The salesman claimed that the car would go from a speed of "0 to 100 in 60 seconds flat."

Diangelo takes the new car to a racetrack and performs a few trial runs to test the car's acceleration. The times and speeds of three trials are recorded in the following tables.

Trial 1

Time (s)	Speed (mph)
5	5
10	10
15	15
20	20

Trial 2

Time (s)	Speed (mph)
0	0
12	20
24	40
36	60

Trial 3

Time (s)	Speed (mph)
0	0
15	15
30	
45	60

Write your answers on another piece of paper. Show all your work to receive full credit.

Part A

For the third trial, Diangelo's stopwatch wasn't working correctly, but he happened to look at his speedometer after 45 seconds and noted that he was traveling 60 miles per hour. Assuming that Diangelo's acceleration was constant, fill in the missing values in the table.

Part B

Draw a graph for Trials 1, 2, and 3 in which the x-axis represents time in seconds and the y-axis represents speed in miles per hour. What do the slopes of these functions represent? During which trial does Diangelo accelerate fastest? Explain your answer.

Part C

Is there any time, x > 0, when Diangelo's speeds and times are the same for two or more of the trials? Justify your conclusion.

NAME _____   DATE _____   PERIOD _____

Performance Task (continued)   POINTS _____

Diangelo wants to test out the car's brakes, so he decelerates as shown in the graph.

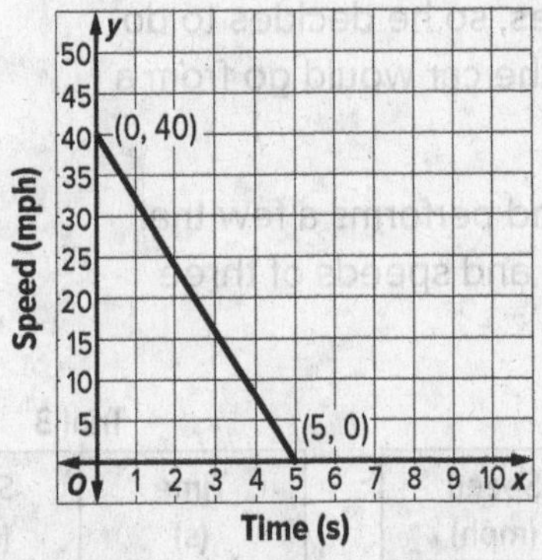

Part D
Write a slope equation in the form $y = mx + b$ for this graph. Assuming this had been a constant rate of deceleration, how fast was Diangelo traveling 4 seconds prior to the start of this trial? Explain your answer.

Part E
If the car travels at $y = x^2$, where y is the speed in miles per hour and x is the time in seconds, how fast would the car be traveling at 0, 1, 2, 3, and 4 seconds? Graph this function using these points and determine if it is linear or nonlinear. Discuss why it is linear or non-linear.

Performance Task (continued)

Chapter 4

Temporary Temperatures

Sasha is measuring temperatures in her area and recording the data for a science experiment. She wants to follow weather patterns to track the rate at which temperatures increase and decrease.

Time (P.M.)	Monday (°C)	Tuesday (°F)	Wednesday (°F)
1:00	10.0	40	30
2:00	12.8	42	36
3:00	15.6	44	40
4:00	18.3	46	42
5:00	21.1	48	43

Write your answers on another piece of paper. Show all your work to receive full credit.

Part A

On Monday, Sasha records several temperatures in degrees Celsius before she realizes that she wanted them in degrees Fahrenheit. She knows that degrees measured in Fahrenheit are 32 more than $\frac{9}{5}$ times the measure of the temperature in degrees Celsius. Determine what Monday's temperatures are in degrees Fahrenheit. Round to the nearest degree.

Part B

Draw separate graphs for the temperature readings on Monday, Tuesday, and Wednesday using degrees Fahrenheit. Determine whether each graph is linear or nonlinear. Explain your decisions.

Sasha argues that, in general, a graph of temperature readings would be nonlinear. Explain why you agree or disagree with her statement.

Performance Task (continued)

POINTS _____

Part C

Sasha draws the following graph of her temperature readings from Friday, where the temperature F is degrees Fahrenheit and t is time in hours since noon.

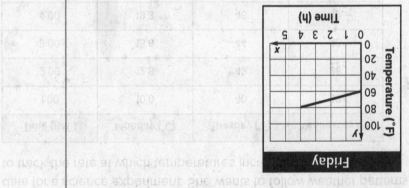

Write an equation for the temperature F at time t. If the temperature trend continues, what will the temperature be at 5:00 P.M.?

Part D

Sasha concludes her research with Sunday's temperature readings. At 1:00 P.M., the temperature was 55°F; at 1:30 P.M., the temperature was 58°F; at 2:00 P.M., the temperature was 57°F; at 2:30 P.M., the temperature was 55°F; and at 3:00 P.M., the temperature was 60°F.

During what time intervals was the temperature increasing? Decreasing? Would this graph be linear or nonlinear?

Part E

Sasha returns the next week for one last reading. She finds the temperature increasing linearly from noon to 2:00 P.M., increasing nonlinearly from 2:00 P.M. to 4:00 P.M., and decreasing nonlinearly from 4:00 P.M. to 7:00 P.M.

Draw a graph that would reflect this information.

Performance Task

Toy Sailboat Race

Maria is going to enter her toy sailboat in a race next Saturday. She is designing different sails to test to see which one she wants to use during the race. The mast of one of her sailboats is 30 inches tall and forms a 90° angle with the deck of her boat. The race regulations state that the sail must be made of canvas fabric and cannot have an area greater than 1 square foot. The following are Maria's three favorite designs. She knows that Sail 1 and Sail 2 are right triangles.

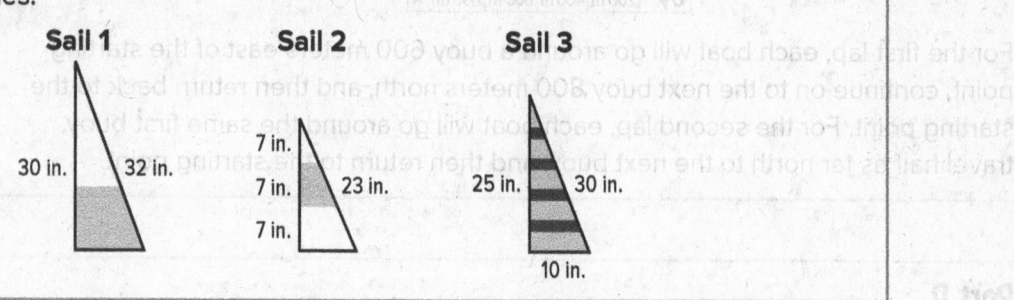

Sail 1   Sail 2   Sail 3

30 in.   32 in.   7 in.   23 in.   25 in.   30 in.
                       7 in.
                       7 in.   10 in.

Write your answers on another piece of paper. Show all your work to receive full credit.

Part A

For Sail 3, will the sail's height run parallel to the mast and perpendicular to the deck of Maria's boat? Justify your answer.

Part B

Maria's brother tells her that Sail 1 will cause her to be disqualified from the race because it does not meet the regulations. Is he correct? Explain why or why not.

Part C

Maria is making a pattern to cut out the fabric for Sail 2. For the striped portion, she needs to know what angles to cut out. If the stripe runs parallel to the boat deck and the top angle of the sail is 24°, what are the measures of the interior angles of the stripe of the sail? Explain your answer.

Performance Task (continued)

The toy sailboat race begins at the buoy shown on the map.

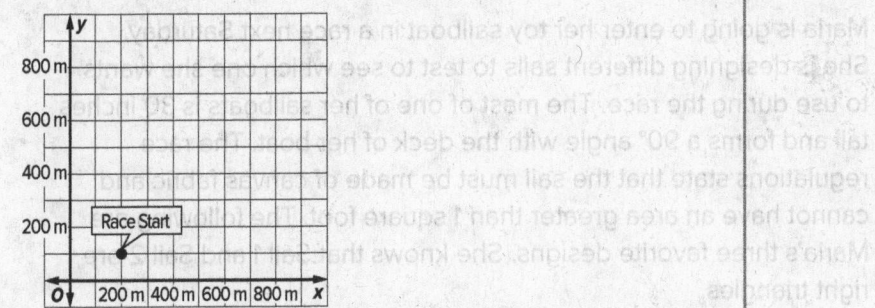

For the first lap, each boat will go around a buoy 600 meters east of the starting point, continue on to the next buoy 800 meters north, and then return back to the starting point. For the second lap, each boat will go around the same first buoy, travel half as far north to the next buoy, and then return to the starting point.

Part D

Label the race map with the coordinates of the other three race buoys. What is the longest leg of the race? Justify your answer.

Part E

Maria assumes that the second lap of the race will be half as long as the first because she will turn her boat back to the starting point after traveling half the distance between the first and second buoy. Is Maria correct? Explain your answer.

Performance Task (continued)

Slide Presentation

Jace is a graphic designer and specializes in creating slide presentations that can be animated when all of the slides are viewed together. A company is paying him to create a presentation about being safe when working in the company's warehouse.

Write your answers on another piece of paper. Show all your work to receive full credit.

Part A

Jace has drawn the following triangle to represent the part of a machine that spins when it cuts.

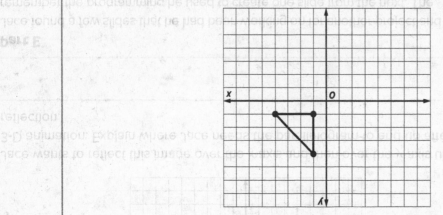

He wants to rotate the image of the triangle around the origin 90°, 180°, and 270° clockwise for several slides to show how fast the part spins when the motor of the machine is running. What would the coordinates of the triangle be on the next three screens? How did you come to these conclusions?

Part B

When Jace tries to program his computer to create the three slides in Part A, he finds that he is not allowed to use rotations. Explain another method that Jace could use to create each of the same slides without using rotations.

Would your solution work for any image? Explain.

Part C

Jace wants to show that no matter the size, sharp edges are not safe. He illustrates this point by using the image in Part A and magnifying it by a factor of 3. His coworker argues that the smaller image will have smaller angles that appear sharper than the larger image. Is Jace's coworker correct? Explain.

Performance Task (continued)

POINTS _____

Part D

Jace draws the parallelogram shown to illustrate a sheet of metal that the company uses.

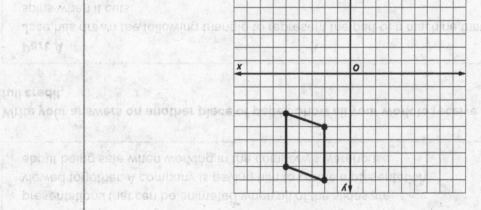

Jace wants to reflect this image over the x-axis and then over the y-axis using 3-D animation. Explain where Jace needs the parallelogram to end up after each reflection.

Part E

Jace found a few slides that he had been working on for another project and cannot remember the programming he used to create one slide from the next. The coordinates of the figure in each of the slides are as follows:

Slide 1: (−2, 2), (−1, 1), (3, 8), (2, 4)
Slide 2: (2, 2), (1, 1), (−3, 8), (−2, 4)
Slide 3: (1, 1), (0.5, 0.5), (−1.5, 4), (−1, 2)
Slide 4: (1, −1), (0.5, −0.5), (4, 1.5), (2, 1)

Describe the transformations from one slide to the next to help Jace re-create the same motions for his current presentation.

Performance Task

Chapter 7

Engineered to Perfection

A bridge connects two cities separated by a river. However, the bridge has been unable to meet increasing traffic demands, so engineers have been asked to construct another bridge several miles south. They are still in the planning stages and currently are preparing blueprints. All units are in feet.

Write your answers on another piece of paper. Show all your work to receive full credit.

Part A

The engineers look at the beam structures and decide where to put them. The beams will look like the following, where $y = 0$ is ground level and $x = 0$ is the center of the bridge:

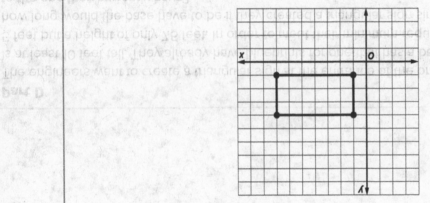

The engineers decide to rotate this beam 90° counterclockwise about the center of the bridge at ground level so that it is on the other side of the center of the bridge. What are the beam's new coordinates?

Upon further inspection, they decide the beams need to be at ground level. What are the new coordinates for the rotated beam after it has been translated to ground level? Explain your answers.

Part B

The top supporting sides of the bridge are made up of right triangles that are 7 feet tall with hypotenuses 9 feet long. Each triangle would be placed on its base with its hypotenuse facing *away* from the center of the bridge. The engineers want to build one of the triangles 0.5 feet to the left of the center of the bridge and 2 feet off the ground level. What are this triangle's coordinates?

Next, the engineers decide to build another triangle on the other side of the center of the bridge, reflecting the first. What are its coordinates? How did you come to these solutions?

Performance Task (continued)

Part C

The engineers are comparing pairs of figures to determine where exactly they want to place them on the bridge. For each pair, explain why they are congruent, similar, or neither.

1) a rectangle with a base of 4 feet and a height of 3 feet and a rectangle with a base of 3 feet and a height of 4 feet

2) a circle with an area of 4π square feet and a circle with a radius of 3 feet

3) a triangle with interior angles of 82° and 75° and the longest side measuring 8.5 feet and a triangle with interior angles of 23° and 75° and the longest side measuring 8.5 feet

4) a cube with a volume of 8 cubic feet and a sphere with a volume of 8 cubic feet

Part D

The engineers want to create a triangular sign at the entrance of the bridge that is at least 10 feet tall. They already have blueprints for one that has a base of 5 feet but a height of only 7.5 feet. In order to meet their minimum requirements, how long would the base have to be if they created a triangular sign similar to the one they currently have?

What would be the ratio of the smaller triangle's perimeter to that of the larger?

What would be the ratio of the smaller triangle's area to that of the larger? Explain your answers.

Performance Task (continued)

Chapter 8

Artsy Smartsy

Suna is extremely creative and thoroughly enjoys arts and crafts. She is constantly creating original knickknacks that she can use for decoration or accessories. She is currently working on three projects:

- One project is a storage unit for her DVDs made from a cylindrical oatmeal container with a wooden dowel inside to keep the DVDs secure. The radius of the hole in the middle of a DVD is one tenth of the diameter of the entire oatmeal container. The height of the oatmeal container is 30 centimeters, and its total volume is 21,195 cubic centimeters.

- Another project is a flower vase made with a painted traffic cone that is 1 foot tall and has a diameter of 10 inches at its opening.

- The third project is a chair made using a large fitness ball with a radius of 3 feet.

Write your answers on another piece of paper. Show all your work to receive full credit. Use 3.14 for π.

Part A

When Suna was making the DVD storage container, she was unsure how large the interior wooden dowel should be. The hardware shop sells wooden dowels with diameters of 2, $2\frac{1}{4}$, $2\frac{1}{2}$, and $2\frac{3}{4}$ inches. Based on the information given, determine which dowel Suna should buy. Justify your answer.

Part B

Suna wants to fill the fitness ball with sand instead of air. However, she only wants to fill it 75% full so that it will not pop when sat on. Explain how many cubic feet of sand Suna will be putting into the fitness ball.

Performance Task (continued)

Part C

Suna wants to make a giant chair with another fitness ball that has a 50% larger radius. She wonders if that would imply that it would also have a 50% larger volume. Explain the change in the volume for any sphere if its radius has been increased by 50%.

Part D

Suna stands the traffic cone vase outside by putting the point down 6 inches into the dirt in her yard. She is worried that when it rains the traffic cone will fill up with too much water and fall over. She predicts that the cone will fall before it gets even halfway full of water. The next day it rains, so Suna decides to check and see if it fell. Just as she makes her way to it, the traffic cone falls. She determines that it had 160 cubic inches of water in it when it fell.

Argue whether Suna's initial prediction was right or wrong. Assume there was no dirt present in the traffic cone before or after the fall.

Part E

When Suna painted the traffic cone, she went over it twice. She only painted the outside portion of the cone that was not being placed down in the dirt. If each container of paint covers 225 square inches, Suna must have purchased *at least* how many containers? Explain.

Performance Task

(continued)

Walking on Sunshine

Suppose you are a local meteorologist analyzing weather patterns in your area. You want to better understand the temperature data you collected before you communicate your findings on the local news station where you work.

Before completing this Performance Task, research and record the daily high and low temperatures for your city from a previous month.

Write your answers on another piece of paper. Show all your work to receive full credit.

Part A

In order to help your team members visualize your data, you decide to make a scatter plot of the daily temperatures. Create a scatter plot of the daily high and low temperatures on the same coordinate grid using a different color and or symbol for the highs and lows. Describe any trends in the data, including clustering and outliers.

Draw the lines of best fit for the high temperatures and the low temperatures. Explain the meaning of any positive or negative correlations. Are the lines of best fit good models of the data? Explain your answer.

Part B

If the readings showed one of the days to have a high of $-5°F$, explain how this would have affected your overall line of best fit for your high temperatures, if at all.

Estimate what the temperatures might be for the next week.

Performance Task (continued)   POINTS

Part C

Create a frequency table for the daily high and low temperatures. Explain what information an observer can get from the frequency table of the high and low temperatures during the month.

Part D

You decide to do further research into your readings by comparing them with years past. To do this, you need the mean, median, mode, and range of your findings. Show what these are for the high and low temperatures. Which value would you use to describe the average high and low temperatures? Explain why.

Page PT1 Studying the Solar System

		Scoring Rubric
CCSS Content Standard(s)		8.EE.1, 8.EE.2, 8.EE.3, 8.EE.4
Mathematical Practices		MP1, MP2, MP3, MP6, MP7
Depth of Knowledge		DOK2, DOK3

Part	Max Points	
A	2	**Full Credit:**

The order of the asteroids is: C, A, B, D, F, E.

Sample answer: I wrote the positive relative positions of the asteroids in scientific notation to make it easier to compare the values from least to greatest.

Asteroid	C	A	B	D	F	E
Relative Position (10^6 km)	-7.5×10^5	0	2.354×10^3	3×10^7	3.4×10^7	1.20×10^{18}

The negative value is the least value, followed by the 0 point. The remaining values can be compared using their powers of 10. Asteroids D and F have the same power of 10, so you compare the decimal portions to determine that 3 is less than 3.4.

Partial Credit will be given for the correct order with no explanation of the reasoning process.

No credit will be given for an incorrect answer.

| B | 1 | **Full Credit:** |

Distance from A:

Asteroid D: 3×10^{25} km

Asteroid E: 1.2×10^{26} km

Since 1.20×10^{26} is 4 times greater than 3×10^{25}, asteroid E is 4 times farther from asteroid A than asteroid E.

No credit will be given for an incorrect answer.

| C | 2 | **Full Credit:** |

Volume of A: $\frac{4}{3}\pi(8^3)^3 = \frac{4}{3}\pi(8)^9 = \frac{4}{3}\pi(2^3)^9 = \frac{4}{3}\pi(2^{27})$

Volume of C: $\frac{4}{3}\pi(2^{-3})^3 = \frac{4}{3}\pi(2^{-9})$

Since 2^{27} is 2^{36} times larger than 2^{-9}, the volume of asteroid A is 2^{36} times greater than the volume of asteroid C.

Partial Credit will be given if the volume expressions are correct, but the scale factor is incorrect.

No credit will be given for an incorrect answer.

| D | 3 | **Full Credit:** |

No, this asteroid does not have the greatest volume.

I need to find the radius of the asteroid to see if it has a greater volume than the other asteroids.

$$V = \frac{4}{3}\pi r^3$$

$$\frac{3}{4}(114) = \frac{3}{4}\left(\frac{4}{3}\pi r^3\right)$$

$$85.5 = \pi r^3$$

$$\frac{85.5}{\pi} = \frac{\pi r^3}{\pi}$$

$$27 \approx r^3$$

$$3 \approx r$$

Comparing the radii of all of the asteroids, $2^{-3} < 1 < 3 < 11^2 < 3^5$. Since $4^4 < 8^3$, I can see that the asteroid does not have the greatest volume.

Partial Credit will be given for correct calculations OR a correct conclusion OR correct reasoning.

No credit will be given for an incorrect answer.

| TOTAL | 8 | |

Part	Max Points	Scoring Rubric
D	2	**Full Credit:** $2{,}000 + 2(1{,}250) - 895 + x = 10{,}000$ $2{,}000 + 2{,}500 - 895 + x = 10{,}000$ $3{,}605 + x = 10{,}000$ $x = 6{,}395$; \$6,395 required to reach the goal Partial Credit will be given for the correct equation OR correct solution. No credit will be given for an incorrect answer.
E	2	**Full Credit:** $5x + 25 + 7x - 3(0.25x - 15.5) + \sqrt{3}\left(\dfrac{x}{\sqrt{3}} - \sqrt{3}\right) + \dfrac{3}{2} =$ $5x + 25 + 7x - 0.75x + 46.5 + x - 3 + \dfrac{3}{2} = 12.25x + 70$ For two weeks, $x = 14$, so $12.25(14) + 70 = \$241.50$. Simplifying each expression yields: $5x + 25$, $6.25x + 46.5$, and $x - 1.5$. We can see that speeding tickets at $6.25x + 46.5$ would give the highest results because x is being multiplied by a greater amount than in the other two expressions. Partial Credit will be given for calculating the combined amount of income generated by the three methods after two weeks OR by identifying and explaining the method that generates income the fastest. No credit will be given for an incorrect answer.
TOTAL	9	

Page PT3 Success on the Road

CCSS Content Standard(s)	8.EE.7, 8.EE.7a, 8.EE.7b
Mathematical Practices	MP1, MP2, MP6, MP8
Depth of Knowledge	DOK2, DOK3

Part	Max Points	Scoring Rubric
A	1	**Full Credit:** $0.35 + 0.01(10) = c$; $0.35 + 0.1 = 0.45$; \$0.45 No credit will be given for an incorrect answer.
B	2	**Full Credit:** Cars going north and south: $1 + 3x = 4(0.5 + 0.75x) - 1$; $1 + 3x = 2 + 3x - 1$ $1 + 3x = 1 + 3x$; Both sides of the equation are equal. Therefore, there are an infinite number of solutions. Cars going west and east: $2 + 3x = 1 + 3x$ simplifies to $2 = 1$, Therefore, there are no solutions. Partial Credit will be given for identifying the number of solutions for cars going north and south OR west and east. No credit will be given for an incorrect answer.
C	2	**Full Credit:** Rate 1: $4 - 3x + 2 - 6 + 2x - 4 = -3x$; $2x - 4 = 0$ $2x = 4$; $x = 2$; 2 cars per minute Rate 2: $\dfrac{3}{2} = \dfrac{4x}{16}$; $48 = 8x$; $x = 6$; 6 cars per minute Rate 3: $2(x - 4) + 2x + \dfrac{1}{2}(2x + 3) - \dfrac{5}{2} = 2 - (3x + 2) - x$ $2x - 8 + 2x + x + \dfrac{3}{2} - \dfrac{5}{2} = 2 - 3x - 2 - x$ $5x - 9 = -4x$; $9x = 9$; $x = 1$; 1 car per minute Therefore, rate 3 at $x = 1$ car per minute allows the fewest number of cars per minute. Partial Credit will be given for calculating the correct number of cars for each rate OR correctly identifying the rate which allows the fewest number of cars per minute. No credit will be given for an incorrect answer.

PT5 Shiny New Car

CCSS Content Standard(s)	8.EE.5, 8.EE.8c, 8.F.3, 8.F.4
Mathematical Practices	MP1, MP2, MP3, MP4, MP7
Depth of Knowledge	DOK2, DOK3

Scoring Rubric

Part	Max Points	
A	1	**Full Credit:** **Sample answer:** If acceleration is constant, the slope $= \frac{60-0}{45-0} = \frac{4}{3}$. Since the function is modeled by $y = mx$, the missing speeds are found by multiplying the time by the slope. $15\left(\frac{4}{3}\right) = 20 \qquad 30\left(\frac{4}{3}\right) = 40$ No credit will be given for incorrect answers.
B	4	**Full Credit:** 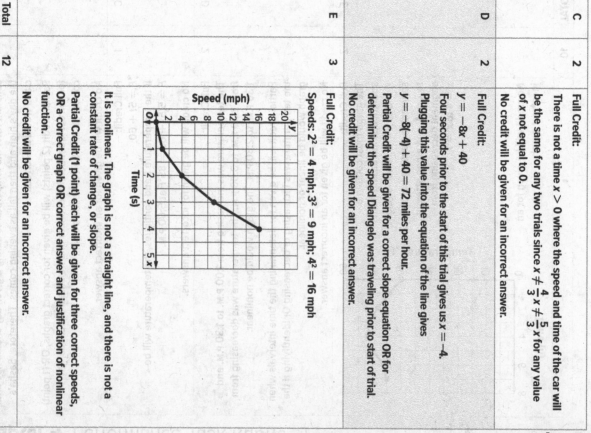 Slope of Trial 1: 1; Slope of Trial 2: $\frac{5}{3}$; Slope of Trial 3: $\frac{4}{3}$; The slopes of the graphs represent the acceleration, or rate of change of the speed, of each of the trials. Diangelo accelerated the fastest during Trial 2. **Partial Credit (2)** points will be given for a correct graph showing all three trials, OR an explanation of what the slope functions represent, and determining in which trial Diangelo accelerated the fastest. No credit will be given for an incorrect answer.
C	2	**Full Credit:** There is not a time $x > 0$ where the speed and time of the car will be the same for any two trials since $x \neq \frac{4}{3}, x \neq \frac{5}{3}x$ for any value of x not equal to 0. No credit will be given for an incorrect answer.
D	2	**Full Credit:** $y = -8x + 40$ Four seconds prior to the start of this trial gives us $x = -4$. Plugging this value into the equation of the line gives $y = -8(-4) + 40 = 72$ miles per hour. **Partial Credit** will be given for a correct slope equation OR for determining the speed Diangelo was traveling prior to start of trial. No credit will be given for an incorrect answer.
E	3	**Full Credit:** Speeds: $2^2 = 4$ mph; $3^2 = 9$ mph; $4^2 = 16$ mph It is nonlinear. The graph is not a straight line, and there is not a constant rate of change, or slope. **Partial Credit (1 point)** each will be given for three correct speeds, OR a correct graph OR correct answer and justification of nonlinear function. No credit will be given for an incorrect answer.
Total	12	

Chapter 4 Performance Task Rubric

CCSS Content Standard(s)	8.F.2, 8.F.3, 8.F.4, 8.F.5
Mathematical Practices	MP1, MP2, MP3, MP4
Depth of Knowledge	DOK2, DOK3

Part	Max Points	Scoring Rubric
A	1	**Full Credit:** (see below)

Time (P.M.)	Monday (°F)
1:00	50
2:00	55
3:00	60
4:00	65
5:00	70

$$F = \tfrac{9}{5}(C) + 32$$
$$F = \tfrac{9}{5}(10) + 32 = 50°F$$
$$F = \tfrac{9}{5}(12.8) + 32 \approx 55°F$$
$$F = \tfrac{9}{5}(15.6) + 32 \approx 60°F$$
$$F = \tfrac{9}{5}(18.3) + 32 \approx 65°F$$
$$F = \tfrac{9}{5}(21.1) + 32 \approx 70°F$$

Since the rate of change is constant, this is a linear function.
No credit will be given for an incorrect answer.

B — 4

Full Credit:

Monday — Temperature (°F): y-axis 20, 40, 60, 80, 100; x-axis Time (h) 0 1 2 3 4 5

Tuesday — Temperature (°F): y-axis 20, 40, 60, 80, 100; x-axis Time (h) 0 1 2 3 4 5

Wednesday — Temperature (°F): y-axis 20, 40, 60, 80, 100; x-axis Time (h) 0 1 2 3 4 5

Monday and Tuesday are linear functions because the rate of change of the temperature over time is constant. Wednesday is a nonlinear function because the rate of change of the temperature over time is *not* constant.

In general, we would not expect temperatures to rise and fall at a constant rate; the temperatures during a given day should rise until the day's high and then fall as evening comes. Therefore, Sasha's claim would be correct.

Partial Credit (2 points) will be given for correct graphs, OR (1 point) for correct identification of linear and nonlinear functions, OR correct justification of Sasha's claim.

No credit will be given for an incorrect answer.

C — 1

Full Credit:
$$F = 5t + 60$$
If the temperature trend continues, the temperature will be
$$F = 5(5) + 60 = 85°F \text{ at } 5:00 \text{ P.M.}$$
No credit will be given for incorrect answers.

D — 2

Full Credit:
The temperature was increasing from 1:00 P.M. to 1:30 P.M. and from 2:30 P.M. to 3:00 P.M. The temperature was decreasing from 1:30 P.M. to 2:30 P.M. The graph would be nonlinear.

Partial Credit will be given for determining the time intervals when the temperature was increasing or decreasing Or identifying if the graph would be linear or nonlinear.

No credit will be given for an incorrect answer.

E — 2

Full Credit:
The graph must contain a straight line increasing from $x = 0$ to $x = 2$, a non-straight segment increasing from $x = 2$ to $x = 4$, and a non-straight segment decreasing from $x = 4$ to $x = 7$.

Temperature (°F): y-axis 10, 20, 30, 40, 50, 60; x-axis Time (h) 0 2 4 6 8

No credit will be given for an incorrect graph.

TOTAL — 10

Page PT9 *Toy Sailboat Race*

Part	Max Points	Scoring Rubric
CCSS Content Standard(s)		8.G.5, 8.G.7, 8.G.8, 8.EE.2
Mathematical Practices		MP1, MP2, MP3, MP4, MP7
Depth of Knowledge		DOK2, DOK3
A	1	**Full Credit:** No, the height of the sail cannot run parallel to the mast and be perpendicular to the deck because the sail is not a right triangle. Using Pythagorean's Theorem to determine if the sail is a right triangle, we see that: $25^2 + 10^2 \neq 30^2$ $625 + 100 \neq 900$ $725 \neq 900$ No credit will be given for an incorrect answer.
B	3	**Full Credit:** Yes, Maria's brother is correct. The area of Sail 1 is greater than 1 square foot and would therefore cause Maria to be disqualified. $30^2 + (\text{base})^2 = 32^2$ $\text{base} = \sqrt{32^2 - 30^2} \approx 11.1 \text{ inches}$ The area of the sail is approximately $\frac{1}{2}(11.1)(30) \approx 166.5$ square inches. The regulations indicate that the sail cannot be larger than 1 square foot, or 144 square inches. So this sail is too large. Partial Credit of 1 point each will be given for the correct base of the triangle, the correct area of the triangle OR for the correct conclusion with justification. No credit will be given for an incorrect answer.
C	2	**Full Credit:** $90°, 90°, 66°, 114°$ Since the triangle is a right triangle, the base angle of the sail is $180° - 90° - 24° = 66°$. Since the stripe runs parallel to the base of the sail, the hypotenuse of the sail is a transversal line. This means that the base angle of the stripe is the same as the $66°$ angle of the sail.

Chapter 5 Performance Task Rubric

Part	Max Points	Scoring Rubric
		The stripe must be perpendicular to the mast, so both of the left-side angles are $90°$. The stripe is a quadrilateral, so the final angle is $360° - 90° - 90° - 66° = 114°$. Partial Credit will be given for 2 or 3 correct angle measures. No credit will be given for an incorrect answer.
D	1	**Full Credit:** Start to buoy 1: 600 meters Buoy 1 to buoy 2: 800 meters Buoy 2 to start: $\sqrt{600^2 + 800^2} = 1000$ meters Buoy 3 to start: $\sqrt{600^2 + 400^2} \approx 721.11$ meters The longest leg of the race is between buoy 2 and the starting point. Legs of the race: No credit will be given for an incorrect answer.
E	1	**Full Credit:** Maria is incorrect. The only distance that is half is the second leg of the second lap. The distance of the first leg remains the same as on the first lap. The distance between the third buoy and the starting point is more than half of the distance between the second buoy and the starting point. No credit will be given for an incorrect answer or the correct answer without justification.
Total	8	

CCSS Content Standard(s)	8.G.1, 8.G.3
Mathematical Practices	MP1, MP2, MP3, MP4, MP7, MP8
Depth of Knowledge	DOK2, DOK3

Part	Max Points	Scoring Rubric
A	3	**Full Credit:** The coordinates of the triangle on the next three presentation slides would be: $90°$: $(x, y) \rightarrow (y, -x)$ The new vertices will be $(1, -1)$, $(4, -1)$, and $(1, -4)$. $180°$: $(x, y) \rightarrow (-x, -y)$. The new vertices will be $(-1, -1)$, $(4, -1)$, and $(-4, -1)$. $270°$: $(x, y) \rightarrow (-y, x)$ The new vertices will be $(-1, 1)$, $(-4, 1)$, and $(-1, 4)$. Each point of the original triangle and its image are the same distance from the point of rotation. I determined in which quadrant a $90°$, $180°$, and $270°$ clockwise rotation would be located. Then I plotted each point the same distance from the origin as its corresponding point in the original triangle. Partial Credit (2 points) will be given for correctly identifying the coordinates of all three clockwise rotations with no explanation OR correctly identifying the coordinates of two clockwise rotations and providing a valid explanation of the process. Partial Credit (1 point) will be given for correctly identifying the coordinates of two clockwise rotations with no explanation OR correctly identifying the coordinates of one clockwise rotation and providing a valid explanation of the process. No credit will be given for an incorrect answer.
B	3	**Full Credit:** Jace could use reflections to create the same slides. For the $90°$ rotation, Jace could reflect the image about the x-axis. For the $180°$ rotation, Jace could reflect the previous image about the y-axis OR the original image about the line $y = -x$. For the $270°$ rotation, Jace could reflect the previous image about the x-axis OR the original image about the y-axis. This only works because the image is symmetric about the line $y = x$. Partial Credit (2 points) will be given for the correct reflections OR (1 point) for the explanation that these replacement reflections only work for special cases. No credit will be given for incorrect answers.
C	1	**Full Credit:** No, Jace's coworker is not correct. When a figure undergoes a dilation of any scale factor, the figure's angle measurements will remain the same. No credit will be given for an incorrect answer or an answer without a correct explanation.
D	2	**Full Credit:** For a reflection over the x-axis: $(x, y) \rightarrow (x, -y)$. The new vertices will be $(2, -8)$, $(2, -4)$, $(5, -7)$, and $(5, -3)$. For a reflection over the y-axis: $(x, y) \rightarrow (-x, -y)$. The final vertices will be $(-2, -8)$, $(-2, -4)$, $(-5, -7)$, and $(-5, -3)$. Partial Credit will be given for one correct answer. No credit will be given for an incorrect answer.
E	3	**Full Credit:** • The transformation from Slide 1 to Slide 2 is a reflection about the y-axis because $(x, y) \rightarrow (-x, y)$. • The transformation from Slide 2 to Slide 3 is a dilation (with center at the origin) with scale factor 0.5 because $(x, y) \rightarrow (0.5x, 0.5y)$. • The transformation from Slide 3 to Slide 4 is a rotation $90°$ clockwise (or $270°$ counterclockwise) about the origin because $(x, y) \rightarrow (y, -x)$. Partial Credit of 1 point will be given for each correct transformation description. No credit will be given for an incorrect answer.
TOTAL	12	

Chapter 6 Performance Task Rubric

Page PT13 Engineered to Perfection

Part	Max Points	Scoring Rubric
CCSS Content Standard(s)		8.G.1, 8.G.2, 8.G.4
Mathematical Practices		MP1, MP2, MP3, MP4, MP7, MP8
Depth of Knowledge		DOK2, DOK3
A 1		**Full Credit:** The rotated coordinates become (−y, x). Therefore, (1, 1), (7, 1), (7, 4), and (1, 4) become (−1, 1), (−1, 7), (−4, 7), and (−4, 1). The new placement of the beam needs to be at ground level; however, it is 1 foot off the ground. Therefore, we need to translate the beam down 1 foot, so (x, y) becomes (x, y − 1). Thus, (−1, 1), (−1, 7), (−4, 7), and (−4, 1) become (−1, 0), (−1, 6), (−4, 6), and (−4, 0). No credit will be given for an incorrect answer.
B 2		**Full Credit:** Using the Pythagorean theorem, we know that: $7^2 + b^2 = 9^2$ $b \approx 5.66$ feet Because the triangle starts at x = −0.5 and y = 2, we see the coordinates are (−0.5, 2), (−0.5, 9), and (−6.16, 2). To reflect a figure over the y-axis, (x, y) becomes (−x, y). Thus, (−0.5, 2), (−0.5, 9), and (−6.16, 2) become (0.5, 2), (0.5, 9), and (6.16, 2). Partial Credit will be given for the correct coordinates of the triangle OR its reflection. No credit will be given for an incorrect answer.
C 4		**Full Credit:** 1) The rectangles are congruent because they have the same shape and size. We know this because the second rectangle can become the first through rotation. 2) The circles are similar because they have the same shape but different sizes. We know this because a circle with a radius of 3 feet has an area of 9π square feet, which is larger than the area of the circle with an area of 4π square feet. Thus, the first can become the second through dilation. 3) The triangles are congruent because they have the same shape and size. We know they have the same shape because the interior angles are the same: 180 − 82 − 75 = 23 and 180 − 23 − 75 = 82. We know they are the same size because the lengths of their longest sides are equal. 4) The cube and the sphere are neither congruent nor similar. Although they have the same volume, their shapes are different. Partial Credit (1 point) will be given for each correct answer. No credit will be given for an incorrect answer.
D 3		**Full Credit:** Because the triangles are similar, we can use ratios to find the measure of the missing side. $\dfrac{5}{7.5} = \dfrac{x}{10}$ $x \approx 6.67$ feet The length of the base of the new sign would be about 6.67 feet. If the height went from 7.5 feet to 10 feet, then the ratio between the two triangles is 7.5:10, which simplifies to 3:4. This is also the ratio for the perimeters. For the ratio of areas, we know $a{:}b = a^2{:}b^2$, $(3)^2{:}(4)^2 = 9{:}16$. Partial Credit (1 point) will be given for each correct answer: length of base of the sign, perimeter ratio, OR area ratio. No credit will be given for an incorrect answer.
TOTAL	10	

Part	Max Points	Scoring Rubric
CCSS Content Standard(s)		8.G.7, 8.G.9
Mathematical Practices		MP1, MP2, MP3, MP4, MP6, MP7
Depth of Knowledge		DOK2, DOK3, DOK4

| A | 2 | **Full Credit:** Sample answer: I need to find the diameter of the large cylinder before I can find the diameter of the hole in the DVD. I can substitute the given information about the oatmeal container into the volume formula and solve for r. $$V = \pi r^2 h$$ $$21{,}195 = (3.14)(r^2)(30) \qquad 15 = r$$ Doubling the radius gives a diameter of $2(15) = 30$ centimeters. Dividing this by 10 gives the radius of the inside of the DVD: $30 \div 10 = 3$ centimeters. This is a 6-centimeter diameter, which is approximately equal to 2.36 inches. The dowel rod with the closest diameter that is not larger than 2.36 inches is the $2\frac{1}{4}$ inch diameter rod. **Partial Credit** will be given for the correct dowel rod conclusion with no explanation. **No credit** will be given for an incorrect answer. |
| B | 1 | **Full Credit:** The formula for the volume of a sphere is $V = \frac{4}{3}\pi r^3$. Plugging in the values, we get $\frac{4}{3}(3.14)(3)^3 = \frac{4}{3}(3.14)(27) = \frac{4}{3}(84.78) = 113.04$ cubic feet. However, Suna wants the fitness ball to be only 75% full. Thus, $113.04 \times 0.75 = 84.78$ cubic feet. **No credit** will be given for an incorrect answer. |

C	1	**Full Credit:** Increasing by 50% is the same as multiplying by 1.5. So, I need to multiply the radius by 1.5 and see if I get the same as multiplying the volume by 1.5. $$V = \frac{4}{3}\pi(1.5r)^3$$ $$= \frac{4}{3}\pi(3.375r^3)$$ $$= 3.375\left[\frac{4}{3}\pi(r)^3\right]$$ Increasing the radius of a sphere by 50% will not increase the volume 50%. Increasing the radius by 50% will increase the volume by 237.5%. **No credit** will be given for an incorrect answer.
D	2	**Full Credit:** The volume of the cone-shaped vase equals $\frac{1}{3}\pi r^2 h = \frac{1}{3}\pi(5)^2 (12) \approx 314$ cubic inches. Since 160 cubic inches is greater than half the volume of the cone, Suna's prediction was incorrect. **Partial Credit** will be given for the correct volume of the cone. **No credit** will be given for an incorrect answer.
E	2	**Full Credit:** Sample answer: Use the Pythagorean theorem to determine that the slant height of the cone is 13 inches. The radius and slant height of the portion of the cone that is to be placed in the dirt are 2.5 inches and 6.5 inches, respectively. The area that Suna painted is equal to the lateral surface area of the whole cone ($\pi r \ell$) minus the lateral surface area of the portion that is below the surface. The area that Suna painted is equal to $(3.14)(5)(13) - (3.14)(2.5)(6.5) = 153.075$ square inches. Multiplying by 2 yields the total surface area: $153.075(2) = 306.15$ square inches. Since each container of paint covers 225 square inches, Suna must have purchased at least two containers. **Partial Credit** will be given for the correct surface area to be painted. **No credit** will be given for an incorrect answer.
TOTAL	8	

Page PT17 *Walking on Sunshine*

Note to Teacher: To complete this Performance Task, students will need to research and record the daily high and low temperatures from a previous month either as class work or for homework. Have students compare and discuss results.

CCSS Content Standard(s)	8.SP.1, 8.SP.2, 8.SP.4, 8.F.5
Mathematical Practices	MP1, MP2, MP3, MP4, MP7, MP8
Depth of Knowledge	DOK2, DOK3

Part	Max Points	Scoring Rubric
A	4	**Full Credit:** Check students' graphs. Students will graph a scatter plot of daily high and low temperatures on the same coordinate grid. Students graph approximate lines of best fit for the high and low temperatures. Students should analyze the graphs and point out any clusters or outlying data and discuss the meaning of any positive or negative correlations.

Sample data:

Day	1	2	3	4	5	6	7	8	9	10	11	12	13	14	15
High (°F)	54	36	48	57	27	27	46	37	36	57	61	72	57	54	54
Low (°F)	21	16	23	28	10	7	21	30	32	32	36	32	41	39	27

Day	16	17	18	19	20	21	22	23	24	25	26	27	28	29	30	31
High (°F)	59	48	63	63	63	43	50	32	51	64	66	39	30	47	54	48
Low (°F)	36	28	31	27	32	21	21	10	9	32	32	18	14	14	32	30

Sample answer: The lines both have a slight positive correlation, meaning that the high and low temperatures are getting warmer. The lines of best fit are not great models of the data because the data points vary greatly from the lines.

Partial Credit (2 points) will be given for the scatter plot and discussion of the trends OR for drawing lines of best fit and discussion of correlation of data.

No credit will be given for an incorrect analysis of the lines of best fit.

B	1	**Full Credit:** **Sample answer:** Since a temperature of −5°F is an outlier, it would cause the line of best fit to give an inaccurate model of the data. The highs next week might be between 57°F and 63°F. The lows next week might be between 32°F and 35°F. **No credit** will be given for an incorrect answer.

C	2	**Full Credit:** Sample frequency table:

Temperature Range (°F)	Frequency of High Temperatures	Frequency of Low Temperatures
0–10	0	4
11–20	0	4
21–30	3	12
31–40	5	10
41–50	7	1
51–60	9	0
61–70	6	0
71–80	1	0

Sample answer: The high temperatures have a mode range of 51–60°F, while the low temperatures have a mode range of 21–30°F.

Partial Credit will be given for the frequency table.

No credit will be given for answers without a table.

D	2	**Full Credit:** **Sample answer:** For the high temperatures: Mean: 49.8, mode: 54, median: 51, range: 45; The mean of 49.8 is the best representation of the averages because the data are evenly distributed. For the low temperatures: Mean: 25.2, mode: 32, median: 28, range: 34; The median of 28 is the best representation of the averages because there are outliers. **Partial Credit** will be given for the averages and ranges. **No credit** will be given for incorrect answers.

TOTAL	9